NATIONAL GEOGRAPHIC SOCIETY
Research Reports

NATIONAL GEOGRAPHIC SOCIETY.

Research Reports

Abstracts and reviews
of research and exploration
authorized under grants from the
National Geographic Society
during the year

1967

Edited by Paul H. Oehser
under the direction of the
Committee for Research and Exploration

NATIONAL GEOGRAPHIC SOCIETY
WASHINGTON, D. C.

*   *   *   *

Contents

Editor's Note

The following accounts published in *National Geographic Society Research Reports, 1965 Projects* and *1966 Projects,* pertain in part to projects that continued into 1967, and no further treatment of them is required in the present volume:

"Archeological Expedition to the Norse Sites at L'Anse aux Meadows, Northern Newfoundland," by Helge M. Ingstad, *1965 Projects,* pp. 123-129.

"Archeological Excavations in Jerusalem, 1964-1967," by Kathleen M. Kenyon, *1965 Projects,* pp. 141-152.

"The 'Acropolis' of Aphrodisias in Caria: Investigations of the Theater and the Prehistoric Mounds, 1966-1967," by Kenan T. Erim, *1966 Projects,* pp. 89-112.

"Mesozoic and Tertiary Vertebrates in California," by William J. Morris, *1966 Projects,* pp. 197-209.

"Biological Exploration of the Northern Cordillera Vilcabamba, Peru," by John W. Terborgh and Theodore R. Dudley, *1966 Projects,* pp. 255-264.

Foreword

The National Geographic Society was founded in 1888 by a group composed largely of Washington scientists for increasing and diffusing geographic knowledge and for promoting research and exploration. The Society's activities toward achieving its second objective date from 1890, when the Society sponsored a geographic and geologic expedition to study the Mount St. Elias Range of Alaska. Since then it has made more than 1,300 grants in support of approximately 1,000 projects in research and exploration. The work has encompassed the broad scope of geography, including such scientific disciplines as geology, paleontology, astronomy, geophysics, oceanography, biology, anthropology, archeology, ethnology, and geographical exploration. The research program has increased as the Society has grown, until today the budget of the Society provides $1,200,000 annually in support of the program.

This is the seventh in a series of volumes that as projected will eventually contain abstracts and reviews of the results of all the research and exploration projects sponsored by the Society since it was established. These are being published volume by volume, first to bring the project up to date as rapidly as practicable and then to work back and report similarly on the less numerous Society-sponsored research projects of earlier years. The present volume contains accounts covering work done under grants made during the year 1967. In some instances, when a continuing research program has been supported by grants over a number of years, and a breakdown of results by year is found impracticable, it has seemed best to include only one résumé for the entire project, with cross references to the main account inserted in other volumes as appropriate. Volumes now in print (1974) cover the following years: 1955-1960, 1961-1962, 1963, 1964, 1965, 1966, 1967.

In presenting the résumés no attempt has been made to standardize the style and specific approach of the investigator, other than to confine each account to reasonable space limitations. In many cases fuller but scattered reports on the work have been, or will be, published elsewhere — in the technical scientific journals, occasionally in the *National Geographic,* or in book form. Published accounts emanating from the research projects are included in the literature references, which each author has been encouraged to supply.

The Committee for Research and Exploration takes this opportunity to thank all the grantees who have cooperated in this publication project. In the years ahead we shall be calling on many of them again in similar fashion, and we solicit their continued help.

Experience with the previous volumes of this series has convinced us that the presentation of research findings as given in these books is of real value to the scientific community. Scholars the world over find this record of the accumulating results of National Geographic Society research grants of real assistance in their own investigations and in the preparation of scientific publications. The general reader also gains new and important knowledge about the current state of research related to geography from each of these volumes.

ALEXANDER WETMORE
Acting Chairman, Committee for
Research and Exploration
National Geographic Society

The Yazidies, "Devil Worshipers" of the Middle East

Principal Investigator: Sami Sáid Ahmed, University of Denver, Denver, Colorado.

Grant No. 603:   In support of an ethnological study of the Yazidies of Iraq, Turkey, Iran, Syria, and Russia.

The Yazidies are an esoteric religious group numbering about 50,000 persons, most of whom live near Mosul, Iraq, in the areas of Sinjar, Baashiqa, and Bihzani. Smaller groups are to be found in southern Russia, in Syria and Iran, and in Turkey near Erivan, Diarbakr, and Bitlis. Their faith prohibits unnecessary association with outsiders, and their sacred books are sealed to unbelievers. Throughout the Middle East the Yazidies are called "devil worshipers."

Scholarly interest in the Yazidies is relatively recent. The few studies that have been made are superficial and far from objective. My purpose in this investigation was to visit the Yazidi areas and attempt to make an objective and comprehensive study of the Yazidi culture and doctrines of faith. The great majority of the Yazidies inhabit an area near Mosul, in northern Iraq. This is the Valley of Lalish, their holy ground, their Mecca, where the tomb of their venerated Shaikh Adi is located. The valley is beautiful, serene, and isolated amid the mountainous terrain. Water is plentiful as there are numerous springs. Every animate and inanimate object on this holy ground is held sacred by the Yazidies — water, trees, stones, and buildings. The life of the people is very simple; most are farmers and shepherds, a few keep vineyards, and a very few are government officials.

Origin

There have been various explanations as to the derivation of the name "Yazidi." One conjecture is that they take their name from Yazid ibn Unaisa, the Kharijite Muslim. Another is that they are named for Yazid, son of Mu'awiyyah, the second Muslim Caliph of the Omayyad Dynasty. In the opinion of some scholars, the group long ago migrated from the city of Yazd and carried the name of their city with them. I was interested to

1

discover the common belief among the people themselves. One Yazidi told me that he believed they were named after Yazid Cyrus Al-Shamsani (Cyrus the Great), founder of the Achaemenid Empire. However, there is no historical evidence that Cyrus was ever referred to as "Yazid." A former Yazidi Prince claimed that they take their name from Yazid the Jaafi (of Yemen), but this is entirely false.[1] The conviction of many with whom I talked is that they were once called Shamsanies, meaning "those of the sun." Veneration of the sun does appear to be entrenched in their faith and strongly points to a Mithraic substratum.

I find the most plausible explanation based on the evidence to be that they were indeed named after the Omayyad Caliph. This Yazid is still regarded as one of their principal deities. However, his name sounds suspiciously similar to *Yazdan* (God), and *yazata* (a term used both in reference to the soldiers of Ahura Mazda in Zoroastrianism and to the nature spirits of the Magi).

Polytheistic Strata

The Yazidies are correctly termed "devil worshipers," but Satan is not worshiped exclusively. Satan is a member of the first of two trinities of the gods, which emanated from God (Yazdan): *First Trinity:* 1, Satan (also referred to as Taus Melek and Ankar); 2, Melak Salem (Gabriel); 3, Shams (Shaikh Shams of Reality, possibly Mithra). *Second Trinity,* emanating from the first and including: 1, Shaikh Adi; 2, Yazid; 3, Jesus Christ. This Shaikh Adi of the second trinity was in fact a Muslim Sufi who died about 1150. To the Yazidies he represents the incarnation of all the other divinities, including Satan. Shaikh Adi is their godhead.

According to Yazdi doctrine, God (the Judeo-Christian creator-God) created seven angels to whom he entrusted the affairs of the world: Azazil (Satan), Dardail (Shaikh Hasan), Israfel (Shams Ul-Din), Michael (Shaikh Bakr), Gabriel (Sajadin), Shamnail (Nasir Ul-Din), and Nurail (Fakhr Ul-Din).

It must be borne in mind that contradictions are rampant in the Yazidi faith. These two sets of trinities and the angelology, in all probability, have been borrowed from Manichaism.

Genesis According to Yazidi Belief

All of mankind, except the Yazidies, is descended from Adam and Eve. The Yazidies are offspring of Shahid, who they claim was a son of Adam born of no mother.

---

[1] Ismail Beg Chol, *The Yazidies, Past and Present*, p. 77. Beirut, 1934.

Tradition encompasses two flood stories. The first flood coincides fairly well with the Biblical account. This relates that a Yazidi woman named Khala Shamsa informed Noah that her oven was flooded. Noah and his men (all of whom were Yazidies) boarded the ark in response to the woman's warning. According to their account, this flood began at Ain Sifni, near Mosul. The sole Yazidi who survived the second flood was a woman named Naomi, a descendant of Melek Miran.

Religious Scripture

The sacred writings of the Yazidies are the *Mishaf Resh* (Black Book) and the *Jalwa,* which sets forth the main points of doctrine on the basis of then current convictions. It is extremely difficult to date these works. One believer informed me that he was in possession of the *Jalwa;* he said this was the only sacred religious text and that it was very different from the known *Jalwa.* Initially I took this claim seriously; however, when I visited his village on two later occasions (fall 1968 and summer 1969), he presented me with two separate and radically different manuscripts. Neither could possibly date back even as far as 30 years, as they often refer to comparatively recent events. It is unmistakably clear that the author of the two documents deliberately created confusion and contradiction between the two works. However, these two manuscripts have been of great value in clearing up many points of doctrine.

According to this teaching the Yazidies firmly believe Satan (Taus Melek) takes special care of them, his chosen people. Satan sends teachers and/or prophets to warn them of imminent dangers. He is said to be present on such occasions as the birth of dynasties and the investiture of kings. The Mishaf Resh lists the following as Yazidi kings: Agricola (probably Tacitus's father-in-law); Ahab (King of Israel, 874-853 B.C.); Ahasuerus (father of Darius); Nasrukh (an Assyrian god mentioned in the Old Testament); Kamush (god of Moab); and Artemis (the Greek goddess).

Ritual Objects

To the Yazidi the most sacred artifacts are seven copper standards called sanjaqs. It is commonly held that these existed before the creation. Each represents a deity. Collectively these standards are considered the banners of Satan (Taus Melek, Yazid, Shaikh Adi, etc.). They are kept in the Khizanat Rahamn at the home of the ruling Prince in Ba'adri. Once a year the Prince permits the sanjaqs to be rented to the Qawwals (Chanters).

The sanjaqs receive a ritual washing and are taken first to the tomb of Shaikh Adi. Then they are carried from one village to another. The entrance of the sanjaqs into a village is a joyous occasion; one of the Chanters precedes the standards, announcing the arrival of these sacred relics. All who view them must be freshly bathed, dressed in white, and barefooted. The villagers welcome the procession with prayer and shouting and dancing. The standards are taken to the home of the most notable villager where the Chanters sing and play tambourines and shababas (horns). And it is here that the people bring their gifts and offerings to the god. No unbeliever is permitted to see the sanjaqs, but reportedly there is an image of a ducklike bird at the top of each standard. A traveler reported that a Yazidi told him that at these ceremonies a sanjaq is placed in relation to seven bolsters and a sacred jug, which obviously must have some religious significance.

The Caste System

There are eight castes in Yazidi society, each of which has its own functions, privileges, and code of social behavior. Intermarriage is not permitted between castes except under extraordinary circumstances. Occasionally marriages are permitted among members of a subclass but only between members of certain families. There are circumstances where special dispensation is granted for members of differing castes to intermarry; e.g., Chanters with commoners; the Pirs of Mohammed Rashan with the Pirs of Jarwana. Converts are not accepted into any caste. The castes are as follows:

1. *The Princes:* This is the highest caste and the one from which the ruling Prince is selected. This group traces direct ancestry to Shaikh Bakr, a member of the house of Shaikh Adi. Shaikh Bakr (identified with the angel Michael) seemingly usurped leadership from the descendants of Shaikh Hasan, also of Shaikh Adi's house, and the person thought to be the author of the *Jalwa*. He was killed in Mosul about 1246. It is entirely possible that Shaikh Bakr arranged with the Chanters to confuse the names of this Shaikh Hasan with that of Hasan Al-Basri (d. 728).

The power of the ruling Prince is absolute in both political and religious matters. He is the recipient of the rental fee from the sanjaqs and of all tithes, gifts, and endowments. If a Yazidi dies leaving no male heir, the ruling Prince receives the subject's estate. The Prince has the power to excommunicate members of the faith, and he cannot be removed from office to which he has been appointed for the duration of his lifetime.

In the physical realm only a member of the Kawchak caste may do the Prince's laundry, and the dirty wash water must be disposed of according to ritual. Upon the death of the Prince his clothes are given to the Grand Shaikh. His widows are prohibited from remarrying since they are considered to have received *mana* (spiritual power) from the Prince.

2. *The Pesmrreyyah:* This caste shares a common ancestry with the Princes; intermarriage is permitted and general privileges are the same. Because of this apparently poor class differentiation, the Pesmrreyyah are decreasing in number.

3. *The Clergy:* This caste is headed by the Baba Shaikh (Grand Shaikh), who is the highest religious authority. He is chosen from the house of Fakhr Ul-Din, and his traditional dress consists of a white garment, white headgear, and a black belt. Upon the death of the Baba Shaikh, tribal chiefs and the heads of the clergy meet to select a successor. The ruling Prince must approve the selection before the new leader assumes his duties.

The Shaikhs (clergymen) are divided into three main subdivisions, the Adani, the Shamsani, and the Qatani. Their dress is similar; all wear white robes, black turbans wound around their heads, and red or yellow girdles. Every Yazidi has his Shaikh to whom he gives tithes and gifts and through whom he seeks forgiveness of sins. Only those clergy belonging to the house of Shaikh Hasan are permitted a formal education; they are the caretakers of the sacred books and, if such is desired, are present at marriage ceremonies.

4. *The Pirs:* Although not members of the Clergy, the Pirs act as advisers to the people concerning religious matters. Each Yazidi has a Pir to whom he offers alms. Members of this caste dress in black and wear white turbans wound with a red scarf with a black plume.

5. *The Faqirs* (Qara Bash): The Faqirs are community ascetics who spend their days in prayer and religious observances. They are highly respected; they neither smoke nor drink. Their clothing is distinctive and is considered sacred. Next to their skin they wear a black wool shirt *(khirqa)* over which is another black garment. The *khirqa* is removed only when worn out, at which time it is placed in a special depository called *khana khirqa* at Lalish or *kani bir akhaii* in Sinjar. The *khirqa* is bound by a red woolen belt *(mahak)*, held by a copper ring *(karim)* that the Yazidies believe was fashioned by God. To complete his attire the Faqir wears a string around his neck *(malfouf)* and a skull cap *(kullik)*.

The Master of the Faqir order is known as the *Kak*. At present he resides in Syria near Aleppo. The Faqaia (female members of the Faqir caste) are headed by a leader entitled *Kabana*. The Faqaia are recruited from among virgins and widows, and they reside at Lalish where they dedicate themselves to the service of the shrines and the holy places in the Sacred Valley.

6. *The Kawchaks:* Any Yazidi can become a Kawchak by completing the initiation, which consists of 1,600 days of fasting, making a visit to all shrines, and adhering to a life of asceticism. The Kawchaks interpret dreams, pray in times of crisis, determine the fate of the dead, and are thought to have the ability to perform miracles. All members of this caste meet once a year with the Baba Shaikh at Lalish to discuss their affairs.

7. *The Qawwals* (Chanters): This caste is designated to sing and chant the rituals and hymns and to lead the dancing at festival and funeral ceremonials. They are entrusted with the responsibility of carrying the sanjaqs from village to village.

8. *The Murids* (Commoners): This caste encompasses all remaining members of the tribe. Their freedom is limited by the faith; they are deprived of many of the social rights enjoyed by other classes and are placed under heavy financial obligations.

Rituals and Beliefs

From observation and inquiry it is clear that this religion embodies beliefs and practices of many other faiths including the Mithraic cults, Zoroastrian, Mazdaean, Manichaean, Hindu, Christian, and, by far the most obvious, Islam.

Fasting: There are two types of fast, public and private. The public fast is termed the "Fast of Yazid" and falls on the first Tuesday, Wednesday, and Thursday of December according to the Eastern calendar. It commemorates the triumph of Cyrus the Great's capture of Babylon in 538 B.C. Private fasting is observed in two sessions of 40 days each. One begins on December 20; the other on July 20. The latter is observed only by the Clergy and the Kawchaks. The first three days are carried out at Lalish. However, odd as it may seem, during this three-day period the fast may be broken whenever a believer brings a meal to the fasting person.

Prayer: There is a daily ritual prayer wherein the Yazidi facing the rising sun kisses the ground and utters a ritualistic formula. The contents of this prayer were given to me several times, but I am convinced that none of the translations is correct. Non-Yazidies are prohibited from watching this observance of worship. Other daily times are set forth as noon, sunset, and before retiring. All avenues to learning the prayers were blocked.

Pilgrimage: Every Yazidi is required to visit the shrine of Shaikh Adi once a year, preferably at the Grand Feast (Juma'yyah, which takes place October 6-13). Reportedly, many Yazidies have begun to take this obligation lightly. In addition to visiting the shrine, the pilgrims must also ascend

Mount Arafat, wash in water from the Zem Zem well, watch the ritual cleansing of the Barshbaki, and partake in something called Qabagh, which involves shooting guns. A bull is slaughtered and cooked, and each pilgrim is advised to partake of this meat. Also, pilgrims are obligated to observe a nocturnal service performed by the Clergy and the Kawchaks called the Sama' (circling around the light).

Transmigration of Souls: This is a deep-rooted conviction. Yazidies believe that after death a man's soul may enter the body of another human or of an animal (depending on the kind of life he has lived). The soul of an oppressor would go to an ass, a liar to a fox; the soul of a selfish and conceited person would be assumed by a snake, and the soul of a Faqir would go to a king.

Baptism: All newborn infants are baptized with water from Ain Al-Baida (Kani asi) at Lalish by a Faqir. All the relatives gather on this occasion of joyous celebration.

Circumcision: The circumcision of young male children is another happy family-type occasion. It is customary for the child's father to invite a man, usually a Moslem, to hold the child during the operation. Drops of blood stain this person's clothing and he is thereafter considered a "blood-brother" *(kirif)* to the child's family. If it happens that the *kirif* is another Yazidi, there can be no intermarriage between the two families for five generations.

There is a peculiar tenet whereby each person must have an eternal brother and/or sister who is a member of the Clergy. This person is available for occasional advice, but doctrine obliges that the Yazidi kiss the hands of his eternal brother and sister daily. Oddly, it is decreed that the eternal brother or sister must cut new shirt collars for his or her "charge" and must be present at his death.

Amulets: Chanters collect the dust from Shaikh Adi's tomb, mix it with holy water, and form small balls called *brats*. These are sold to believers and everyone seems to have a *brat*. These must be carried at all times and eaten in case of illness. Some years ago a couple ate a *brat* together as a contract of marriage. At present if a man, even by mistake, gives a *brat* to his wife, she is considered divorced.

Marriage: Doctrine permits every man to have four wives. Because of the prevailing extreme poverty, most are content with one. Princes and Clergy ordinarily are the only men who can afford to support their limit in wives.

A marriage concerns both families involved. If the girl's parents refuse the suitor, the young couple can elope *(netish)* and hope that someone will intercede and pacify the angry parents. The bride's dowry usually goes to her parents. It is not unusual for wives to be considered chattel; they may even serve as collateral on a mortgage or may be used as a stake for gambling.

In former times marriage contracts were unnecessary, and it was a simple matter for a woman to leave her husband or to run off with another man. However, one Prince instituted the obligatory marriage contract testified by two witnesses. No marriage may be performed on Wednesdays or during the month of April. A Yazidi cannot marry the sister of his divorced or deceased wife or the wife of his deceased brother or uncle. Neither can he marry the sister of any girl to whom he was once engaged. Any Yazidi woman who is suspected of having sexual relations with a nonbeliever is either killed by her relative or is excommunicated and expelled by her community.

The formula for divorce is simple. The husband tells his wife, "You are my mother, or Pir, or Shaikh." However, he can take her back any time he so chooses.

Funeral and Burial Customs: At the time of death, a Yazidi is surrounded by his Shaikh, his Pir, and his eternal brother and sister. They dissolve *brats* in water for him to drink. After death they wash the body, put *brat* dust on the eyes and hands, and enshroud it in white cotton fabric. At the gravesite a Chanter tutors the dead *(tarqiniyyah)*. Burial takes place amid the sound of tambourines, shababas, and mourning women. Occasionally the dead person is buried in his best clothes (and jewelry if a woman). Sometimes a bed is placed in the grave. Mournful gatherings to commemorate the loved one's death are held on the third, seventh, and fortieth day after burial. Cemeteries are located in the vicinity of shrines so that people can visit them often, bringing food and offerings in remembrance of the dead.

Religious Holidays: The Yazidi holy day is Friday. Yazid's Feast (Bilanda), on January 8, marks Yazid's birth. Some believe this coincides with Cyrus's entry into Babylon. Sari Sali (New Year Festival) takes place on April 14 and celebrates Satan's (Taus Melek's) descent to earth to deliver the Hebrews from Pharaoh. To mark this occasion, young girls decorate their homes with red anemones. Forty days of fasting beginning July 20 and December 20 are both terminated by feasting. The Grand Feast (Juma'yyah) is held on October 6-13. Every Yazidi is required to visit the shrine of Shaikh Adi annually and traditionally go there at this time. The Qurban Feast takes place on the ninth and tenth days of the twelfth month of the Moslem calendar. It marks the redemption of Ishmael by the Lamb (Satan) sent to Abraham. The time is also designated for pilgrimage to the tomb of

Shaikh Adi. Three days of fasting, December 14-16, are climaxed by a Ramadan feast. Shaikh Adi's birthday is celebrated on December 25. Other holidays are Khidr Al-Yas in mid-February and Qadr Night on the fifteenth of the eighth month of the Moslem calendar. On the latter many go to Lalish for all-night prayer and the reading of specific verses from the Koran.

Religious Taboos: A Yazid may not speak any word containing the sounds *sh* and *ṭ*. For instance, it is forbidden to say aloud the words *shikkat* (matches), or *shaṭṭ* (river) for they contain the letters from the word Shaitan (Satan). Words that rhyme with Shaitan are forbidden, such as *sulṭan* and *qiṭan*. Neither may the Yazidi utter any word containing an *l* sound, such as *la'ana* (curse) or *mia'al* (slippers), as this also is somehow considered derogatory to Taus Melek.

Dietary restrictions are numerous. The Yazidi may not eat fish, out of respect to Jonah; roosters, out of respect to Satan; or deer meat, for it is said that deer eyes resemble those of Shaikh Adi, and deer were the prophet's cattle and therefore prohibited to the people. Okra, gourds, beans, cabbage, rabbit, pigeon, and pork are taboos, and one may not look at, plant, or eat lettuce.

No Yazidi home may have a bathroom or sewer (this prohibition may represent Zoroastrian influence). The Yazidi may not spit on the ground or urinate while standing. Men must put on their trousers while sitting down and may not remove them completely for sexual intercourse. The Yazidi may not go to sleep facing the direction of Shaikh Adi's tomb, and all the faithful are prohibited from entering churches, mosques, or schools.

Conclusion

The Yazidi religion, social structure, and economy are unique in today's world. The system is so arranged that few families benefit, but all seem content to uphold the supremacy of the privileged castes. The two sacred books are cleverly written to confuse, contradict, and forever subject this people to ignorance and obedience. The religion has borrowed heavily from others in the area, and embodies something of the entire religious experience of the Middle East.

SAMI SÁID AHMED

Underwater Archeological Expedition to Turkey, 1967

Principal Investigator: George F. Bass, University Museum of the University of
Pennsylvania, Philadelphia, Pennsylvania.

Grant No. 609:   For investigation of Roman shipwrecks off the coast of
Yassi Ada, Turkey.[1]

The expedition of the University Museum of the University of Pennsylvania and the National Geographic Society sent to Turkey in 1967 had
two separate objectives: To develop more efficient methods of underwater
excavation and to experiment further with underwater search and survey
techniques. It was hoped that both would lead to significant archeological
results.

The site chosen for excavation was a late Roman shipwreck, of uncertain
date,[2] lying on a slope 120 to 140 feet deep near Yassi Ada (Flat Island).
Found by Peter Throckmorton a decade earlier (Throckmorton, 1960,
1964; Frost, 1962), the wreck was visible only as a mound of amphoras protruding from the sandy bottom; it had served as a "target" for our earlier experiments, in 1964, to map a site photogrammetrically from our two-man
submarine *Asherah* (Bass and van Doorninck, 1969; Karius et al., 1965).

So that we might better determine what methods of excavation needed
greatest improvement, Frederick van Doorninck made an efficiency study
of our excavation of a 7th-century Byzantine wreck, also at Yassi Ada,
between 1961 and 1964 (Bass, 1968b, 1970; Bass and van Doorninck,
1969). Diving logs showed that during those four summers we had dived
on a total of 211 days, making 3,533 individual dives (usually in pairs or in

---

[1] Additional support was provided by Nixon Griffis, the National Science
Foundation, the Triopian Foundation for Archeological Research, and the U. S.
Navy (Office of Naval Research, Supervisor of Salvage, Deep Submergence Systems Project, Naval Oceanographic Office, and Naval Research Laboratory; this
included funds and equipment for perfecting our system of photogrammetric
mapping and for evaluating several types of side-scanning sonar).

[2] The wreck was believed to be of the 5th or 6th century A.D., on the basis of
its amphora types, but further excavation in 1969 provided material to indicate
a date during the second half of the 4th century (Bass and van Doorninck, 1971).

teams of up to four divers). This resulted in a total work time on the wreck of 1,243 man-hours, of which van Doorninck calculated only about 1,080 were necessary for the actual excavation (the remaining time was spent making a documentary film, taking nonscientific photographs, making unnecessary measurements, etc.). Total necessary work time was spent as follows:

Task	Number of hours	Percent of total
1. Removal of sand, shell, etc.	694	64
a. Air lifting: 224 hours		
b. Sweeping by hand: 470 hours		
2. Making plans (photography and drawing)	204	19
3. Removal of amphoras, anchors, small finds	115	11
4. Bringing up hull remains	41	4
5. Other (anchoring barge, pinning down wood, measuring wood, closing down each season, etc.)	24	2

We had spent four summers with an average of a dozen divers a summer, yet had the same excavation been on land five men working normal 8-hour days could have produced the same number of man-hours in just one month. Greater efficiency was needed, for if we could excavate a ship of similar size in only two summers we would obviously halve such annual expenses as transportation, rental of local boats, salaries, shipping, and customs, etc.

There were two approaches to reducing the number of summers spent on a similar underwater site:

1. Increase the daily number of man-hours on the site, so that a total of 1,000 to 1,200 could be reached in two rather than four summers. This could be accomplished by:
   a. Increasing the number of divers on the staff.
   b. Increasing the duration of decompression following each dive, thereby allowing longer dives.

2. Increase the amount of work accomplished during each man-hour, by the introduction of better techniques, so that 1,000 to 1,200 man-hours might not be required.

We decided on both approaches, realizing that the cost of each season would be greater than that spent on the Byzantine ship. First we enlarged

FIG. 1. Methods of excavation used at Yassi Ada, 1967.

the staff considerably: G. F. Bass, director; Claude Duthuit, chief diver; Don Wilson and John Cassils, physicians; Susan Womer Katzev, Jane Cook, and Eric J. Ryan, artists; Charles Nicklin, Paul Fardig, Robert Hodgson, and Mustafa Kapkin, photographers; Bennett Jones and Matt Kaplan, architects; William Maggs, mechanic; Ann Searight, conservator; Donald M. Rosencrantz, electrical engineer; Laurence T. Joline, Oguz Alpözen, Peter Fries, Oktay Ercan, Birol Kutadgu, Belkis Mutlu, Judy Hodgson, Irene Maggs, and Anna McCann; and archeology students Frank Bartell, W. Willson Cummer, Jana Hesser, Gail Hillard, Cynthia Jones, Michael L. Katzev, Regnar Kearton, Sanford Low, Hugh Mullenbach, David I. Owen,

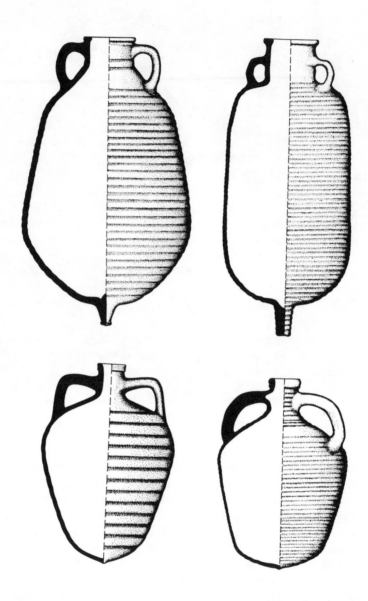

FIG. 2.   The four major amphora types from a Late Roman wreck at Yassi Ada.

Nancy Palmer, Marilyn Rosenberg, Orhan Gürman, Marie Ryan, Kenneth Sams, Stuart Swiny, Ted Worth, and Laina Wylde; Sarah Cummer, Crisa Kearton, Susan Owen, Joyce Ryan, Judy Sams, and Jack Sasson also assisted; Lt. Cmdr. John Ulrich and Andrew Wright were sent by the Supervisor of Salvage, U. S. Navy, to assist in expedition preparations. Yüksel Eğdemir served as archeological commissioner for the Turkish Department of Antiquities, and Mehmet Turguttekin, captain of the trawler *Kardeşler*, was once more in charge of all local logistics.

We were able to increase individual diving times for the 20 to 25 divers included in this staff by the use of a submersible decompression chamber (SDC), which allowed up to four divers at a time to decompress for long periods in dry comfort. The SDC, built on my design by Galeazzi of Italy, had two hatches: (*a*) (see fig. 1) for entry and exit, and (*b*) for the attachment of a one-man portable recompression chamber for the removal of a stricken diver to a large chamber on the surface in case of emergency (the SDC was also designed to lock onto the surface chamber, but we lacked lifting facilities at Yassi Ada to raise the SDC out of the water). A cable ran down from the SDC to 5 tons of sheet metal (*c*) piled on the sea bed and chained together; the cable passed through a pulley and ran up the slope to a chainhoist on Yassi Ada, where one man could raise or lower the SDC to the desired depths for decompression. An air hose and a telephone line (*d*) also ran from the island.

For the second approach, that of improved techniques, we devised a number of tools. On the Byzantine wreck we often had hesitated to use an air lift near fragile remains, but sand swept by hand forms large mounds on the site, and the removal of these takes valuable time. In 1967 we were able to speed sand removal by the use of a large air lift and a high-pressure water jet. For the air lift (*e*), which was assembled from sections of aluminum pipe 10 inches in diameter, we laid 70 feet of "railroad track" along the lower side of the wreck; the track was made of two industrial monorails, turned upside down and kept parallel by wooden ties. The bottom of the air-lift pipe was secured inside a "hood" (*f*) cut from an oil drum; passing through this hood was a pipe axle for the pair of two-wheeled trolleys that ran under the tracks. The upper end of the air-lift pipe was buoyed by an air-filled oil drum (*g*) so that the air lift, in effect, hung upside down from the monorails. One (*h*) or, more often, two hoses from compressors on the barge above entered the hood to supply the necessary air to the lift.

We dug a trench beneath the air-lift tracks by means of a water jet (an ordinary fire-hose (*i*) connected to an irrigation pump on the diving barge) and swept sand from the wreck into it either by hand or by water jet for later, fast removal; the potentially destructive water jet could be used with more freedom than we had anticipated for the layer of sand covering this wreck proved to be several feet thick in places — much deeper than that which we had encountered on the neighboring Byzantine wreck.

We mapped the site photographically by two methods, one photogrammetric. For the latter, a pair of motorized cameras *(j-j)* with special underwater lenses were mounted on the *Asherah,* along with a pair of

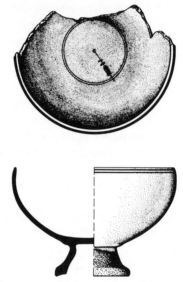

FIG. 3.   Example of glazed bowl from wreck of around 1600, at Yassi Ada.

stroboscopic lights *(k-k),* and a television-camera "view finder" *(m)* connected to a small TV monitor inside the submarine's pressure hull; also inside the hull, a camera automatically photographed a counter and tilt and depth indicators whenever a stereophoto was taken. Normal aerial survey techniques and equipment were used in making 3-dimensional plans from the stereo pairs.

Although this method of mapping, designed by Donald Rosencrantz, worked well (Bass and Rosencrantz, 1968), an unforeseen delay in the arrival of the *Asherah* in Turkey led us to map the site during the first part of the summer by our older method; we photographed 2-meter squares from a photo-tower *(n)* resting on a scaffolding of angle-iron, which we moved from the Byzantine wreck. This technique necessitates numerous corrections for parallax and scale, as well as separate vertical measurements.

As usual, all artifacts and wood fragments were tagged with numbered plastic labels, and wood was pinned to the sea bed with sharpened bicycle spokes to prevent its moving. A metal detector *(o)*, provided by the Research Laboratory for Archaeology and the History of Art, Oxford, located iron remains beneath the sand, often at some distance from the wreck; these remains were in the form of concretions, which we cut open to serve as molds for rubber casts of the original objects (Bass and van Doorninck, 1969). Amphoras were raised to the surface in a large wooden basket *(p)* attached to a balloon capable of lifting 1,000 pounds, but fragile timbers were carried by divers in a long wire basket *(q)* as they walked up the slope to Yassi Ada, about 100 yards away; a hose *(r)* from a compressor on the barge provided air for the balloons used on both baskets.

Our underwater telephone booth, designed by Michael and Susan Katzev, was a hemisphere of clear plastic *(s)*, 4 feet in diameter, anchored to 1,500 pounds of ballast with angle-iron legs. From it a telephone line and air hose *(t)* ran to the surface. The "booth" allowed conversations with the barge and between divers, but more importantly it served as an air-filled haven for divers in trouble (a spare tank was strapped to a leg of the booth for emergencies).

During the summer we mapped and removed most of the cargo, comprising just over 1,000 amphoras of four types (fig. 2). Part of the remarkably well preserved hull of the ship was revealed, but no traces of the ship's galley were found in 1967. Lying partly over the Roman wreck were the timbers of another ship, of uncertain date [3] and purpose (fig. 1); a few bowls of glazed terracotta (fig. 3) were the only objects found on board.

Our second objective was the further experimentation with search techniques, and we hoped to find one or both of the deep wrecks sought unsuccessfully in 1965 using a Towvane, television, and a proton magnetometer (Bass and Fernald, 1971). We had learned at that time that the sea bed in each search area, being flat, level, and sandy, was ideally suited for side-scanning sonar with its great range. With support from the U. S. Navy, we were to use and evaluate three different sonar systems.

The first unit was designed and built by the Marine Physical Laboratory of the Scripps Institution of Oceanography of the University of California; Maurice McGehee, Tony Boegeman, and Bruce Luyendyk accompanied it from Scripps to operate and maintain it. The sonar "fish" was towed behind

---

[3] A silver coin of Philip III of Spain (1578-1621) was found on this wreck in 1969.

and below the 65-foot trawler *Kardeşler,* with a pair of paper recorders in the *Kardeşler's* hold recording sound waves reflected from the sea bed out to 600 feet on either side. For navigation, three shore-based transit operators, with transceivers, simultaneously recorded bearings on the *Kardeşler's* mast every 2½ or 5 minutes and radioed these to the trawler where they were plotted on a chart. In the Arap Adasi search area, near Marmaris, where a bronze bust of "Demeter" had been netted some years earlier, over 100 targets about 265 feet deep were recorded; this number was reduced to the dozen or so most likely to represent shipwrecks. Bad weather limited to only two mornings the search in the area near Yalikovak where a bronze Negro youth and a statuette of Isis had been found, but a promising target was recorded there as well. This target was later recorded again by the EG&G sonar system operated by Martin Klein (the third system to be evaluated was damaged too badly for field repair during shipment). A dive with the *Asherah* revealed it to be an ancient cargo.[4]

REFERENCES

BASS, GEORGE F.
    1965. The *Asherah*: A submarine for archaeology.   Archaeol., vol. 18, no. 1,
        pp. 7-14, illus.
    1966. Archaeology under water, 244 pp., illus.   Thames & Hudson, London;
        Frederick A. Praeger, New York. (Revised edition, Penguin Books,
        Ltd., Harmondsworth, England, 1970.)
    1968a. New tools for undersea archeology.   Nat. Geogr. Mag., vol. 134, no. 3,
        pp. 402-423, illus.
    1968b. Underwater archeological expedition to Turkey.   Nat. Geogr. Soc.
        Res. Rpts., 1963 Projects, pp. 21-34, illus.
    1968c. The Turkish Aegean: Proving ground for underwater archaeology.
        Expedition, vol. 10, no. 3, pp. 3-10, illus.
    1970. Underwater archeological expedition to Turkey, 1961-1962.   Nat.
        Geogr. Soc. Res. Rpts., 1961-1962 Projects, pp. 11-20, illus.
BASS, GEORGE F., and FERNALD, RUSSELL
    1971. Underwater archeological explorations in Turkey.   Nat. Geogr. Soc.
        Res. Rpts., 1965 Projects, pp. 15-22, illus.
BASS, GEORGE F., and JOLINE, LAURENCE T.
    1968. Problems of deep wreck identification.   Expedition, vol. 11, no. 1,
        pp. 9-12, illus.

----

[4] Subsequent examinations of all the major targets with television (Bass and Joline, 1968) revealed that two of those in the Marmaris area were also ancient wrecks. The wreck in the Yalikovak area was also seen to have table ware and roof tiles from the galley as well as objects which appear to be nonceramic among its amphoras.

BASS, GEORGE F., and KATZEV, MICHAEL L.
1968. Tools for underwater archaeology. Archaeol., vol. 21, no. 3, pp. 165-173, illus.

BASS, GEORGE F., and ROSENCRANTZ, DONALD M.
1968. A diversified program for the study of shallow water searching and mapping techniques. Office of Naval Research Report. (No. AD 686 487, Clearinghouse [CFSTI], Springfield, Va.)

BASS, GEORGE F., and VAN DOORNINCK, FREDERICK H., JR.
1969. Excavations of a Byzantine shipwreck at Yassi Ada, Turkey. Nat. Geogr. Soc. Res. Rpts., 1964 Projects, pp. 9-20, illus.
1971. A fourth-century shipwreck at Yassi Ada. Amer. Journ. Archaeol., vol. 15, no. 1, pp. 27-37, illus.

FROST, HONOR
1962. Under the Mediterranean, 278 pp., illus. Routledge and Kegan Paul, London. (American edition, 1963, Prentice-Hall, Englewood Cliffs, New Jersey.)

KARIUS, RUDLOF; MERIFIELD, PAUL M.; and ROSENCRANTZ, DONALD M.
1965. Stereo-mapping of underwater terrain from a submarine. Pp. 1167-1177 *in* "Ocean Science and Ocean Engineering" (Transactions of the Joint Conference, Marine Technology Society and American Society of Limnology and Oceanography, Washington, D. C., June 1965).

THROCKMORTON, PETER
1960. Thirty-three centuries under the sea. Nat. Geogr. Mag., vol. 117, no. 5, pp. 682-703, illus.
1964. The lost ships: An adventure in undersea archaeology, 260 pp., illus. Little, Brown & Co., Boston and Toronto. (English edition, 1965, Jonathan Cape, London.)

GEORGE F. BASS

The Regulation of Body Temperature by Bluefin Tuna

Principal Investigator: Francis G. Carey, Woods Hole Oceanographic Institution, Woods Hole, Massachusetts.

Grant Nos. 638, 706,   To conduct a physiological study of body-temperature
783.   regulation and swimming performance in the bluefin tuna
    (Thunnus thynnus Linnaeus).

Our interest in body-temperature regulation in the bluefin tuna started in 1966 when John Teal and I, hearing that tuna were warm, went on a long-line cruise of the R/V *Delaware,* of the Bureau of Commercial Fisheries, out of Gloucester to see for ourselves if this was so. Tuna and some species of sharks do have high body temperatures, and we began a program of experiments and observations through which we have learned much about these fishes and how they maintain their temperature. We published our first paper that year (Carey and Teal, 1966) before we had applied for National Geographic Society support. Here we gave our basic observations of temperatures in tuna, discussed why the warm fish are interesting, and described some of the anatomical features that allow them to warm their bodies. In the summer of 1966 we worked on bluefin caught in commercial fish traps in Provincetown, Massachusetts, and from those temperature measurements saw indications that the bluefin could control its temperature. Although the water temperature at the trap varied, the temperature of the fish tended to remain the same. To explore this further we wanted to measure temperatures of tuna caught at the northern and southern ends of their range, where we would find extremes of water temperature. The Society supported our field work in the summer of 1967 when we went to Bimini in the Bahamas where the water was as warm as 29° C. (82° F.) and to Nova Scotia and Newfoundland waters where we sought low water temperatures. These data formed part of our paper on regulation of body temperature by bluefin tuna (Carey and Teal, 1969b), in which we summarized our tuna-temperature measurements from many different times and areas and showed how the temperatures of the fish tend to remain constant whether the water they are swimming in is warm or cold.

By the winter of 1967-68 we had decided that it would be necessary

BLUEFIN #13   10 JULY 1970

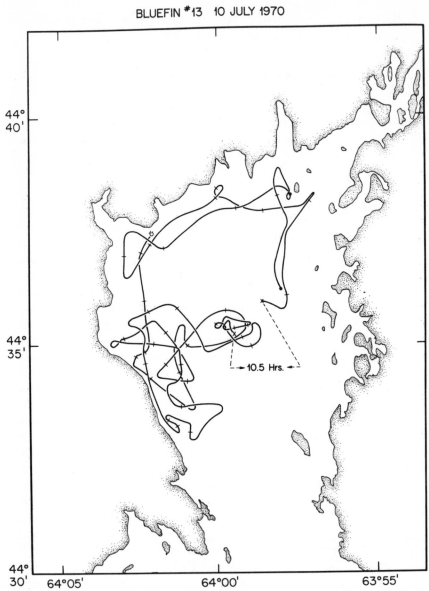

FIG. 1.   The track of bluefin no. 13, July 10, 1970, in St. Margaret Bay, Nova Scotia.

to follow the temperatures of free-swimming fishes, first, because we had encountered considerable skepticism that tuna were normally warm; there was a feeling that their high temperatures were a result of strenuous exercise during capture or were due to some other artifact. A more serious problem had to do with the way our information on temperature regulation had been obtained. We had measured temperatures of fish caught in varying water temperatures over a wide span of time and location. It is well known that fish adapt quickly to various environments, and it seemed possible that the apparent temperature control we observed was an acclimation involving tissue and enzyme changes over an extended period of time rather than the rapid thermoregulation that mammals are capable of. If we could put a device on a free-swimming tuna and follow its body temperature as it changed water temperature, we could soon find what sort of temperature control it was using. At the same time we would still doubt that tuna were not normally warm. We decided to press this experiment during the following season and gained National Geographic Society support for the field work.

Our visit to St. Margaret Bay, Nova Scotia, that summer convinced us that we should return there to work on bluefin. The year 1967 had been a very good one for the Coolen Brothers who ran the traps in St. Margaret Bay, and they took some 700 giant bluefin during the month of July alone. The Coolens were very helpful, and the nature of the traps used there made it much easier to let a fish out than the kind used in Provincetown. St. Margaret Bay seemed like a much better place to work on bluefin than anywhere else, and in 1968 we applied to the Society for support for an expedition there.

While working in Provincetown during the summer of 1967 we tried to follow the temperature of a tuna swimming on the end of a long wire while we chased after it in a little boat. In these attempts the fish either died or got around a lobster pot or some kelp and pulled off the wire. After a good deal of effort we abandoned this idea in favor of an acoustic telemetry system. During the winter we designed and constructed the necessary transmitters and receiving system. The transmitters were small and designed to fit a tuna's back or in its stomach. They broadcast information on the fish's body temperature and the water temperature where it was swimming at a changing pulse rate of 21-kilocycle sound. The various transmitters had life spans of 6 hours to 3 days and could be heard from 1.5 to 5 miles. We would follow the fish by using a steerable hydrophone, which was highly sensitive in one direction. By rotating the hydrophone we would find the strongest signal and steer the boat toward it, thus following the fish.

We had high hopes when we set out for St. Margaret Bay that summer but were disappointed to find that the tuna had not arrived and did not come during the several weeks we hung around. That summer the bluefin tuna had gone to the northern bays of Newfoundland, and when it seemed that we would not get fish in St. Margaret Bay we went off to Newfoundland to try and rescue something from the season. We were disappointed there also, for although the bluefin were abundant there was no commercial

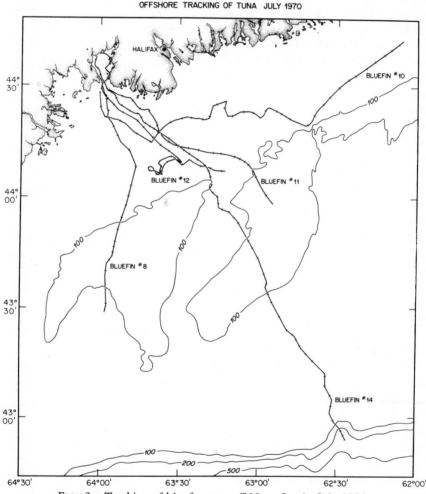

OFFSHORE TRACKING OF TUNA   JULY 1970

FIG. 2.   Tracking of bluefin tuna off Nova Scotia, July 1970.

fishery for them, and bad weather and an inadequate vessel kept us from catching any ourselves. We felt really defeated when we went home, but our spirits recovered with time and we decided to try again the following season.

In 1969 we had support again from the National Geographic Society and also from the Bureau of Sport Fisheries, and the two sources provided enough means for our field work during the summer of 1970 also. Working in cooperation with the Fisheries Research Board of Canada, we had the use of one of its research vessels the first summer. Although satisfactory, the boat was crewed only on an 8-hour-day basis, and while we succeeded in implanting transmitters in four fish we could follow them only for a few hours before the working day was up and the fish had to be abandoned. However, we were delighted to find that our equipment worked very well and that we could record temperatures from free-swimming fishes. They did stay warm during the time that we followed them, showing that the high temperature in tuna was a normal condition, not just an artifact of capture. The temperature control experiment was not a success that summer however. None of the fish changed their water temperature for a long enough time to make a convincing experiment, and we returned to St. Margaret again in 1970.

In the summer of 1970 we chartered a 60-foot line vessel, *Ella & Roby,* from Port La Tour, Nova Scotia, for the month of July. This was an able boat with a two-man crew who were used to staying at sea for days at a time. There were plenty of fish that summer, and we succeeded in implanting transmitters in both the muscle and the stomachs of bluefin. We were fortunate enough to have some of these fish swim from warm to cold water and were much interested to see that their body temperatures did not change but were held constant, showing the type of thermoregulation that mammals are capable of. The results of these temperature experiments are in a report entitled "Temperature Regulation in Free-swimming Bluefin Tuna" (Carey and Lawson).

It was an exciting experience following these great fish. Most of them moved directly down the bay and out to sea, swimming a steady 3 to 6 knots but occasionally stopping in shoal areas for 1/2-hour to 1-hour periods before going on. On one occasion the fish we were following was a member of a school of four that we saw breaking water in pursuit of bait. We were pleased to see this indication that our telemetry device did not disturb the fish's normal activity. One fish remained in the bay, wandering about near the surface. We left it at night and picked it up again the following morning and followed it for another day (see fig. 1). Our tracking gear

Fig. 3. The *Ella & Roby*, rigged with tracking gear for following bluefin tuna.

worked very well, and it was very easy to stay with a fish. Some of the tuna that went out to sea seemed to follow a constant course day and night with little variation; others changed direction or went along the coast. Figure 1 shows the course taken by some of these fish. Our last fish was followed for 56 hours and went 130 miles to sea to the edge of the continental shelf. We plan to write a paper on the behavior of these fish as we followed them, where they spent time, how they swam, and what water temperatures they sought.

REFERENCES

CAREY, FRANCIS G.
    1973. Fishes with warm bodies. Sci. Amer., vol. 228, no. 2, pp. 36-44, illus.
CAREY, FRANCIS G., and LAWSON, KENNETH D.
    1973. Temperature regulation in free-swimming bluefin tuna. Comp. Biochem. Physiol., vol. 44A, pp. 375-392, illus.
CAREY, FRANCIS G., and TEAL, JOHN M.
    1966. Heat conservation in tuna fish muscle. Proc. Nat. Acad. Sci., vol. 56, no. 5, pp. 1466-1469, illus.
    1969a. Mako and porbeagle: warm-bodied sharks. Comp. Biochem. Physiol., vol. 28, pp. 199-204, illus.
    1969b. Regulation of body temperature by the bluefin tuna. Comp. Biochem. Physiol., vol. 28, pp. 205-213, illus.
CAREY, FRANCIS G.; TEAL, JOHN M.; KANWISHER, JOHN W.; LAWSON, KENNETH D., and BECKETT, JAMES S.
    1971. Warm-bodied fish. Amer. Zool., vol. 11, pp. 137-145, illus.
CAREY, FRANCIS G.; TEAL, JOHN M.; and KLEIJN, K.
    1972. Body temperatures of black-tip sharks, *Carcharinus limbatus*. Deep-Sea Res., vol. 19, pp. 179-181.
LAWSON, KENNETH D., and CAREY, FRANCIS G.
    1972. An acoustic telemetry system for transmitting body and water temperature from free swimming fish, 21 pp., illus. Woods Hole Oceanographic Institution, Woods Hole, Massachusetts.
LINTHICUM, D. SCOTT, and CAREY, FRANCIS G.
    1972. Regulation of brain and eye temperatures by the bluefin tuna. Comp. Biochem. Physiol., vol. 43A, pp. 425-433.

FRANCIS G. CAREY

Calypso Oceanographic Researches, 1967

Principal Investigator: Jacques-Yves Cousteau, Institut Océanographique, Monaco.

Grant Nos. 657-659: In continuation of the Society's support of Captain Cousteau's underwater research.

Study of the Vertical Migrations in the Sea

In April 1967 a study of the vertical migrations of marine organisms was undertaken by scientists and divers aboard the *Calypso* by direct observation of the migratory movements, using the SP-350 diving saucer. The saucer descended to approximately 300 meters and recorded the various manifestations of life in terms of time and depth, as well as the direction of migratory movements, either according to the average direction of immediate displacement or the displacement of zones of life between the descent and ascent of the saucer. The complete exploration (descent and ascent) lasted between 50 minutes and 1 hour 25 minutes. The speed of both the descent and the ascent was essentially the same, averaging between 8 and 12 meters per minute.

Because these migrations were related to the phenomena of the DSL (Deep Scattering Layer) and took place around the setting and rising of the sun, the dives were scheduled in the evening at dusk and at night (4 dives) or in the morning at dawn (2 dives). They were performed in the Indian Ocean along approximately 800 miles between lat. 00°25′N. and 01°00′S. and between long. 69° and 56°E. The average depth in this entire region is more than 2,000 fathoms. The dives were made on April 9, 10, 11, 13, and 17. The four evening dives took place on April 9, 11, 13 (at night), and 10 (right after sunset). The two dives at dawn were made on April 11 and 17, the hour of sunrise corresponding approximately to the saucer's arrival at 300 meters. The first observation made was that the evening dives allowed one to observe a relatively stabilized situation, whereas during the dives at dawn it was possible to witness the actual displacement of the layers of organisms as they returned to the bottom with the light drawing near.

In all the dives made after sunset there was first a layer of clear water and then somewhat lower was a zone of murky water, beginning several meters below the surface and extending over several dozens of meters.

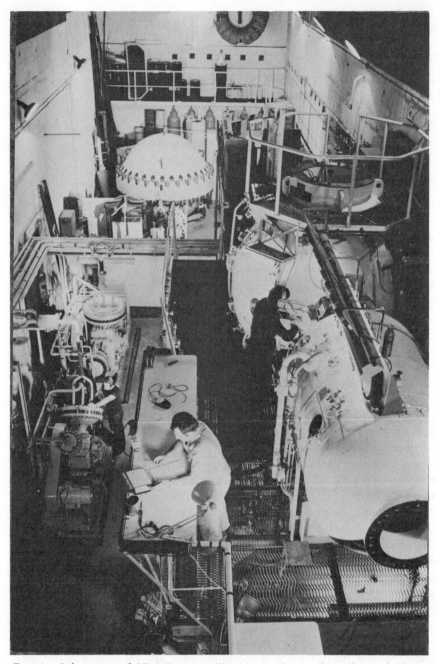

FIG. 1. Laboratory of High-Pressure Physiology, Center for Advanced Marine Studies.

This zone offered a rather precise maximum of density of organisms at about half the distance from its lower and upper extremities. During these dives small, shiny fishes and squids were found along with shrimps and small crustaceans. Particularly dense concentrations of these organisms were visible at 50 meters on April 9 and at 70 meters on the 11th and 13th. Under the zone of life, crawling near the surface, on the 11th and 13th a second zone of dense life was seen that made the water murky at a considerably lower depth of 180 meters; live plankton, shrimps, and jellyfishes were evident. During the first dive performed on the 9th, a diffusion layer identified by the sounder at 270 meters, on 12 and 34 kilocycles, seemed to spread out in front of the saucer's projectors — a fact that could be compared to a similar phenomenon observed in 1954, also in the Indian Ocean, with the first automatic Edgerton cameras with flash. The diffusing layer on the recorder of the sounder disappeared at the spot where the cameras and their flash were located.

During all the dives performed at dawn several meters beneath the surface (25 meters on the 11th, 45 meters on the 17th) an intense zone of life was observed that made the water murky but was laid out in various ways. On the 11th, the maximum of life and opacity was much closer to the surface than the deep limit of this zone, and this limit descended to about 10 feet between the two passages of the saucer. On the 17th, when the dive was made closer to sunrise than it was on the 11th, there was no maximum of life and opacity, and this zone, which extended from 45 to 90 meters at the time of the saucer's descent, had immersed to a depth of 70 meters and reached 160 meters during the ascent of the machine. During these two dives the saucer observed many fishes, shrimps, and squids swimming toward the bottom, as well as some "peas" agitating with disorganized and very rapid movements — which could be identified, thanks to a careful scrutiny, as very small shrimps doubled over, their tails swimming very rapidly in every direction, with the cloud moving toward the bottom. Toward 300 meters there is a zone of dense and muddy waters. This migratory movement toward the bottom seems to begin precisely before dawn and draws to the bottom layers of dense life that has accumulated during the night near the surface, separating the migrating organisms into several groups. This would explain the presence of these layers of muddy waters at 300 meters, the point at which the saucer would have joined up with the fastest swimmers, the shrimps and the siphonophores.

Conshelf IV

After the success of the Conshelf III experiment, a new type of equipment became necessary in order to execute the Conshelf IV project. The objective of Conshelf IV was to carry out operations from the experimental submarine *Argyronète* below 600 meters.

The year 1967 was devoted to the construction and mounting of the sphere with the existing caissons and to conducting a series of experiments on animals at the Laboratory of High Pressure Physiology, under the direction of Prof. Jacques Chouteau of the University of Marseille School of Science.

The Spherical Caisson: The sphere was built by assembling two hemispheric segments, the latter for the purpose of diminishing the areas where it would be impossible to create any openings (screens, doors, etc.). The two segments were made by forging iron plates 80 millimeters thick. All the doors were polished after the thermal treatment. The construction was completed in 10 months, including installation of two high-pressure filters for the regeneration system and two caissons for superpressurization. Upon its arrival in Marseille, and after an assemblage with one of the existing caissons, the sphere was connected to the following apparatuses:

- high-pressure regeneration
- vacuum
- pressuring
- physicochemical control
- low-pressure regeneration
- pressurized water

Inside, the equipment was installed so as to be easily disassembled, for 2-man experiments. For animal experiments it was necessary to disassemble this equipment, take the floor apart, and install a new one for the animals (goats). The animals' food, stocked in the sphere during the entire experiment, was automatically replenished as the animals consumed it. The installation was completed by setting up a measuring and recording bay for the physical parameters — temperature and pressure — at various points.

During June the so-called "Boucanox" experiments were undertaken for the purpose of studying the phenomena resulting from anoxia and to determine the goats' extreme point of resistance. In order to check the results of a preceding experiment ("Ursula") we proceeded to the "Boucazote" O_2-N_2 experiments, to find out whether the same hypoxic troubles would disappear by raising the partial pressure of oxygen. The result was confirmed by a mixture (O_2-N_2) having approximately the same specific weight as the one used in "Ursula" (O_2-He).

Photographic Equipment

The problem of photography arose while a study was being made of the construction of the two small 500-meter submarines designed for *Calypso* equipment. With the motion-picture situation resolved by the two 16- and 35-millimeter outside hull cameras, several alternatives were offered:

(1) To replace one of the motion-picture cameras with an Edgerton photographic camera, couple with an electronic flash.

(2) To use an inner photographic unit.

(3) Not to install a photographic camera but to use the film of the 35-millimeter motion-picture camera by selecting certain images.

In the first case, besides a consideration of costs, it would be necessary to build a special box, the weight and size of which would correspond to those of the motion-picture camera. In the second, it would be difficult to pilot a machine and manipulate a still camera at the same time. In the third, the quality of the motion-picture images would not be so good as that of the stills. For cinematographic reasons, the first alternative was temporarily dropped but remains under study. Thus, the third solution remained, allowing for an important choice of the film images (35-millimeter camera, 130-meter reels, 18-millimeter Cook lens, 9.8 TGA, 1/50 shutter speed, F-2.8 —with two 750-watt quartz iodide lamps). At the same time, the second solution remains partly valid in certain cases where the submarine is placed at the bottom or where it is interesting to photograph close-ups with a reflex finder.

In a field such as underwater exploration, nothing is definitive. A high degree of flexibility of equipment as well as of manpower is needed in order to adapt to different types of problems and working conditions.

REFERENCES

AQUADRO, C.-F., and CHOUTEAU, JACQUES
  1967. Problems of extreme duration in open sea saturation exposure. Chap. 10 (pp. 98-108) *in* "Underwater Physiology," C. J. Lambertsen, ed. Williams & Wilkins Co., Baltimore.
CHOUTEAU, JACQUES
  1969. Saturation diving: The Conshelf experiments. Chap. 21 (pp. 491-504) *in* "The Physiology and Medicine of Diving and Compressed Air Work," 532 pp., illus. Peter B. Bennett and David H. Elliott, eds. Baillière, Tindall & Cassel, Ltd., London.

CHOUTEAU, JACQUES; COUSTEAU, JACQUES-YVES; and ALINAT, J.
   1967. Manifestations hypoxiques lors de la respiration sous pression de mélanges respiratoires (O_2-He; O_2-N_2) normoxiques. Influence de la masse spécifique du mélange. Journ. Physiol., Paris, vol. 59, no. 4, p. 376
CHOUTEAU, JACQUES; COUSTEAU, JACQUES-YVES; ALINAT, J.; and AQUADRO, C.-F.
   1967a. Expérimentation animale de séjour prolongé en oxygène-helium de 41 à 58 bar. Journ. Physiol., Paris, vol. 59, no. 1 bis, p. 225.
   1967b. Sur les limites physiologiques d'utilization du mélange respiratoire oxygène-helium par la plongée et les séjours prolongés sous pression. Compt. Rend. Acad. Sci. Paris, vol. 264, pp. 1731-1734.
   1968. Sur les limites physiologiques de la plongée à saturation à l'air et aux mélanges synthétiques (O_2-N_2, O_2-He). Rev. Physiol. Subaq. et Med. Hyperbare, vol. 1, no. 1, pp. 38-44, graphs.
NATIONAL ACADEMY OF SCIENCES and NATIONAL RESEARCH COUNCIL
   1967. Proceedings of the Third Symposium on Underwater Physiology, Washington, D. C., March 23-25, 1967.

JACQUES-YVES COUSTEAU

Radiotelemetry Research on Large Western Mammals in Yellowstone National Park, Wyoming, 1967

Principal Investigators: Frank C. Craighead, Jr., Atmospheric Sciences Research Center, State University of New York at Albany, and Environmental Research Institute, Moose, Wyoming; and John J. Craighead, Montana Cooperative Wildlife Research Unit, Missoula, Montana.

Grant No. 643: For continuation of study of large mammals in Yellowstone National Park by means of radiotelemetry.

A cooperative ecological research project to develop and employ radiotelemetry techniques for studying grizzly bears *(Ursus arctos horribilis),* elk *(Cervus canadensis),* and black bears *(Ursus americanus)* was continued through 1967. Cooperating and supporting agencies included the National Geographic Society, National Science Foundation, Atomic Energy Commission, Philco Corporation, National Park Service, U. S. Fish and Wildlife Service, Wildlife Management Institute, Environmental Research Institute, and the Yellowstone Park Company (which contributed buildings and utilities in the Park). Research team collaborators included Frank C. Craighead, Jr.; John J. Craighead; Joel Varney, Philco Corporation; Hoke Franciscus, Carlisle, Pennsylvania; and Jay Sumner and Henry McCutchen, Montana Cooperative Wildlife Research Unit.

Our experience in telemetering body temperature from free-roaming elk (Craighead and Craighead, 1966, 1972) paved the way for attempting to telemeter a nychthemeral body-temperature recording from a "hibernating" black bear. Participation in Dr. Vincent J. Schaefer's Seventh Field Research Expedition in Yellowstone Park provided the opportunity to do this (Craighead and Craighead, 1967). During the winter of 1967 we made three trips to the winter den of a black bear located on the Gibbon River in Yellowstone National Park. Our objective was to telemeter simultaneously the body temperature of the bear, the den temperature, and the ambient air temperature. The first trip was made on January 26-28, the second on January 30-31, and the third on February 20-21.

On the morning of January 27 we injected the bear with 125 milli-

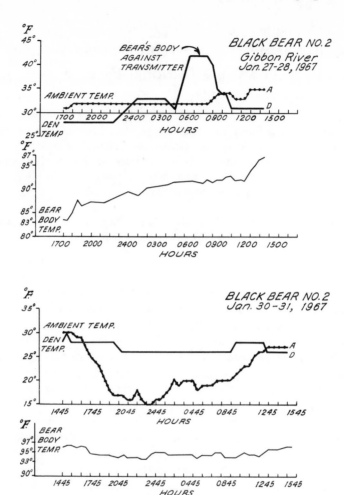

FIG. 1.   Graph of den, ambient-air, and body temperatures, black bear no. 2.

grams of sernylan (phencyclidine hydrochloride). This was a dose of about
1 milligram (100 mg. per cc. solution) per pound of body weight. Following
anesthetization, we shaved a small area at the back of the bear's neck, made
a 2.5-centimeter incision, and inserted the temperature probe to a depth of
about 4 centimeters. The incision was then sutured and disinfected. The
bear's rectal temperature taken about 2 hours after immobilization was
96.0° F. After returning the bear to its den we monitored the bear's temperature, the temperature of the den chamber, and the outside ambient air

temperature each half hour by radio from our camp in the canyon below the bear's den. Three transmitters were employed, and all three simultaneously transmitted the data on a frequency of 32.01 MHz. Differences in pitch and pulse rate enabled us readily to differentiate the signals and to count with a stop watch the pulse from each transmitter (Craighead and Craighead, 1972a). The ambient air temperatures were obtained by use of a standard thermometer and by telemetry. Plans to record body temperature with an automatic chart recorder could not be carried out because of a delay in getting the equipment.

At 1700 on the 27th we began monitoring the radio signals. We obtained a body temperature of 83.5° F., a den temperature of 28° F., and an outside ambient air temperature 31° F. (fig. 1). The body temperature of 83.5° F. was in contrast to the earlier rectal temperature recording of 96.0° F. This drop of 12.5° was apparently due in part to chilling while we were working with the bear as well as to the drug effect. Such an effect has been observed with this drug in some monkeys and in the *Anabis* baboon.

At 1200 the next day (January 28) the bear's body temperature registered 92.0° F. The animal was resting but awake. At this time a flash used to take a photograph of the bear in the den alerted and disturbed him and he came out of the den. Minutes later he had climbed the snow slope above the den and his body temperature registered 91.7° F. At 1230, with the bear still in the snow above the den, the transmitter recorded a body temperature of 91.5° F. and at 1248, 48 minutes after leaving the den, a temperature of 91.5° F. Approximately an hour after the animal left the den at 1305, the body temperature was 93.5° F.; at 1320 it was 94.5° F.; and by 1430 it had climbed to 96.7° F. There was no immediate or rapid increase in body temperature coinciding with the bear's strenuous physical exertion. There was, however, a temperature rise of 4.7° F. 2½ hours following the exertion and at a time when the bear was relatively inactive. The temperature rise cannot be interpreted as a local heat increase from musuclar activity. It may be associated with a normal rise in the bear's diurnal-nocturnal temperature rhythm.

We returned to the den site on January 30 to monitor the body temperature of the bear during a 24-hour period. The bear was not disturbed, and temperature recording began at 1445 on January 30. Over the period the temperature of the den varied from 26° to 30° F. but remained relatively constant at 26°-28° F. The ambient air temperature varied from 15° to 30° F. The bear's body temperature dropped to a minimum of 93.7° F. and reached a high of 96.2° F., a spread of 2.5° F. (fig. 1). In general, the variation in body temperature coincided with the variation in outside air tem-

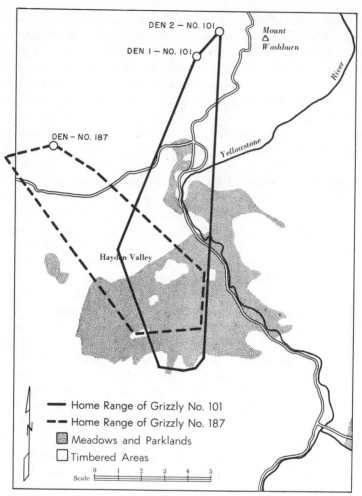

FIG. 2.   Grizzly home ranges, 1967.

perature as well as with the more constant den temperature. Although the
bear was in a darkened den where day-night variations in light intensity
were slight, his body temperature showed a diurnal-nocturnal temperature
rhythm (fig. 1).

On February 20 we returned to the black-bear den to obtain another
nychthemeral body-temperature pattern. We hoped to measure the bear's
body temperature under conditions of deeper sleep and lower environmental temperatures. A brief period of monitoring indicated that the

temperature probe had pulled out of the bear, and so we were unable to obtain another 24-hour body-temperature pattern. The temperature probe was functioning, however, and we were able to record temperatures of the microclimate between the bear and his well-insulated bed. The winter bed was fashioned from a mixture of dry pine needles and finely shredded twigs. This porous insulation created a microclimate between the bear and its bed with a temperature approaching that of the bear's body. The maximum temperature reading of 96.7° F. probably occurred with the probe under a portion of the bear's body where the hair was thin and heat conduction from the body efficient. When the bear moved, the distance between the bear's body and the probe altered, causing brief temperature changes that fluctuated over a 40-minute period from 96.5° to 83.0° F.

In an attempt to simulate the conditions of maximum heat, we placed a thermometer between a human body and several layers of underwear, shirt, and down jacket. The temperature recorded in this manner was 95.0° F., or 1.7° F. lower than the maximum recorded for the bear's bed. All electronic equipment was subsequently checked and found to be functioning properly; therefore the temperature recording of 96.7° F. ($\pm 1°$) for the bear's cutaneous temperature or for his bed must be accepted as approximately correct. A probable explanation is that the bear's deep-body temperature at the time was close to 100.0° F., a temperature attained in summer when the bear is nonlethargic. The unusual alertness and activity exhibited by the bear suggest that such an increase in body temperature may, in fact, have occurred.

The microclimate between the bear and its bed constitutes an area estimated at approximately three-quarters of the bear's body surface when curled in sleep. The insulated bed was 18 inches deep, 30 inches in diameter, and cuplike in shape, with nearly perpendicular walls against which the bear's body fit snugly. When the bear was curled in a sleeping position, he was slightly below the rim of the cup in a microclimate where temperature changes were minimized.

The temperature of the den chamber or cave (space above and around the bed) remained quite constant, responding slightly to changes in outside ambient temperatures, as revealed by the graph (fig. 1). Body heat that radiated from the exposed portion of the sleeping bear (one-fourth his body area) was trapped in the upper reaches of the low cave. This exerted only a slight warming effect on the entire interior of the den.

As indicated earlier, the bear's rectal temperature was 96.0° F. following immobilization; the body-temperature variations over the 24-hour monitoring period (January 30-31) ranged from 93.7° to 96.2° F. This suggests that the deep-sleep or dormancy temperature may be influenced by the environmental temperature or microclimate enveloping the bear and that this in turn may to a considerable extent vary with or even be regulated by the bear's thermoregulatory processes.

In contrast to this animal, another black bear observed in winter sleep prepared no bed whatsoever and slept on the bare earth floor of the den chamber. The den was in a thermal area and was warmed by a thermal spring. The temperature of the den or microclimate approached room temperature, and thus a warm and constant environmental temperature comparable to the black bear in his insulated bed was attained by other means and no insulated bed was needed or prepared.

Hedge et al. (1965), reporting on studies of winter lethargy of black and grizzly bears in captivity, found that two black bears and one grizzly bear as cold weather developed (as low as $-60°$ F.) gradually spent more time in dens. All three bears became dormant in the sense that they did not leave the curled-up position for as long as a month at a time.

The black bear we have reported on here and one other were lethargic under natural hibernating conditions but not in a state of deep dormancy. This does not infer that in the course of the winter they did not attain a state of hypothermic lethargy, but only that when we observed them they were readily roused and on occasions quite active. They were not exposed to den environmental temperature conditions as low as those of Hedge's bears in captivity. Possibly the microclimate temperature determines the degree of lethargy needed and achieved by a bear in its winter den. Winter-sleep conditions of wild bears may vary greatly with individuals and may also vary greatly from those observed under conditions of captivity. Extended periods of monitoring deep-body temperature and bed and den temperatures of different bears under a variety of deep-sleep conditions should reveal not only significant interrelationships between body temperatures and environmental temperatures but also factors influencing the degree of winter lethargy.

One female grizzly was instrumented in an attempt to determine the period of developmental arrest from conception to implantation. Delayed implantation has been conclusively demonstrated in the grizzly bear (Craighead, Hornocker, and Craighead, 1969), but the length of the delay period is unknown.

Some animals were instrumented in order to test newly developed equipment and others in order to gather biological data.

Table 2 presents data on the size of four additional grizzly-bear ranges (Craighead and Craighead, 1969). Female no. 40 has been instrumented

TABLE 1.—GRIZZLY-BEAR RADIO-LOCATING DATA, 1967

Bear no.	Number of days radio operating	Number of days attempted to locate by radio	Number of days no attempts to locate by radio	Number of days successful in locating	Percent days successful from attempts made to locate	Number of days visual sightings attempted with aid of signal	Number of days visual sightings were made	Percent of sightings successful from attempts made	Remarks
40	16	14	2	13	93	1	0	0	
101	49	38	11	36	95	16	12	75	
187	65	59	6	54	92	9	7	78	
188	15	13	2	13	100	0	0	0	
Totals	145	124	21	116	94%	26	19	72	

TABLE 2.—GRIZZLY-BEAR RANGES DETERMINED BY RADIO TRACKING, 1967

Bear no.	Tracking dates	Animal tracking days	Number of days located or sighted	Area of range in square miles	Remarks
188	8/22 – 8/26	15	13	6.7	Lone three-year old male
40	9/5 – 9/14	16	13	11.1	Lone sow (pregnant)
187	9/11 – 9/26 9/4 – 11/7	65	54	39.8	Lone sow (pregnant)
101	9/6 – 9/28 10/19 – 11/13	49	36	43.1	Sow with yearlings

FIG. 3. Immobilized black bear at entrance to den being fitted with a radio-collar for telemetering body temperature.

for seven consecutive years, and the size of her home range and her centers of activity within her home range have been accurately determined and thoroughly described. Four of her winter dens have been located by the

FIG. 4. Natural rock cave used by black bear for winter den. Bear within den has just been injected with immobilizing drug sernylan.

use of radio, and this information is presented in Craighead and Craighead (1972b). Information on home and seasonal ranges and daily, seasonal, and migratory movements of 23 grizzlies radiotracked during a seven-year period will be presented in a report, "Home Ranges and Movements of Instrumented Grizzly Bears."

During 1967, home ranges were determined for females no. 187 and 101, table 2. No. 187 was a 4½-year-old female known to have mated and thought to be pregnant. Her prehibernation movements were closely monitored. She made two treks to her den before finally returning to hibernate. Female no. 101 had one yearling and two adopted ones. Throughout the summer they traveled, slept, and foraged together and were apparently inseparable. Both of the adopted yearlings nursed the female. The female, however, hibernated with only her single offspring; the two adopted yearlings denned within the home range of their mother (sow no. 40), but their den or dens were not located.

We disturbed no. 101 at her den while tracking her; she abandoned the den and then selected a new site and dug another den within a period of about a week. Her activities during this time were closely monitored by radio. Details of the behavior and movements of females nos. 187 and 101 will be reported in greater detail in future reports.

Two black bears were instrumented during 1967 to determine movements and ranges. Bear no. 1 had also been instrumented the previous year.

On September 19, 1966, a young adult male black bear (no. 1) was instrumented with an extended-life transmitter and tagged with a color marker at Canyon Village. This instrumentation was a preliminary attempt to test the radiotracking system on this species and to obtain data on movement and homing behavior. On September 23, 1966, the bear was retrapped at Canyon Village by National Park Service rangers and released at Hayden Valley, seven airline miles to the south of Canyon. On September 30 the bear was located in a denning area near Lake, approximately 15 miles south of Canyon. The bear remained in this area, moving in and out of its den. The signal from the bear was monitored throughout October. The last signal was obtained on October 29 when the bear finally denned for the winter.

The following summer black bear no. 1 was seen at Tower and on August 3, 1967, he was immobilized and the radio-collar removed. The distance from Lake to Tower is 25 airline miles. On September 12, 1967, the bear was trapped in Canyon Village 10 airline miles south of Tower and again was instrumented with an extended-life transmitter. He remained in the Canyon area until September 17, after which the signal was lost. On September 25 the signal was detected near Lake in the same area where he had denned the previous year. A final signal was picked up on October 2 and the bear denned after this date.

Several features of this animal's movements are of interest. The distance the bear moved from one extreme of his range to the other was 25 airline miles. In making this movement he crossed Dunraven Pass and negotiated other rugged mountain terrain. Timing of movements for both years shows a high degree of correlation. The bear denned in the same area both years. No defense of a home range was observed. He entered the home ranges of other black bears and at times foraged jointly with these bears. We obtained no evidence from this animal that the black bear in Yellowstone is territorial.

Black bear no. 3 was trapped November 20, 1967, at Mammoth as it was preparing to den. It was instrumented with a radio and released in the Old Faithful area approximately 25 airline miles away on November 21.

From November 21 to 29 this bear wandered in the vicinity of the release site making no attempt to home to the site of capture. The animal was monitored by radio and visually tracked in about 10 inches of snow. Between November 21 and 29 the bear located a rocky cliff with numerous natural caves. Tracks showed that the bear had traversed the area back and forth, entering and leaving caves. It seemed certain that the animal was

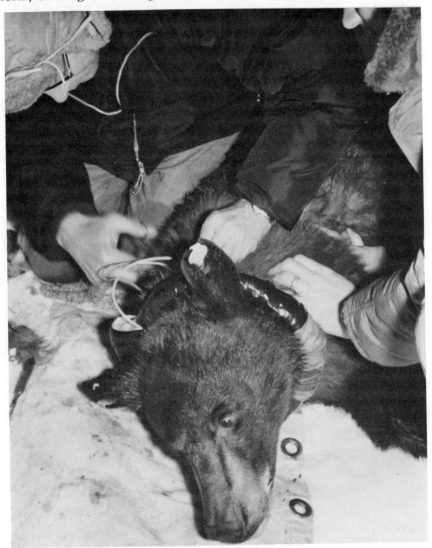

FIG. 5.   Suturing temperature probe in neck region of black bear.

FIG. 6. Disturbance causes bear to leave den. Black bears and grizzlies, though lethargic during winter sleep, can readily be aroused to action.

seeking a winter den site. We lost the radio signal in this area on November 29 and presumed the bear had denned since no tracks leaving the area were located, nor was the signal picked up after that date.

It is of interest that black bears released in a similar manner during the summer months normally home to the area of capture. Winter conditions and perhaps the onset of lethargy drove bear no. 3 to "hibernate" near the release site.

During 1967 work was completed on a two-year study of instrumented and color-marked elk in the Old Faithful and Norris areas of Yellowstone. Movement and range data obtained from seven cow elk instrumented for a total of 1,216 days are being compiled in a separate report.

Inquiry from biological researchers concerning application of our radiotracking system for big-game animals has increased steadily. Specific requests for information and help have come from Dr. Charles Jonkel, Canadian Wildlife Service; Jack Lentfer, Alaska State Fish and Game Department; and Thor Larson, Norwegian Polar Institute, University of Oslo, Norway. These biologists are conducting research programs on the polar bear *(Ursus maritimus)* but do not have access to biotelemetry equipment or to researchers experienced in the development and use of such equipment. At the invitation of Dr. Jonkel we made a trip to Hudson Bay in September 1967 to confer on the feasibility of utilizing our electronic equipment on the polar bear. At Churchill we met and conferred with Dr. Albert W. Erickson, University of Minnesota, Dr. Vagn Flyger, University of Maryland, and Mr. Larson.

Funding was provided by the U. S. Bureau of Sports Fisheries and Wildlife, the Canadian Wildlife Service, the National Geographic Society, and the Environmental Research Institute. Our objectives were to familiarize ourselves with the polar-bear environment and field research conditions in order to assist and advise our colleagues and to demonstrate in the field the use of our equipment. We were prepared to instrument and track two polar bears and to leave the equipment with Dr. Jonkel. The equipment consisted of two transmitters, two receivers, a quad antenna, and other items of gear.

As the Canadian researchers were unsuccessful in capturing polar bears during our brief stay, we were unable to instrument any animals. However, we demonstrated the use of our equipment to the biologists present and tested it under arctic-tundra conditions. Tests showed the equipment would be effective. From the informal conference and field testing, we concluded that we could contribute substantially to the International Program of Polar Bear Research by providing the researchers with minimal equipment needs and on-the-spot aid in assembling and utilizing our biotelemetry system. There was unanimous agreement that this approach would be far superior to independent development and

FIG. 7.   Instrumented black bear in den with body-temperature transmitter around neck. The transmitter beside his head was used to transmit den temperature but in this case was moved by bear. (See fig. 1.)

experimentation by individual researchers in the field of biotelemetry. Programs in Alaska, Canada, and Norway could be initiated much faster, at far less expense, and with much less work and frustration if the polar-bear researchers could use a perfected radiotracking system and have competent field instruction and consultation during the initial stages of their programs.

Similar requests for aid in biotelemetry have come from Dr. Hugh Lamprey, Serengeti Research Institute; Dr. G. Schaller, Arusha, Tanzania; Dr. V. Sokolov, Academy of Science, Moscow, U.S.S.R.; and K. S. Dharmakumarsinhji, Vice Chairman for Wildlife, Bombay, India. Numerous requests have been received from United States biologists, including Dr. Maurice Hornocker, University of Idaho, who is working on the cougar *(Felis concolor),* and Dr. Richard Taber, University of Montana, working on mule deer *(Odocoileus hemionus)* and the bighorn sheep *(Ovis canadensis).*

FIG. 8. Insulated bed of black bear. A microclimate formed between bear and bed.

During 1967 emphasis was placed on development and testing of equipment for automatically recording telemetered information from wild, free-roaming animals. Three automatic recording systems were developed and tested. These were:

1. Equipment designed for 48-hour continuous recording on tape. Automatic recording was 1 minute in every 15. Radio signals were received through our standard tracking receiver on a frequency of 32.02 MHz. The taped information was summed and printed out by a totalizer (fig. 9).
2. A totalizer with direct printout and continuous recording of the information signal (for example, body temperature). This equipment totalized and printed out every 5 minutes.
3. Recording equipment with demodulator and battery operated Rustrak recorder.

All the above equipment is portable, battery operated, and designed for cold-weather operation.

New transmitters that were developed and tested for use with the automatic recording equipment consisted of:

1. A two-channel body-temperature transmitter for measuring body temperatures simultaneously at different depths (4 and 7 centi-

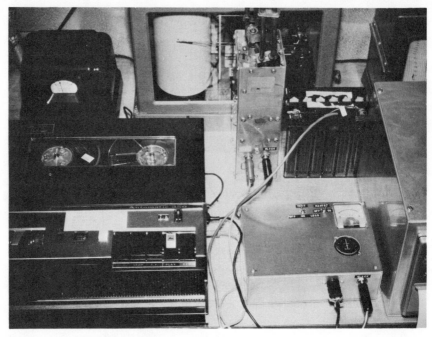

FIG. 9. Automatic recording on tape with printout on paper chart by totalizer at right.

meters) in the animal's body. Resulting temperatures can be correlated with animal behavior and activity.

2. An ambient-temperature transmitter for use in correlating animal behavior and changes in body temperature with fluctuations in ambient-temperature conditions.

3. An accelerometer transmitter for detecting and measuring changes in animal activity such as resting, walking, running, and feeding.

A multiplex box was constructed to switch alternately between inputs allowing sequential sampling from the various transmitters.

Preliminary analysis and breadboarding work were done on a chart recorder intended for use with the body-temperature transmitter and ambient-temperature transmitters. The results of this investigation show that it would be difficult to meet the desired accuracy limits in the case of the body-temperature transmitter with the present pulse-rate method, although satisfactory results can be obtained with the ambient-temperature transmitters.

A preliminary design for a recording circuit utilizing a Rustrak chart recorder and a digital period-measuring converter was completed. This circuit was not breadboarded because its usefulness is limited by the requirement for a 117 V AC power source. The objective of obtaining temperature measurement accuracy to 0.1° F. with a fully portable recording system can best be met by changing to a system utilizing subcarrier modulation rather than the present pulse-rate frequency modulation at a low repetition rate. Future work will proceed in this direction.

REFERENCES

CRAIGHEAD, FRANK C., JR.
 1971. Biotelemetry research with grizzly bears and elk in Yellowstone National Park, Wyoming, 1965. Nat. Geogr. Soc. Res. Rpts., 1965 Projects, pp. 49-62, illus.
CRAIGHEAD, FRANK C., JR., and CRAIGHEAD, JOHN J.
 1967. Seventh Yellowstone Field Research Expedition. Atmospheric Sci. Res. Center State Univ. New York at Albany Publ. no. 45. pp. 61-71.
 1968. Radiotracking of grizzly bears in Yellowstone National Park, Wyoming. Nat. Geogr. Soc. Res. Rpts., 1963 Projects, pp. 59-67, illus.
 1969. Radiotracking of grizzly bears in Yellowstone National Park, Wyoming, 1964. Nat. Geogr. Soc. Res. Rpts., 1964 Projects, pp. 35-43, illus.
 1970. Radiotracking of grizzly bears in Yellowstone National Park, Wyoming, 1962. Nat. Geogr. Soc. Res. Rpts., 1961-1962 Projects, pp. 63-71, illus.
 1972a. Radiotracking of grizzly bears in Yellowstone National Park, Wyoming, 1959-1960. Nat. Geogr. Soc. Res. Rpts., 1955-1960 Projects, pp. 55-62, illus.
 1972b. Grizzly bear prehibernation and denning activities as determined by radiotracking. Wildl. Monogr. 32, 35 pp., illus.
 1973. Radiotracking of grizzly bears and elk in Yellowstone National Park, Wyoming, 1966. Nat. Geogr. Soc. Res. Rpts., 1966 Projects, pp. 33-48, illus.
CRAIGHEAD, JOHN J., and CRAIGHEAD, FRANK C., JR.
 1966. Radiotelemetry of large western mammals, progress report 1965-1966. AEC Contract no. AT (45-1)-1929.
CRAIGHEAD, JOHN J.; HORNOCKER, MAURICE; and CRAIGHEAD, FRANK C., JR.
 1969. Reproductive biology of young female grizzly bears. Journ. Reprod. Fert. Suppl., vol. 6, pp. 447-475.
HEDGE, R. S.; FOLK, GEORGE E., JR.; and BREWER, MAX C.
 1965. Studies on winter lethargy of black and grizzly bears. Proc. 16th Alaskan Sci. Conf. (AAAS), vol. 16, pp. 31-32.

FRANK C. CRAIGHEAD, JR.
JOHN J. CRAIGHEAD

Search for the Ivory-billed Woodpecker

Principal Investigator: John V. Dennis, Princess Anne, Maryland.

Grant No. 664:   In support of a field study of the status of the American ivory-billed woodpecker *(Campephilus principalis).*

The reported sighting of an ivory-billed woodpecker twice on December 10, 1966, in the Neches River Valley of Texas, and continuing reports of the occurrence of this supposedly extinct bird in the region through that winter led to speculation that there might still be some hope for this species (Dennis, 1967). Evidence pointed to the possibility that a very few of the birds might have survived in the heavily timbered Big Thicket of eastern Texas. The last positive evidence of the ivorybill in that State in the form of actual specimens collected dates back to 1904. A National Geographic Society grant made in November 1967 enabled me to spend over half a year in eastern Texas for the purpose of substantiating, if possible, the existence of this bird and if still present ascertaining its numbers, whereabouts, and adaptations to changing conditions. The following is a condensed account of the search. The results cannot be called overly optimistic.

I realized that it was essential to gather and evaluate as much information as possible from reliable observers on the recent whereabouts of the bird, rather than waste time making a superficial coverage of large areas. But whom could I rely upon for accurate reporting? A year after I had made my first sightings on the Neches above Dam B, where others vouched for having seen the bird, I could find no fresh debarking of newly dead trees, nor did I make any further sightings or hear call notes. One report, that of a writer-photographer and his wife, who said that they had watched a feeding ivorybill for half an hour, seemed worth investigation, and I brought it to the attention of photographer Frederick K. Truslow. He went to Texas, set up headquarters near the locality of the suspected sighting, and made a number of trips into the area but with completely negative results. Also we made personal contacts with dozens of people in the Big Thicket region who either had professional knowledge of the ivorybill or who appeared qualified to help us. Although many of their reports seemed to be based upon the long-standing confusion of the ivorybill with the pileated woodpecker, a few appeared reasonably possible. I was particularly impressed by the observations of V. J. Withers, a veteran hunter and backswoodsman, who reported small details of plumage and behavior that matched my acquaintance with the generally similar Cuban ivorybill. On the several occasions that Withers had chanced upon an ivorybill he had been driving swamp roads in a pickup truck. As is true of the wild turkey, the ivorybill, from Withers's accounts, allows close approach by a vehicle but vanishes instantly from a person on foot. His sightings were in the Neches Valley about 8 miles north of Evadale, in a highly timbered region with many large oaks, cypress, and sweetgums. I made a likely sighting in this area in February 1967, and several other reports came from this same locality.

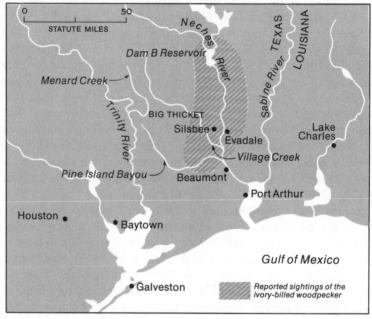

FIG. 1.   Map of the Big Thicket area.

Another very convincing report came in January 1968 from Peter Koch, a naturalist-photographer of Alpine, Texas, who reported seeing first a single bird, and then the next day a pair of ivorybills, in the Pine Island Bayou region of the lower Neches. He was able to follow a pair on foot for some distance and was briefly within camera range, but unfortunately he did not have time to set up his equipment.

Late in February 1968 we began to get reports of ivorybills from a small virgin-timber tract on Village Creek, a tributary of the Neches. Visiting the tract on the morning of the 25th, we taped what to us were unmistakable call notes of the ivorybill. We were highly elated over this and sent copies of the tape to the National Geographic Society. Dr. Alexander Wetmore, Dr. John W. Aldrich, and others at the Smithsonian Institution who heard it agreed that it appeared to check with the ancient recording. The tape became, however, the object of controversy, and later, when it was studied at the Cornell Laboratory of Ornithology, it was, in the opinion of the director, Dr. James Tate, too poor in quality to permit satisfactory identification.

At least half a dozen birdwatchers visiting Menard Creek, a tributary of the Big Thicket's Trinity River, reported hearing "tin trumpet" calls of the ivorybill at sundown. Yet on several visits neither I nor Peter Isleib, an ornithologist-photographer with me, heard the notes. Although we continued to receive reports of ivorybills in widely scattered parts of the Neches Valley and the Big Thicket through May 1968, we made no sightings of our own and found no reason for a return visit of Mr. Truslow.

All in all, the study yielded meager evidence of the ivorybill's existence, but the following conclusions may be stated:

1. Possibly two or three pairs of ivorybills may remain in the Big Thicket region of Texas.

2. Reported sightings indicate that the habitat of the ivorybill, one of the wariest of birds, may now be confined to cypress and hardwood bottomlands in big river valleys and a few tributary wilderness areas.

3. Undoubtedly, one reason for the ivorybill's decline may be its inability to compete successfully for food (and possibly for nesting sites) with the pileated woodpecker, which has greatly increased in numbers during this century through a wide variety of habitats. But loss of habitat and persecution at the hand of man remain basic reasons for the ivorybill's extirpation.

REFERENCES

DENNIS, JOHN V.
    1967. The ivory-bill flies still. Audubon Mag., vol. 69, no. 6, pp. 38-45, illus.
TANNER, JAMES T.
    1942. The ivory-billed woodpecker. Nat. Audubon Soc. Rpt. no. 1, 111 pp.,
      illus.

JOHN V. DENNIS

Prehistoric Dwellings in
Katmai National Monument, Alaska

Principal Investigator: Don E. Dumond, University of Oregon, Eugene, Oregon.

Grant No. 623: In support of the excavations of prehistoric aboriginal dwellings in Katmai National Monument, under the auspices of the University of Oregon and the National Park Service.

The direct and practical aim of this project was the excavation of aboriginal dwellings in the vicinity of the headquarters of Katmai National Monument (figs. 1, 2) that would be suitable for consolidation as tourist displays. The more purely scientific aim was to increase the existing archeological sample of implements and of nonportable cultural features representing certain prehistoric periods of special interest.

In the field excavations of 1967 I was assisted by Kenneth Luepke, Robert L. A. Mace, and Joe D. Stewart. The actual partial reconstruction of the single dwelling ultimately chosen for preservation was made by me, working alone, in 1968. The display aspect of the project has been reported as required by the contract between the University of Oregon and the National Park Service (Dumond, 1969b). The more strictly scientific results are summarized here.

Background

The first exploratory archeological excavation in the vicinity of Monument headquarters was done in 1953, under the auspices of the Katmai Project (Luntey, 1954), when two men from the University of Oregon tested one location (designated BR1; see fig. 2) on Brooks River (Davis, 1954).

In 1960 the University of Oregon began a program unrelated to the earlier test, fielding archeological research parties that worked at Brooks River (among other places) in 1960, 1961, 1963, 1964, and 1965; this research was financed largely by three separate grants from the National Science Foundation, with additional support both from the Bureau of

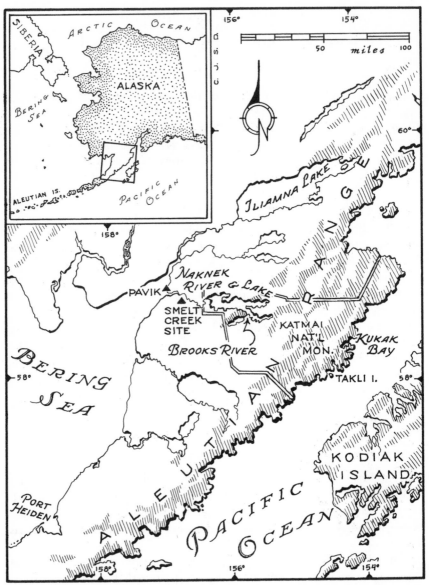

FIG. 1. The northern Alaska Peninsula. (Drawn by Carol Steichen Dumond.)

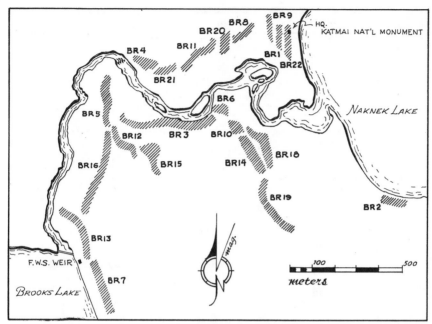

FIG. 2. Brooks River. Numbered locations are areas of prehistoric occupation, most of which lie along beach ridges and terraces formed during the evolution of the modern river bed. (Drawn by Carol Steichen Dumond.)

Commercial Fisheries of the U. S. Fish and Wildlife Service and from the National Park Service.

This later work resulted in the definition of a sequence of cultural phases thought to be generally representative of the area of the Naknek Lake and River drainage system and of nearby portions of the Bering Sea coast. These phases, as they are now dated by extensive radiocarbon determinations, are shown in figure 3. More synthetically, the prehistory of the Naknek drainage has been described (e.g., Dumond, 1969a) by means of four cultural periods, each of which is represented by one or more phases. These periods will be described briefly.

Kittewick period—Lasting from 2500 ± 100 to 1900 ± 100 B.C., this consists of the time represented by a single phase, the *B.R. Strand* phase. Before 1967 the small collections assigned to this phase consisted chiefly of chipped cutting and scraping implements, to which a few well-made polished slate lance blades were attributed only hesitantly. The 1967 results will be described below.

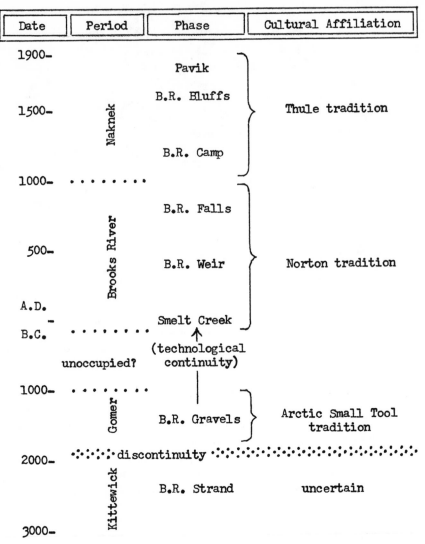

FIG. 3.   Sequence of phases in the Naknek drainage.

Gomer period — This time is represented by a single phase, the *B.R. Gravels* phase, now dated from 1900 ± 100 to 1000 ± 100 B.C. Before 1967 five habitations of the period had been tested or completely excavated, and a number of additional collections had been made from temporary campsites. Implements were predominantly of delicately flaked chalcedony, consisting of small bipointed endblades, burins, microblades, and well-chipped scrapers, together with small adz blades with polished bits, and with a few larger flaked knives. Affiliation with the Arctic Small Tool tradition (Irving, 1962, 1970) is unmistakable. In 1967 one additional habitation of the period was excavated completely, two others were tested extensively, and a third was tested briefly. The major work of that season is described below.

Between implements of the Kittewick period and those of the Gomer period there is virtually no continuity whatever. In view of this, and of the apparently almost instantaneous transition from one to the other, it is concluded that the initiation of the Gomer period occurs with the arrival of a new (northern) people who replaced the earlier occupants. The Gomer period was followed by a time in which Brooks River in the upper Naknek drainage, the site of much of the work, was apparently not occupied; whether the entire drainage system was similarly unoccupied is not known, but it seems unlikely.

Brooks River period — This time is represented by three phases — *Smelt Creek, B.R. Weir,* and *B.R. Falls* — and lasts from 200 ± 100 B.C. to A.D. 1000 ± 100. All phases may be assigned to a general Norton tradition, which takes its name from the Norton culture of Cape Denbigh, described by Giddings (1964), and which apparently developed from the earlier Arctic Small Tool tradition. Locally, the Smelt Creek phase saw the introduction of Norton-style pottery, an obvious import from the north and ultimately from Asia. Continuity with the preceding Gomer period is strong in stone implements, however, with some implements of the two periods being indistinguishable: both Gravels and Smelt Creek people used identical small stone-adz blades and made some similar small chipped projectile points. The B.R. Weir and B.R. Falls phases are recognizably different from each other and from Smelt Creek, but all are obviously joined together in a local evolutionary sequence in which the most Norton-like (Smelt Creek) phase developed into the later phases in turn. All of them include similar fiber-tempered pottery. During the period the use of polished slate implements increased steadily. Although it is possible that the reoccupation of Brooks River during the Smelt Creek phase represented another new influx of people to the Naknek drainage system, continuity in stone implements is strong enough that out-and-out population replacement in the entire Naknek area seems unlikely. No additional excavations in deposits of this period were made in 1967.

Naknek period — This, too, includes the time represented by three phases—*B.R. Camp, B.R. Bluffs,* and *Pavik*—lasting from A.D. 1000 ± 100 to A.D. 1900, and pertaining to what may be called the Thule tradition, a late outgrowth of the Norton manifestation. With the first of these local phases there appears a major reliance upon the polishing of slate for tool manufacture, a form of pottery in which the fiber inclusions have been largely replaced by gravel, and the use of the sunken house entrance; all these continue throughout the period. The Pavik phase dates from the time of Russian occupation and includes iron, window glass, and glass beads, with a decrease in the use of stone implements of all sorts. In 1967 two houses of the earliest phase of this period (B.R. Camp) were excavated completely. One of them was that chosen for reconstruction in 1968.

Excavations in 1967

The experience of the five previous field seasons had indicated that two locations in particular promised the availability of relatively undisturbed habitations—that designated BR20, and the combined areas of BR12, BR15, and BR16 (fig. 2). The periods of occupation were thought to be substantially different for the two areas: the second millennium A.D. for the former (B.R. Camp phase) and the second millennium B.C. for the latter (B.R. Gravels phase).

Testing in both areas narrowed the choice to two units in the BR20 locality (dwellings designated BR20-2-A and BR20-2-C), to two at BR15 (BR15-2 and BR15-3), and to one at BR16 (BR16-3). Of these, only BR20-2-A, BR20-2-C, and BR15-2 were excavated completely. Any of these three would have been adequate for consolidation and display. BR20-2-A was chosen for the final reconstruction because of its size, its convenient location for display purposes, and because it—unlike its neighbor BR20-2-C—did not fill completely with water in excessively rainy weather. Results of excavations are described briefly.

BR15-2—The plan and sections of this house are shown in figure 4. The presumed post holes in the floor were visible only as stains; this is the first habitation of its period in which floor posts were even ambiguously observable. The house was excavated by its builders into a surface that at the time was covered with a layer of volcanic ash that now appears a noticeable yellow, and which is rather distinctive in the Brooks River area; this ash has been designated *volcanic ash G* (Nowak, 1968) in the local sequence of ash deposits, and is known to have been deposited around 1900 B.C. (Y-931; Stuiver and Deevey, 1962). Spots of this ash scattered through the fill above the house floor suggest that some sod was used in building the ab-

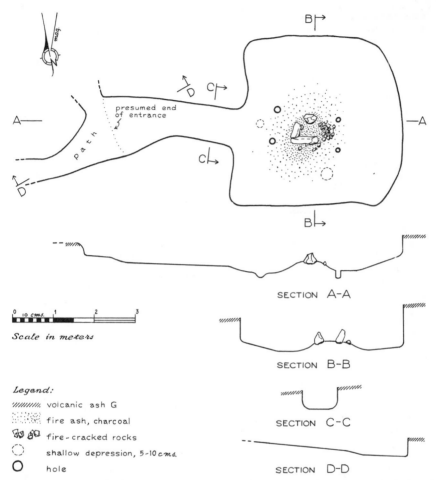

Legend:

////// volcanic ash G

fire ash, charcoal

fire-cracked rocks

shallow depression, 5-10 cms.

○ hole

FIG. 4. House BR15-2, B.R. Gravels phase, dating around 1450 B.C. (Drawn by Carol Steichen Dumond.)

original roof. Timbers did not survive, except that in one side of the house the presence of rather slender pieces of charred wood suggests the presence of a light framework of poles. A radiocarbon date from this charcoal is 1450 ± 110 B.C. (I-3115; Buckley and Willis, 1970). The 65 artifacts recovered in the house indicate affiliation with the Arctic Small Tool tradition, so that the house is assigned to the B.R. Gravels phase of local culture.

BR15-3 and BR16-3 — These habitations were similar in form to BR15-2, squared and with sloping entrance passages that were excavated no more

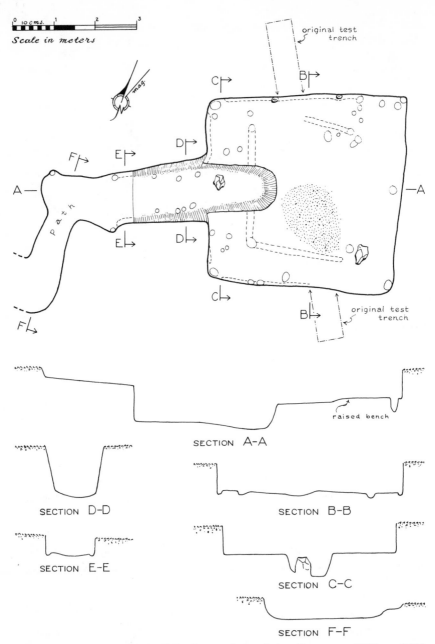

FIG. 5.   House BR20-2-A, B.R. Camp phase, dating from A.D. 1200 to 1300.
(Drawn by Carol Steichen Dumond.)

deeply than the house floor itself. Neither revealed evidence of floor posts. Like BR15-2, both are assigned to the B.R. Gravels phase; together they yielded 85 implements.

BR20-2-A — Plan and sections are given in figure 5. In all, 120 stone implements and 34 potsherds were recovered from the entire house excavation, although fewer than one-half of these were actually from the floor of the house and entrance, the remainder coming from one or more camps made in the depression formed by the house after its roof caved in. The artifacts and the stratigraphic position of the house beneath a noticeable deposit of what is designated *volcanic ash C* (Nowak, 1968), which dates from around A.D. 1400, cause it to be assigned without hesitation to the B.R. Camp phase. However, it was obviously excavated through an underlying deposit of B.R. Weir phase materials, and in one place into an even lower deposit of B.R. Gravels phase occupation debris. A deposit of charcoal in one corner was first thought to probably relate to house BR20-2-A itself. A radiocarbon date from the charcoal, however, was A.D. 260 ± 110 (I-3116; Buckley and Willis, 1970). Inasmuch as this is a completely acceptable date for B.R. Weir phase materials, it seems clear that the charcoal pertained to the underlying occupation. At any rate, the fact that the house did not predate any volcanic-ash deposit earlier than that of ash C indicates that it could under no circumstances have been constructed earlier than about A.D. 1000. And because ash C itself was deposited around A.D. 1400, it is equally clear that the house must have been built before that time. In view of the fact that the house had actually caved in and been camped on *before* the deposition of ash C, it is certain that the house was not built at the very end of the A.D. 1000-1400 period. A reasonable and conservative estimate of the date of the construction would then be between A.D. 1200 and 1300.

BR20-2-C — This house, the location of which is shown in figure 6, was substantially similar to BR20-2-A, although somewhat smaller (about 3 by 4 meters). The walls were extremely irregular, presumably from a combination of aboriginal digging and sloughing. It had not been built with base logs such as were present in the front two-thirds of BR20-2-A, which served to keep the wall of that house from being gradually moved irregularly outward. In addition, BR20-2-C had been reoccupied after its first construction by people who changed the floor plan somewhat — adding an earthen bench where there had apparently been none — and who added numerous posts, presumably to support an aging, weakening roof. BR20-2-C yielded in all 237 stone implements and 17 potsherds, some of which were not from the two occupations of the house itself, but from later camps

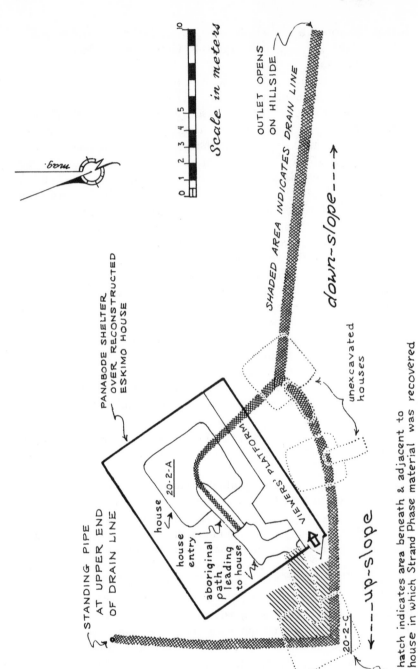

Scale in meters

STANDING PIPE
AT UPPER END
OF DRAIN LINE

PANABODE SHELTER
OVER RECONSTRUCTED
ESKIMO HOUSE

SHADED AREA INDICATES DRAIN LINE

OUTLET OPENS
ON HILLSIDE

down-slope - - - →

20-2-A

house

house
entry

aboriginal
path
leading
to house

VIEWERS PLATFORM

unexcavated
houses

20-2-C

- - - up-slope

hatch indicates area beneath & adjacent to
house in which Strand Phase material was recovered

FIG. 6.   The trench at BR20-2. (Drawn by Carol Steichen Dumond.)

made in the depression left when the house collapsed. Like BR20-2-A, and for identical reasons, the house itself and the campsites on its fallen roof were all assigned to the B.R. Camp phase.

BR20-2 trench — As indicated earlier, heavy rains during the 1967 field season caused ground water to rise in the BR20-2 excavation unit. Although house BR20-2-C was flooded almost brimful, house BR20-2-A received water only in the deep part of its sunken entrance. Nevertheless it seemed clear that if the habitation were to be reconstructed for display purposes it would have to be drained in some manner.

Accordingly, a Y-shaped system of trenches, some 57 meters in total length and in most places 0.75 meter in width, was excavated as indicated in figure 6, so that the entrance itself could be drained directly and so that perforated soil pipe could be placed upslope of the house in order to lower the level of ground water. This trench, excavated stratigraphically into sterile soil at all but its hillside outlet at the east end, provided an excellent, if somewhat irregular, test of locality BR20. As shown, the 90° bend in the trench in the southwest was set across — and dug substantially below — the floor of house 20-2-C.

The stratigraphy of the upper levels of the trench was similar to that of the house excavations. Below volcanic ash C were encountered diagnostic B.R. Camp phase implements; these were especially plentiful in two houses of Camp phase type, also beneath volcanic ash C, that were encountered and cut through by the trench (fig. 6). Lower still, and separated from Camp phase deposits by additional layers of volcanic ash, were materials assignable to the B.R. Weir phase. In addition, in the short section of trench running beneath house 20-2-A itself, under the Weir phase deposit, was encountered a deposit of ash G and a portion of a B.R. Gravels phase habitation.

Some 20 centimeters beneath the top of sterile beach gravel, and more than 2 meters below the modern surface, the first B.R. Strand phase implements were recovered in the main trench about 2.6 meters east of the southeast corner of house BR20-2-C. With this discovery, the area enclosed in the 90° bend of the trench was cleared as indicated by the hatched area in figure 6, and about 17 square meters of undisturbed occupation debris of the B.R. Strand phase were exposed, extending beneath the major portion of the sunken entrance of BR20-2-C. The relatively thin (2-10 centimeters) layer of debris, apparently the remains of a substantial camp but not of a constructed house, had been deposited while the BR20 location formed the shore of Naknek Lake. The 5 to 30 centimeters of sterile beach gravel, much of it partially cemented, that now covers it must have been swept over the area by a storm on the lake, only shortly after its occupation. Most of the deposit was also covered by an undisturbed layer of volcanic ash G. A radiocarbon determination on the charcoal of the layer itself yielded a date of 1950 B.C. ± 120 (I-3114; Buckley and Willis, 1970).

Implements of the Strand phase deposit totaled 61, nearly doubling the existing sample of this little-known phase and adding to it pieces of two flat lamps of stone. Furthermore, the undisturbed position of these artifacts in partially cemented gravels provided unmistakable evidence of the validity of the association of handsome knife and lance blades of polished slate with other rather crude implements of chipped stone, thus confirming what had previously been indicated but not attested to the point of certainty.

While the deposit itself was being excavated, heavy rains again raised the water table, unhappily cutting short the exploration, although providing an effective (and successful) test of the drainage potential of the trench and of the line of soil pipe that was installed within it.

Summary

As indicated above, the Naknek drainage archeological sequence, represented at Brooks River, had been worked out fairly thoroughly before the beginning of the project described here. In the earlier seasons, however, the primary emphasis had been on the development of the temporal sequence, which meant that some desirable and more extensive work in individual phases had been curtailed.

Although five B.R. Gravels phase habitations similar to that of BR15-2 had already been excavated completely or in large part, none of them had provided information regarding the nature of the structure that seems indicated in BR15-2. Furthermore, no habitation of the B.R. Camp phase had previously been cleared. The excavation of two Camp phase houses provided not only additional information regarding implements of that phase but also the first confirmation of a suspicion that the Camp phase saw the initial use of the deeply sunken entrance passage in the Naknek drainage, and indeed may also have seen the first winter occupation of Brooks River itself since the close of the Gomer period two millennia earlier.

The significance of the B.R. Strand phase deposit encountered in the drainage trench at BR20 has already been touched upon. The Strand collection from Brooks River is now sufficient to allow at least a preliminary assessment of the cultural affiliations of the people represented. In brief, much of the chipped-stone industry is strongly reminiscent of that known from about the same time and largely confined within the Alaskan interior, such as at Onion Portage (specifically, the Portage complex; Anderson, 1968), and which intruded to the coast only rarely (as, for instance, at Security Cove; Ackerman, 1964).

On the other hand, the substantial presence of large knives and lance blades of polished slate, and of flat lamps of stone in which presumably sea-mammal oil was burned, suggests a strong influence from contemporary people of the Pacific coast (Clark, 1968; Dumond, 1968). With artifacts hinting at the presence of two traditions sealed together beneath sterile beach gravels, accidental mixture of artifact complexes pertaining to two different aboriginal societies seemed highly unlikely. It was therefore first thought that the Strand phase represented a single acculturated people, either coastal folk who had received strong influence from the interior, or interior dwellers who had been seduced by a measure of coastal living. Inasmuch as it has been more common in Alaska for interior people to take up the use of coastal implements than for the reverse to occur (see, for example, de Laguna, 1947, p. 268ff.), I suggested that these earliest known inhabitants of the upper Naknek drainage were probably interior people (Indians?) who had embraced some coastal ways (Dumond, 1969a, 1971).

Although this possibility cannot now be ruled out entirely, further examinations of collections from the Pacific coast and from interior Alaska would seem to indicate that the affinity of the Strand phase people lies much more strongly with folk of the Pacific coast than elsewhere. The simplest interpretation at this time, then, is that the earliest known human use of the Brooks River area was by people of the Pacific coast. This was clearly not the case during later times, however, for beginning around 1900 B.C., with the arrival of the people of the B.R. Gravels phase, and continuing thereafter, the area was occupied by peoples of northern derivation, the probable direct ancestors of modern coastal Eskimos (Dumond, 1965, 1969a, 1971).

REFERENCES

ACKERMAN, ROBERT E.
    1964. Prehistory in the Kuskokwim-Bristol Bay region, southwestern Alaska. Washington State University Laboratory of Anthropology Report of Investigations, no. 26.
ANDERSON, DOUGLAS D.
    1968. A Stone Age campsite at the gateway to America. Sci. Amer., vol. 218, no. 6, pp. 24-33, illus.
BUCKLEY, JAMES D., and WILLIS, ERIC H.
    1970. Isotopes' radiocarbon measurements VIII. Radiocarbon, vol. 12, pp. 87-129.

CLARK, GERALD H.
  1968. Archaeology of the Takli site, Katmai National Monument, Alaska. M.A. thesis, University of Oregon, Department of Anthropology. University Microfilms M-1439.
DAVIS, WILBUR A.
  1954. Archaeological investigations of inland and coastal sites of the Katmai National Monument, Alaska. Report to the U. S. National Park Service Archives of Archaeology, no. 4.
DE LAGUNA, FREDERICA A.
  1947. The prehistory of northern North America as seen from the Yukon. Mem. Soc. Amer. Anthrop., no. 3. Suppl. to Amer. Antiq., vol. 12, no. 3, pt. 2.
DUMOND, DON E.
  1965. On Eskaleutian linguistics, archaeology, and prehistory. Amer. Anthrop., vol. 67, pp. 1231-1257, illus.
  1968. On the presumed spread of slate grinding in Alaska. Arctic Anthrop., vol. 5, no. 1, pp. 82-91, map.
  1969a. Prehistoric cultural contacts in southwestern Alaska. Science, vol. 166, pp. 1108-1115, illus.
  1969b. Reconstruction of an aboriginal dwelling in Katmai National Monument, Alaska, 52 pp., illus. Report to the National Park Service, Department of Anthropology, University of Oregon. (Duplicated.)
  1971. A summary of archaeology in the Katmai region, southwestern Alaska. University of Oregon Anthropological Papers, no. 2.
GIDDINGS, JAMES LOUIS
  1964. The archeology of Cape Denbigh, 331 pp., illus. Brown University Press, Providence, Rhode Island.
IRVING, WILLIAM N.
  1962. A provisional comparison of some Alaskan and Asian stone industries. *In* "Prehistoric Cultural Relations between the Arctic and Temperate Zones of North America," John M. Campbell, ed. Arctic Inst. North America Techn. Pap., no. 11, pp. 55-68.
  1970. The Arctic Small Tool tradition. Proc. 8th Int. Congr. Anthrop. and Ethnol., Tokyo 1968, vol. 3, pp. 340-342.
LUNTEY, ROBERT S.
  1954. Interim report on Katmai Project, Katmai National Monument, Alaska, 138 pp. National Park Service, Washington, D. C. (Duplicated.)
NOWAK, MICHAEL
  1968. Archeological dating by means of volcanic ash strata. Ph.D. thesis, University of Oregon, Department of Anthropology. University Microfilms 69-6654.
STUIVER, MINZE, and DEEVEY, EDWARD S.
  1962. Yale natural radiocarbon measurements VII. Radiocarbon, vol. 4, pp. 250-262, chart.

DON E. DUMOND

Sonar Search at Ashdod, Israel

Principal Investigator: Harold E. Edgerton, Massachusetts Institute of Technology, Cambridge, Massachusetts.

Grant No. 672: For experimentation with newly developed sonar apparatus in underwater archeological research at Ashdod, Israel.

The main goal of this study was to find, off the coast of Israel, the harbor that certainly must have served the ancient city of Ashdod. A second objective was to locate wrecks that would bring an understanding of the ships that were used and their cargoes. Although we were unsuccessful in our primary objectives, our experiences should be recorded since the results may be helpful to others who will follow us in the search.

Side-looking 12 KHZ sonar, vertical-penetration-sonar of 5 KHZ, and a boomer of about 2 KHZ were used during November and December 1967 to study the offshore ocean adjacent to the recognized ancient Ashdod harbor settlement called Ashdod-Yam (Azotus Paralus), some 4 kilometers south of the modern port of Ashdod and west of the ancient Ashdod site.

A thick layer of sand has apparently covered the area studied, except for a spectacular outcrop of sandstone rocks that are roughly parallel to the shore at a distance of 2.4 kilometers. Three stone anchors were found in this rock area, two of which were brought to the surface by divers. In our opinion it is not coincidental that the rocks are almost exactly opposite to the ancient site of Ashdod-Yam. They could have been an important breakwater during a time when the water level was lower than at present. The ancient walls of the Ashdod-Yam have been dated as 1000 B.C. The sea at this time could have been much shallower than at present (Emery et al., 1967), and the rocks might have been exposed as important breakwater structures.

The map (fig. 1) shows the general area from the modern Ashdod harbor to the site of the ancient city on the shore, which is about 4 kilometers to the south.

A sonar search of the shallow waters off the areas shown in area A of figure 1 did not reach any subbottom structures down to about 3 meters

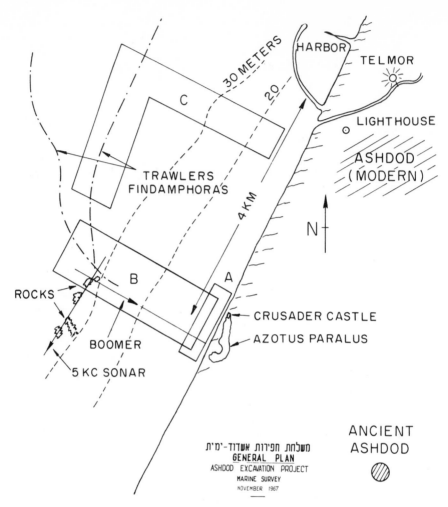

FIG. 1.   A map of the area studied with sonar techniques.

below the bottom. A 5 KHZ pulse sonar was used for this experiment. Possibly deep in the sand there are structures that could not be reached by our 5 KHZ signals.

Side-looking sonar (12 KHZ) was used to scan a large area, shown roughly as B and C on figure 1. The side-scan sonar technique is illustrated in figure 2. The system is of importance since it reveals surface variations

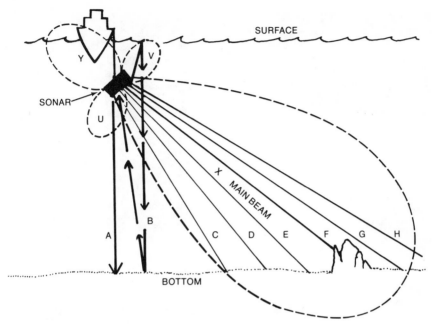

FIG. 2. Diagram showing how a sonar beam can be used as a side-looking sonar.

and the system covers a large area compared to vertical sonar as the survey ship slowly traverses a known course.

There was enough sound from side lobes (V, U of fig. 2) to give a direct transducer-to-bottom time and a transducer-to-source-to-bottom time for most of the time. This information is useful since both the transducer depth and the water depth are then measured. The sonar signals reflected from the bottom depend upon the nature of the bottom. An irregularity as indicated on F of figure 2 will give a stronger reflection of sound than the smooth sand bottom at C to E. Our sonar gave the same beam pattern in all directions, in contrast to most side-looking sonars, which have a narrow beam in the vertical axis in order to obtain increased resolution of sonar targets. As a result, our sonar gave inverted U-shaped signals from small targets since we could "see" them before and after our closest distance to the target as the ship passed the target. This property is sometimes an advantage when making a search for a small or specular object.

We found that the transducer performance is better when it is suspended on a cable below the ship so that the bubbles of air generated by waves and wake are not in the sound path. Our transducer was mounted on

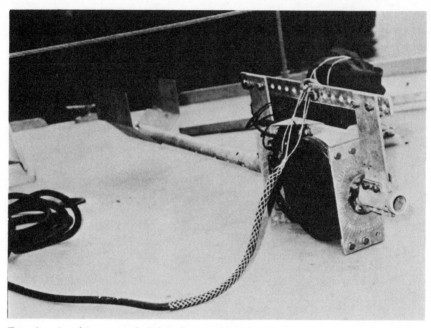

FIG. 3. A cable-suspended fish for carrying a 12 KHZ transducer at adjustable angles for both vertical and side scan applications.

a fish that was suspended by the electrical cable. It could be lowered about 12 meters below the surface. However, at 1 or 2+ knots, the tow angle caused the fish to rise somewhat. Operation in water depths of 2 to 20 fathoms was made with a beam angle of 10° to 20° from the horizontal. A small angle gave a longer distance "look" and less sound reflection from the immediate bottom.

Figure 3 shows an EG&G, Inc. 12 KHZ transducer mounted on a fish so that the transducer can be changed to any desired angle. The assembly is suspended below the ship by the electrical cable. The recorder (EG&G type 254) contains a driver for the sonar and an amplifying circuit to receive the signals and send them to the recording part of the instrument.

One of the targets, observed by the 12 KHZ side-looking sonar at point 12, was investigated by divers. It was found to be an amphora (Byzantine) fragment with an eroded area in the sand around it, as shown in the sketch (fig. 4).

Figure 5 shows a side-looking sonar record of the out-cropping narrow ledge of rocks which is about 2.5 kilometers to the west of the Crusader Castle (fig. 1).

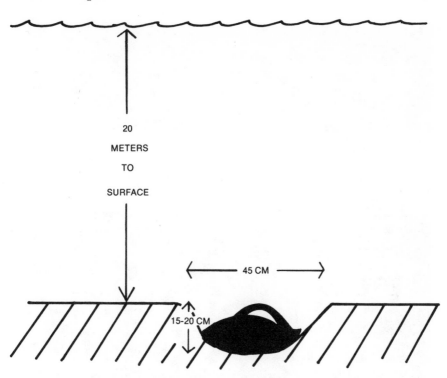

FIG. 4. "Target" that was located by the side-scan sonar of figure 3.

A fisherman, Abraham Levkonia, showed us where these rocks were, and then the rocks were located on the map (fig. 1) by data taken from the shore by two transits whose position was known. Our divers reported that the northernmost rock was covered with fishing nets lost from draggers. A second dive was made to another rock some 100 meters south. The divers described a vertical rock rising 10 meters above the sea bed with a 5-meter-deep cave below the sea bottom on the western wall of the rock. Two stone anchors of the Phoenician type were found at the base of this rock. Another stone anchor of the same type was found at still another rock formation to the south. Figure 8 shows one of the stone anchors.

A 5 KHZ sonar record was made roughly from the north to the south-west in an attempt to include most of the rock peaks, which are located at the west end of area B in figure 1. A part of this record over one of the southern peaks is shown as figure 6. Note that the 5 KHZ penetrates into the sediment material between the rocks. A penetration of about 7 meters

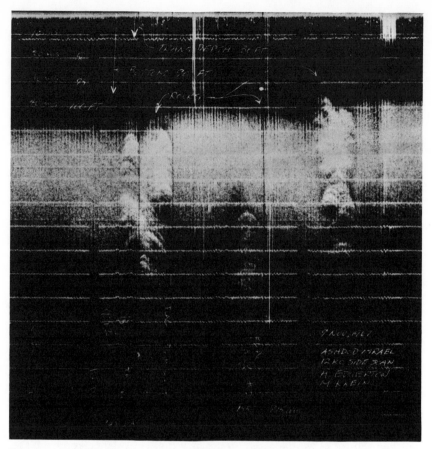

FIG. 5. A side-looking sonar record of a series of outcropping sandstone rocks, as observed by the 12 KHZ system of figures 2 and 3.

is observed in some places. It is possible that a completely covered wreck in the sand could be detected by this penetrating sonar, but the sonar must be directly over the target.

Boomer records — Seismic profiling equipment of the electromagnetic "boomer" type (EG&G 1000 w.s. boomer) was made available by Dr. David Neev of the Ministry of Development, Geological Survey, Jerusalem. The equipment was operated at 200-watt-seconds energy into the standard boomer transducer, which was suspended at the side of the ship. An 8-ball hydrophone on a boom, on the other side of the ship, was used to pick up

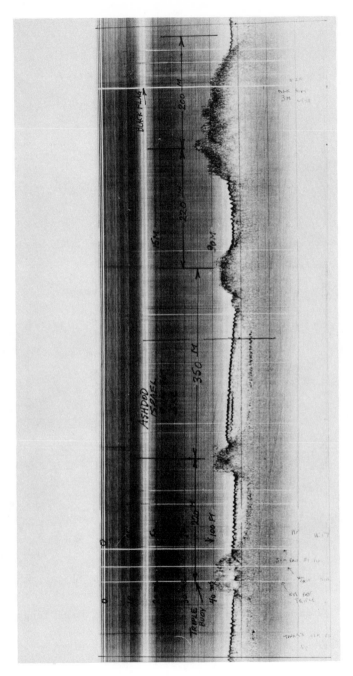

FIG. 6. A subbottom penetration record of the "Rock" area of figure 1 made with a 5 KHZ pulsed sonar.

78

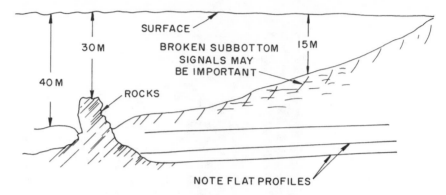

FIG. 7. Sketch showing observed features on a "boomer" 2 KHZ record of the rock-to-shore profile.

FIG 8. Stone anchor recovered by divers off Ashdod, Israel. Length, ca. 45 centimeters.

the reflections from the bottom and subbottom.

Figure 7 shows a sketch of a boomer record made through the rock area toward the shore (see fig. 1). Features to notice are:

1. The flat horizon below the sand.
2. The irregular signals about halfway from the shore to the rocks.
3. The manner in which the rocks extend below the sand on both sides.

The surveyed tracks of the small ship that carried the side-scan sonar are shown as figure 9, as prepared by the Israeli Highway and Survey Department. Sonar signals of interest are marked to aid the divers to find them. It was possible for the surveyors to locate a buoy over any of these targets.

Our expedition emphasized the importance of survey and search techniques to underwater archeology.

Acknowledgments

This expedition was under the sponsorship of the Carnegie Museum, Pittsburgh; the Undersea Exploration Society of Israel; and the Department of Antiquities and Museums of Israel. Major financial support was furnished by the Foreign Program, Office of International Activities, Smithsonian Institution, Washington, D. C.

Dr. James L. Swauger was head of the project, with Dr. Moshe Dothan (Israel) as chief archeologist; Elisha Linder served as field director. The Ashdod Port Authority supplied ships and support, thanks to Gen. Haim Laskov, director general of Israel Port Authorities, and Capt. Moshe Alon of the Ashdod Port. Dr. David Neev (Israel) supplied a boomer seismic system with supporting supplies and personnel.

The expedition is complementary to the shore excavations that were currently underway at Ashdod as reported by Dothan.

Others contributing time, funds, equipment, and interest were Dr. Louis Wolfson (Boston), Raymond Peabody (New London, Connecticut), Walter Feinberg (Newton, Massachusetts), and Nixon Griffis (New York), the National Geographic Society, the Massachusetts Institute of Technology, and EG&G, Inc. (Bedford, Massachusetts).

Peter and Joan Throckmorton, Dr. M. Littman, Skuka Shapiro, Hayim Stav, and Joseph Levy assisted in our work. The survey was accomplished with the aid of Yair Goldman of the Israel Highway and Survey Department of Solel-Boneh.

Dr. David Neev and his group from the Ministry of Development operated the boomer sonar equipment.

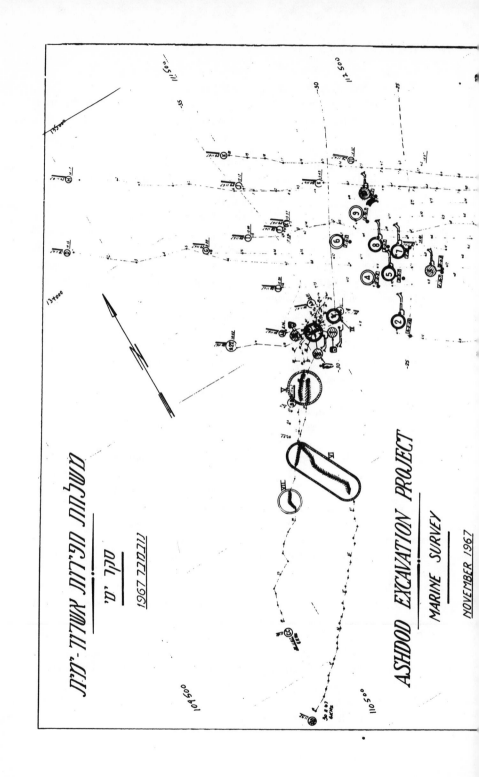

ASHDOD EXCAVATION PROJECT

MARINE SURVEY

NOVEMBER 1967

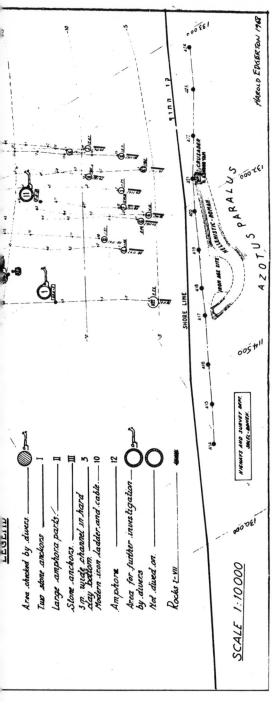

Fig. 9.   Chart showing the tracks of the ship for side-looking sonar and the targets disclosed.

REFERENCES

DOTHAN, MOSHE

  1963a. The first controlled excavation of a city of the Philistines: Revealing the
      past of ancient Ashdod. Illustr. London News, vol. 243, no. 6487,
      pp. 904-906, illus.

  1963b. The Philistines in decline: Ashdod Babylonian, Persian, Hellenistic and
      Maccabean. Illustr. London News, vol. 243, no. 6488, pp. 944-946,
      illus.

  1967. Ashdod, a city of the Philistine Pentapolis. Archeology, vol. 20, no. 3,
      pp. 178-186, illus.

EMERY, K. O.; WIGLEY, R. L.; BARTLETT, ALEXANDER S.; and RUBIN, MEYER

  1967. Freshwater peat on the Continental Shelf. Science, vol. 158, pp. 1301-
      1307, illus.

HAROLD E. EDGERTON
ELISHA LINDER
MARTIN KLEIN

Samosata Archeological Excavations, Turkey, 1967

Principal Investigator
and Director: Theresa Goell, New York City.

Grant No. 648:   In support of an archeological excavation of the mound of
                    Samosata in Turkey.

The urgency for explorations at Samosata-on-the-Euphrates in 1967 was to anticipate the consequences of the Turkish Government's project to build a dam for irrigation and power generation at Halfeti on the Euphrates (map: fig. 1) southwest of Samosata, the capital of the Anatolian-Iranian-Macedonian dynasty's kingdom of Commagene, during the Hellenistic-Roman era. The flooding of the river valley, from Halfeti to the Gerger area including Samosata, is one of the government's reclamation projects, such as the Keban dam now being completed on the same river north of Malatya. Accelerated archeological excavations are being conducted there by Turks and foreigners in order to gain a glimpse of its ancient cultures before they disappear forever under the rising waters. This fate awaits Samosata when the Halfeti dam is completed.

Ancient Samosata (today the modern Turkish town of Samsat) is located on the west bank of the Euphrates River, about 500 meters above sea level in the Vilayet of Adiyaman in southeastern Turkey. Samsat lies between the mouths of the Kâhta Chai (Hellenistic river Nymphaios) to the northeast and the Göksu (Hellenistic river Singa) to the southwest, the latter crossed by an L-shaped Roman bridge now in ruins; both mountain streams flow into the Euphrates (see Dörner and Naumann, 1939). Samosata was one of the main crossings of the latter; farther south near modern Birecik was the famous ancient river-crossing Apameia-Zeugma (Strabo, Geography, XIV, ii, 29), today spanned by a modern concrete bridge.

We made our first trial trench on the summit of the citadel-acropolis — the mound of Samosata — in the late summer of 1964 after closing that season's explorations on Nemrud Dagh, site of the *hierothesion* and tumulus-tomb of King Antiochus I of Commagene (ruled ca. 69-34 B.C.). Our archeological objectives in excavating on the mound of the Commagenian capital city Samosata were stated in Goell, 1967, as follows: "In the upper level,

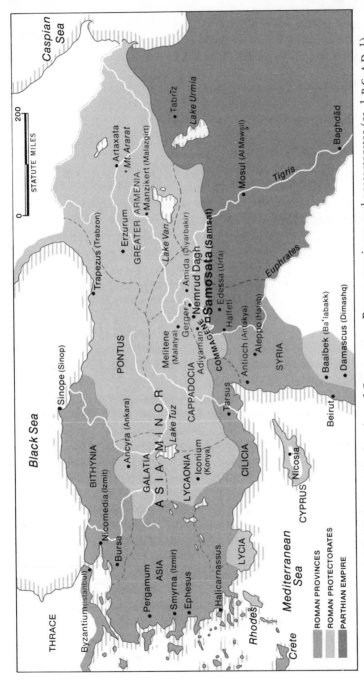

FIG. 1. Map of Asia Minor showing location of Commagene, Roman provinces, and protectorates (ca. 1 B.C.–A.D. 1).

about 1.50 meters below the surface, we found a number of storage rooms with vats, apparently belonging to the medieval palace complex of rooms. Our 1967 season of work will concentrate on following up the architecture of the medieval store-rooms [presumably 12th or 13th century A.D.] and enlarging the area in order to reveal a more comprehensive picture, going down in depth to the levels of Antiochus' Hellenistic dynasty and its foundation. We also planned to uncover the levels to the beginning of the settlement of Samosata in at least the Chalcolithic period at the base of the mound where there are two natural springs gushing from it [and one of the reasons why the early settlement was founded here]. The area around it is strewn with man-made [it is to be read "hand-made"] painted Chalcolithic ceramics, connecting Samosata with the prehistoric cultures of Anatolia, Mesopotamia and Syria. [A span of time of at least 6,000 years is represented.]" (Fig. 2.)

Comparatively little appears in ancient literature to enlighten us about Samosata. We therefore depend on the physical remains preserved in the citadel-mound to fill the lacunae in our knowledge of its history, cultures, religion, political and economic manifestations, and the everyday life of the peoples who occupied it and its environs. Laminated like a layer cake, owing to the overlay of ancient occupation levels, and rising on its eastern side to a height of about 60 meters above the present river level, the mound dominates the surrounding deep valley with its ancient shores at various terrace levels of the Middle Euphrates Rift (fig. 3).

Because of Samosata's situation as a hub of trade and military routes, it was the perpetual battleground of ambitious and conflicting powers and marked by their influences. Among these powers can be counted the pagan Hittites, Hurrians, Assyrians, Urartians, Babylonians, Aramaeans, Medes, Persians, Greeks, Romans, the Christian Byzantines, Moslem Arab Ommayads and Abbasids, Asiatic Moslem Mongols, the central Asian Moslem Turkish Seljuks who become the "Founding Fathers" of Turkey, the European Latin Crusaders, the Turkish Mameluke rulers of Egypt, the Osmanli Turks, conquerors of Byzantium=Constantinople (modern Istanbul), the capital of the Byzantine Empire in 1453; and finally Kemal Pasha, known as Atatürk, liberator and founder in 1923 of the modern Republic of Turkey.

The changing cultural influences that poured in left their mark on the region. At the same time influences streamed out, in particular the Iranian-Anatolian religious cults of the sun-god Mithra and of Jupiter-Dolichenus, the Hellenistic-Hittite-Hurrian god standing on an animal. Apart from references in Assyrian cuneiform records of the 9th-8th centuries B.C., and in classical literature of Strabo, Pliny the Elder, Josephus, Cassius Dio, Plu-

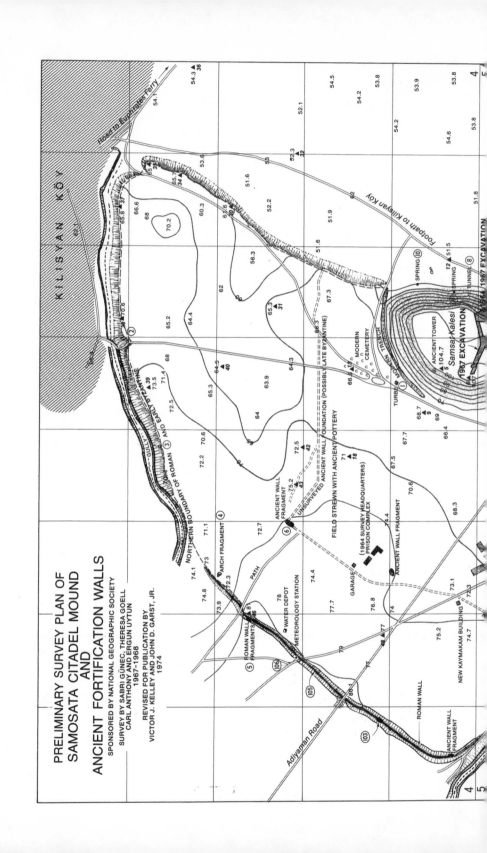

PRELIMINARY SURVEY PLAN OF
SAMOSATA CITADEL MOUND
AND
ANCIENT FORTIFICATION WALLS

SPONSORED BY NATIONAL GEOGRAPHIC SOCIETY

SURVEY BY SABRI GÜNEC, THERESA GOELL
CARL ANTHONY AND ERGUN UYTUN
1967–1968

REVISED FOR PUBLICATION BY
VICTOR J. KELLEY AND JOHN D. GARST, JR.
1974

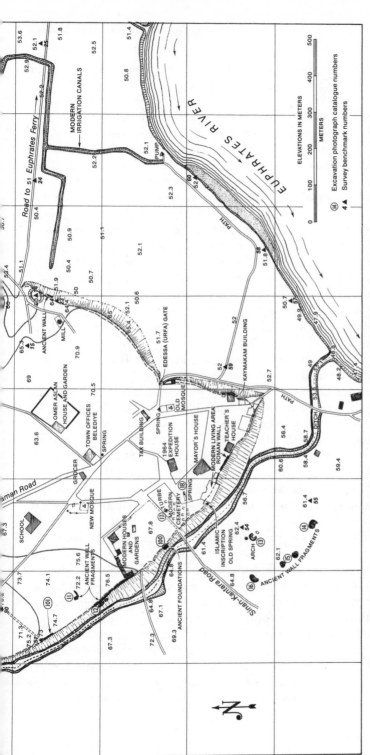

FIG. 2. Preliminary topographic survey plan of the citadel-mound and city fortification wall of Samosata.

tarch, Ammianus Marcellenus, the Byzantine writer Procopius, and others, we know little historically about Commagene.

During the later Hittite-Assyrian period of the 9th-8th centuries B.C., the city-state of Kummukhi occupied what was later the district of the Hellenistic period city Samosata, the capital of Commagene (hellenized Kummukhi). It was a vassal and ally of the Kingdom of Urartu of the Lake Van district of northeast Anatolia and an ally of the Late Hittite city-kingdoms of north Syria, including Carchemish, Sam'al (modern Zinjirli), Gurgum-Marqisi (modern Marash), etc., against the Assyrians. Conquered by the latter in 708 B.C., Kummukhi became an Assyrian province and administrative center. The region was conquered by the Medes, the Persians, and Alexander the Great but disappeared from known recorded history until it appeared again in the arena of warfare in 69 B.C. as the hellenized kingdom of Commagene, its king Antiochus I (ruled ca. 69-34 B.C.) an ally of Tigranes the Great of Armenia in the last Mithridatic war with Rome. In 64 B.C. Pompey the Great included Commagene as an autonomous kingdom in his reorganization of the East. It acted as a buffer state between Rome and the Parthians to the east.

Antiochus I of Commagene, a god in his lifetime, was the "god-intoxicated" monarch who built on the holy summit of the Taurus (now called Ankar and Nemrud Dagh) his last resting place — the unique conical rock tumulus-tomb and syncretistic outdoor sanctuary or *hierothesion* (place holy to the gods), adorned with colossal sculptures and reliefs of himself, his ancestors, and deities. His Holy Edict *(Nomos)* inscribed in Greek on Nemrud Dagh gives us his genealogy, claiming descent from the Achaemenids (Darius), the Macedonians (Alexander the Great), the Seleucidae of Syria, and his local Anatolian ancestors. In this edict he states that he is building his last resting-place according to the best arts of his ancestors. Samosata is about 30 miles south of Nemrud Dagh; its summit, about 7,150 meters above sea level, can be seen shimmering like a mirage in the brilliant sunshine.

Commagene was one of the divisions of Syria under the Macedonian ruler Seleucus I (358-280 B.C.), successor in the East of Alexander the Great. Ptolemy, the governor satrap of Commagene, broke away from the Seleucidae in the 2d century B.C. to form an independent dynasty and kingdom lasting until A.D. 72. From 83 to 69 B.C. the kingdom was dominated by Tigranes the Great of Armenia. The city, about 500 meters above sea level, was the hub of at least four trade and military routes crossing the Taurus, Anti-Taurus, Amanus, and Caucasus Mountains from east, west (the Mediterranean Lands), and north. Other roads came from eastern and southerly

FIG. 3. Mound of Samosata seen from the west, looking south toward the Euphrates River.

directions of the Euphrates—from Mesopotamia, Syria, Egypt, Persia, Central Asia, and far-off China and India. Whichever powers held Commagene with its many river crossings could also control these strategic routes. Our explorations in Samosata, called the *zeugma* or bridge of the Euphrates (see Strabo, above), did not disclose remains of an actual bridge over the Euphrates; but the *passage* of the river, then as today, must have been by means of a ferry or militarily by a pontoon bridge supported by inflated animal skins. Even today men swim across on animal skins in the same manner as depicted on British Museum Assyrian reliefs of the 8th century B.C. (see Barnett, 1959), and a flat-bottomed ferry is punted across the swift river from Samsat to Kantara in the Vilayet of Urfa (ancient Edessa) on the east bank.

Samosata, the strategically located fortified city with citadel-acropolis of the local Commagenian dynasty, was besieged by Lucullus in 69 B.C. and by Mark Antony in 38 B.C., on which occasion Herod the Idumaean rushed with troops from Palestine to Samosata to help him; Herod, later crowned by the Romans as King of Judea, was known as Herod the Great.

For about a hundred years after Antiochus I, Commagene's dynastic succession is not clear, but it was involved with the Romans' eastern ambitions. Commagene's sympathy leaned toward Parthia. Between A.D. 17 and

38 it became a Roman province, but in A.D. 38 Antiochus IV of Commagene was enthroned by the emperor Caius (Caligula) and was the last reigning monarch of the local dynasty; he was dethroned by Vespasian in A.D. 72 for allegedly plotting with the Parthians against the Romans. Commagene became the northern part of the Province of Syria and a military station of Roman legions guarding it against the Parthians and Sassanians, the successors of the Achaemenid Empire. The Euphrates remained as the fluid frontier between the East and the West. In A.D. 114 Hadrian, during his Parthian war, captured Samosata, which apparently was in the hands of the Parthians at that time.

In the 1st century A.D. a contemporary of Augustus and Tiberius, the Greek writer Strabo (born in 63 B.C. at Amaseia, Pontus, in central Turkey; died ca. A.D. 24) described Samosata (Geography, XVI, ii, 3): "Commagene is rather a small district. It contains a strong city, Samosata, in which was the seat of the kings. At present it is a [Roman] province. A very fertile but small territory lies around it. Here is now the zeugma, or bridge, of the Euphrates, and near it is situated Seleucia, a fortress of Mesopotamia, assigned by Pompey to the Commageneans." The present-day agricultural village Lidar situated opposite, to the northeast of Samsat, on the east bank of the river (in Urfa Vilayet), would seem to be the lost fortress of Seleucia. I made a surface examination of the great mound of Lidar in 1967 and brought to light potsherds ranging from the Early Bronze Age to the medieval Turkish-Seljuk glazed ware of the 12th-13th centuries A.D., resembling ceramic material of the same periods found at Samsat.

In the 3d century A.D., during the reign of Diocletian, the capital of the region was transferred southwest from Samosata to Hierapolis where the seat of the Great Mother Goddess of Syria was located. Commagene was renamed Euphratesia after the river and appeared in the wars of the Byzantine-East-Romans and the Persians (Procopius, Wars, I, vii, 2; I, xviii, 2). Its role as an administrative center was reduced, but the city retained some of its fame as the birthplace of the satirist Lucian of Samosata (born A.D. 120) and of Paul of Samosata, the first bishop of Antioch, who was removed in A.D. 272 for heresy.

The Sondage of 1964 and Excavations of 1967

We excavated in Samosata from July to September 1967 to fulfill our objectives, which were formulated on the basis of the large volume and variety of finds of our 1964 preliminary sondage. The 1967 excavations were conducted under the sponsorship of and with the general financial

FIG. 4. Mound of Samosata: Upper plateau, looking toward the medieval keep, or entrance gate, and the Euphrates River.

support of the National Geographic Society; the Bollingen Foundation, Inc.; the Archaeological Society of Staten Island, New York; *Scientific American;* and Mr. and Mrs. Philip Godfrey. We used the equipment acquired in previous years for the Nemrud Dagh excavations under the auspices of the American School of Oriental Research (Goell, 1957, 1961, 1968, 1969).

As in former years, the work was conducted under my direction, and I acted also as architect, photographer, and restorateur. The basic technical staff consisted of the following: Carl Anthony, architect-surveyor, Columbia University; the late Sabri Günenç, topographical surveyor, Ankara; Jean Doak, draftsman-recorder, Cooper Union College, New York; and Jon Spence, visiting photographer and restorateur. Lt. Col. John D. Yarbrough stayed for a short period as geographical adviser and led the exploratory trip made with me on the Euphrates (see below). The commissioner, Adnan Misir Bay, representing the Department of Antiquities of the Turkish Republic, archeologist and assistant at the Urfa Archeological Museum, negotiated formalities between the excavators, the landowner of the excavation-site Mahmud Tas, and the local officials and inhabitants. We appreciate the cooperation received from the Turkish Government officials in Ankara

—the general director of antiquities Hikmet Gürçay Bay, the assistant for excavations Burhan Tezcan Bay, and Raci Temizer Bay, director of the Archeological Museum, Ankara.

The actual digging was done by local inhabitants of Samsat. A group of local Lycée students helped clean the ceramic finds and record their provenance. All ceramics and small finds were stored in the Archaeology Museum, Gaziantep. A considerable mass of bones found in the excavated levels was also stored there and await analysis. Metal objects were brought for photography, drawing, cataloguing, and storage to the Archaeology Museum, Ankara. The preliminary classification and evaluation of our Islamic finds would not have been possible without the invaluable generous briefing and tutelage of Ralph Pinder-Wilson, deputy keeper of the Department of Antiquities of the British Museum. For all earlier periods, Dr. Richard D. Barnett, keeper of the West Asiatic Department, was my constant guide and critic. I am profoundly indebted to him; but I take the responsibility for any errors.

The preliminary excavations were confined to the east-central periphery of the upper level of the citadel-mound (figs. 4, 5). Its top appears deceptively level to the eye; in the following description it is referred to as the "plateau." Today its dimensions are far smaller than originally when it was occupied by buildings and the outer periphery was surrounded by medieval fortification walls. With the disappearance of this girdle wall due to weathering and plundering the mound's slopes were eroded and gouged away. The ancient stratified building walls, which had extended to the mound's edge, were sheared off. Until recently, whatever stones remained on the mound's surface provided a ready quarry for village constructions, a fate suffered by most ancient sites.

At present the plateau measures about 250 meters from north to south and 150 meters from east to west. It is roughly bow-shaped with an eroded deep indentation on the central eastern side. Approximately 50 meters in height, with almost vertical steep outer slopes, its base is more extensive than the plateau; the upper surface decreased in area as the mound rose with each successive occupation level. (Figs. 2-6).

In the Middle Ages Samosata was mentioned by Muslim geographers and historians (see Le Strange, 1890, 1905). During the period of the Arab Ommayad Caliphate (A.D. 661-750) centered in Damascus, and the Arab Abbasid Caliphate (A.D. 750-1258) with seat in Baghdad, the citadel and city were known as Sumaisât, "a very strong fortress." Mas'udi, the Baghdad historian (A.D. 943), in his *Meadows of Gold* (i, 215) writes, "The Kala'ah Sumaisât is also called the Kala'ah at Tîn (Fort of Clay)." Istakhri (A.D. 951), the Persian historian from Istakhr near Persepolis, described Sumaisât as follows: "A small city on the Euphrates, with lands watered by irrigation, and by the rains. There is a fortress here. The drinking water is from the Euphrates" (Istakhri, 62; Ibn Haukal [A.D. 978], 120, copied by Abu-l-Fidâ [A.D. 1321], 267). From Istakhri's comment on the source of the drinking water, we may infer that Samosata's Roman aqueduct was no longer in use. The River Nymphaios (modern Kâhta Chai) brought fresh mountain drinking water from the Nemrud Dagh region to the aqueduct passing through Alahan, a short distance west of the spot where the Nymphaios joined the silted Euphrates. Remnants of the aqueduct's stone arches, rock-cut canals, and mountain tunnels parallel the river's western flank. Yakut (A.D. 1225), Greek by birth and a slave in Baghdad, takes first rank among Muslim geographers. In this great *Geographical Lexicon,* iii, 151, he reports that "Sumaisât is a town on the west bank of the Euphrates. It has a castle. In one quarter of Sumaisât Armenians dwell."

On the southern end of the mound, high medieval castle walls, constructed of reused limestone masonry blocks from earlier periods, survive (figs. 2, 3, 4). On the southeastern side of the mound slightly below the plateau, a length of a massive foundation wall and a large limestone block with traces of a relief, apparently from a monumental Roman building, appear. No traces of the superstructure have survived, but we assume from the references by Mas'udi that the main superstructures of the citadel's girdle and castle walls were made of clay. The technique used in their construction was probably stamped clay or unfired sun-dried clay bricks. Traditionally Anatolian, the Early Bronze Age fortification walls at Tarsus and the Late Bronze Age walls of Hittite Hattusas (today Boghazköy) were made of clay. In medieval Baghdad, the round capital-city built on the Tigris by the second Abbasid Caliph Mansur in about A.D. 762, the double walls were made of huge sun-dried bricks (see Le Strange, 1900). Samosata's fortress was one of the links in the chain of fortifications (the Thûgur) that separated from and defended the Moslem South against the Christian Byzantine North (Le Strange, 1890).

Surface finds and topography indicated that we should begin to excavate on the eroded central eastern periphery of the plateau facing the Euphrates (figs. 4-6) and dig down through cultural sequences totaling a depth of at least 50 meters, reaching back chronologically from the end of the Seljuk period about A.D. 1300 to the anticipated Chalcolithic, about 5000 B.C. The combination of limited time and funds, with the staggering heat and the frequent wind and dust storms, was an unending challenge. The need to employ unskilled local labor, inexperienced in archeological exca-

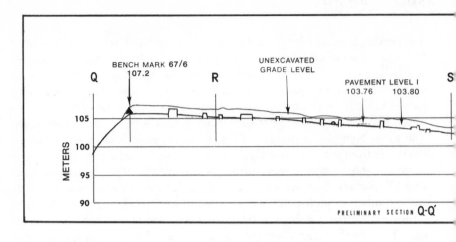

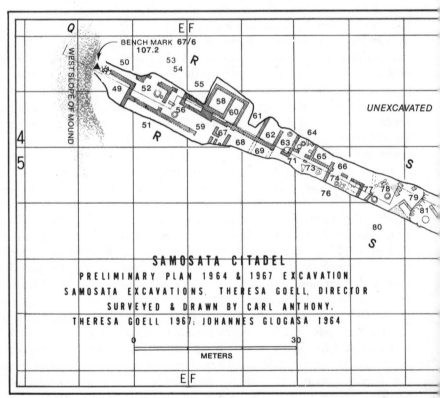

FIG. 5. Mound of Samosata: *Upper figure,* preliminary section of the mound's plateau
east-side excavatio

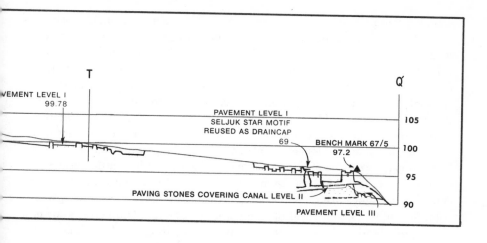

T   Q'

PAVEMENT LEVEL I
99.78

PAVEMENT LEVEL I
SELJUK STAR MOTIF
REUSED AS DRAINCAP
69   BENCH MARK 67/5
97.2

105

100

95

90

PAVING STONES COVERING CANAL LEVEL II

PAVEMENT LEVEL III

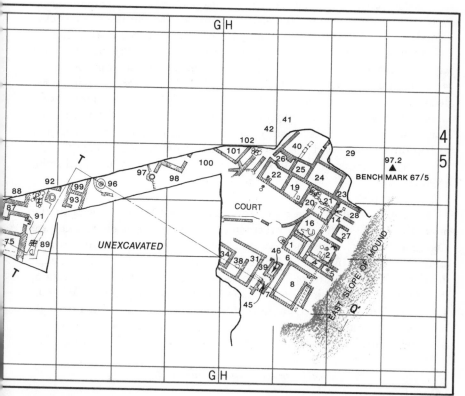

G H

41
42
102
101   40
100   26   29
97   22   25   24   97.2
98   BENCH MARK 67/5
92   19
88   99   96   20   21   23
93   COURT   28
87   16   14
91   1   27
75   89   UNEXCAVATED   34   46   6
38   31   39   5
8
45

4
5

EAST SLOPE OF MOUND

Q'

G H

el I (Seljuk Period). *Lower figure,* plan of the mound's plateau at Level I (Seljuk Period);
east-west trench.

vation techniques, also was a relevant factor in planning our field work.

In former years, before Byzantine and Islamic studies had received their present appreciation, it was taken for granted that the finds from Late Roman-Byzantine and Islamic upper levels of a habitation mound, particularly ceramic material, would be discarded and reported only briefly, if at all. Only inscriptions and material of earlier periods such as Sumerian, Assyrian, Babylonian, Hittite, Persian, Greek, Roman, etc., were considered worthy of learned and systematic attention. It is for this reason that the dwelling places and evidence of daily activities — the genre material — of the Late Roman-Byzantine-medieval Islamic periods are still so little known to us. On the other hand, the monumental structures of East and West — churches, mosques, tombs, colleges, palaces, caravanseries, sculpture, wall paintings, mosaics, and royal objects — are documented and better known.

Consequently, when we began to dig our trial trench in 1964 (figs. 4-6) and uncovered immediately below the plateau surface a rich and varied yield of ceramic fragments and artifacts representing the Islamic-medieval period, we welcomed this opportunity to augment and record so much new information concerning its daily life. Returning here in 1967 (figs. 5, 6), we were determined to give these upper Islamic levels the comprehensive archeological treatment for which they clamored, although in so doing we delayed reaching the hoped-for lower levels of Antiochus's Hellenistic-Commagenian dynasty to bring to light his royal palace and administrative center. We had been eager to clear the Samosata remains of Antiochus I and to coordinate them with his last resting place on Nemrud Dagh (Goell, 1957 etc.; Honigmann, 1924; Weissbach, 1920; Humann and Puchstein, 1890).

The complex of architectural remains of the medieval upper layers that we have excavated to date represents only a fraction of the area of the mound's plateau. The architecture and artifacts we brought to light are among the most comprehensive and enlightening of the Seljuk period known in Turkey (figs. 5, 6). The Seljuk palaces excavated at Kubadabad in central Turkey south of Iconium (Konya) had a different motivation; they were the royal residences or summer palaces of King Keykubad I (A.D. 1235) (T. T. Rice, 1961). Our citadel-residence at Samosata was a strategic military and administrative center controlling the military and trade routes converging there (Ramsay, 1890).

The Objectives and Finds, 1967

LEVEL I:

Citadel-Mound. Our first objective was to continue to excavate in extent and depth the trench begun in 1964 on the east-central periphery of the summit (figs. 2, 4, 5, 6). We dug an east-west trench beginning on the western summit periphery and joined it to the eastern area brought to light in 1964 (figs. 4-6). Both areas of the plateau were excavated simultaneously in order to determine the chronological and cultural relationships between the known eastern habitation and the western areas of the uppermost level (designated as Level I) of the mound. We ascertained the cause of the pronounced difference in elevation of these areas; on the western side of the plateau at Bench Mark 67/6 the elevation level was 107.2 meters, which was 10 meters higher than the elevation of Bench Mark 67/5 at 97.2 meters on the eastern periphery. Clearance of the upper strata of Level I soon showed that the building foundations and clay room floors on the west side of the east-west trench were terraced, stepping down on the east toward the Euphrates (fig. 5, *upper*). The foundations were constructed of rubble consisting of reused Roman, Byzantine, and Islamic building stones, bearing inscriptions with Arabic letters, column and capital fragments, moldings, etc., of destroyed earlier buildings. Pebbles and mud-mortar were used as binding and leveling materials.

Above the foundations, the walls of clay, which during the ravages of time had melted back into earth, concealed and protected the substructures and artifact remains (figs. 4-6). Subsequent plowing on the plateau had disturbed the rooms and their contents, particularly the Islamic medieval clay vessels, which were ground into sherds. No wooden roof beams survived, although we had anticipated finding them on the floor levels where they might have fallen during the Mongol attack on the citadel. The roofs most likely were flat, with surfacing of stone-rolled clay as they still are today in Samsat and the Euphrates-Tigris landscape. It seems probable that the precious wooden supporting posts and roof-trees were carried away for secondary use after the destruction and abandonment of the citadel. We found no ashes as evidence of a general conflagration.

When surveyed and drawn the east side of the trench (the enlarged area of the 1964 excavations) (figs. 4-6), with its complex of rooms, produced a typical Middle Eastern courtyard plan, known from earliest times. A portion of its stone pavement survived in the court. We cleared a series of chambers of larger and smaller units comprising utility rooms with dressed limestone doorways and stone pavements, ovens, storage bins, and light- or stairwells leading to the flat roofs, which could also be used for the storage, cleaning, and drying of grain and fruit and for sleeping during Samsat's long hot summers. There were washrooms, pits, and drainage canals under rooms and passages; a deep stone-lined cesspit under the court; and well-constructed sanitary installations.

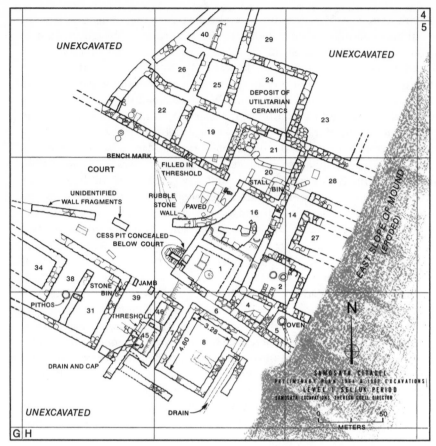

FIG. 6.   Detail of east area of excavations at Level I (Seljuk Period).

Metal. From the number of metal objects, particularly iron "horse-shoes" and partitioned stone mangers, it appears that a part of the eastern area was used for stables and storerooms. Iron scythes, saws, cooking utensils, nails, bolts, hinges, doorstops, and hooks were found. Iron arrows, scale-armor fragments, and sheets of iron (? shields) probably were evidence of the Mongol invasion and defense in the 13th century.

Ceramics. The ceramics found in upper Level I indicated occupation during the 12th-13th centuries A.D. Absence of any ceramic fragments attributable to a 14th-15th centuries' occupation of the early Ottoman period indicated that the citadel was abandoned for habitation purposes from the late 13th century, after the Mongol invasion, until the present day.

In the western trench (fig. 5, *left*) a number of clay ovens, hearths, large heavy ceramic basins, and a variety of the 12th-13th century ceramic vessels appeared in what were apparently kitchen installations capable of serving great numbers and contemporary with the ceramic finds of the area on the eastern side of the plateau.

Because of the presence of types of glazed and luster luxury wares, as well as plain utility vessels present, it is likely that the complex was part of the administrative residence of the governors or emirs of the city during the Seljuk and Mameluke period. However, no Egyptian-Mameluke ware was found. The western trench was too narrow to provide a comprehensive view of the general layout of the building area (fig. 5). Only further excavation can determine whether the building plan on the west side of the plateau was similar to the east, with courts surrounded by units used as residence, harem, administrative offices, guards' quarters, etc. (figs. 5, 6).

The large variety of preserved ceramic styles in Level I of the east and west united trenches can be assigned, on the basis of comparison with finds at other sites in Turkey, Syria, Palestine, Egypt, and Persia, to the 12th and 13th centuries. The luxury wares included luster-painted; green and turquoise glazed Kashan (Persia) and Rakka (Syria) types of underglazed painted vessels; and glazed molded and carved relief decorated vessels. Very characteristic of the Seljuk period are the lead glazed polychrome *sgraffiato* or incised ware, known also as Crusader's ware; the Persian type of *champlevé;* and characteristic Byzantine *"elaborate* ware" prevalent in the palace ware of Constantinople (D. T. Rice, 1930).

The luster vessels show the clear relationship among Turkey, Persia, Syria, and Egypt. One fragmentary green celadon-colored glazed jar, with overglaze bronze luster painted pattern, closely resembles Syrian Rakka vessels. But ours was very crudely made and the workmanship unskilled. It hardly seems likely that it was produced in Rakka and hauled to Samosata. The latter city, or nearby inland caravan cities such as Edessa, Harran, and Hisn Mansur (Adiyaman), if not Samosata itself, must have possessed pottery kilns.

In Konya (ancient Iconium) in central Turkey, the capital of the Seljuk rulers, the Seljuk Karatay Medrese (College) (A.D. 1251), today a Ceramic Museum, houses a fine collection considered to have been made locally of Persian-Kashan luster types of tiles recovered from the Palace of Alaeddin and from the Palace of Keykubad I at Kubadabad. If so, there is no reason why the Samosata wares could not have been made locally in eastern Turkey during the same medieval Seljuk period.

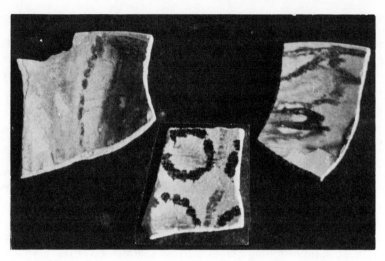

FIG. 7.   Abassid polychrome glazed ceramic bowl fragments, Samarra ware type
(ca. A.D. 9-10). About one-half actual size.

Utility wares abundant at Samosata included jugs with pear-shaped body
form, glossy red-slipped with or without incised and plastic decoration, high
neck, one vertical handle, flat base, and gritty sandy apricot core. They were
still *in situ* on the floor, especially in Room 24 (fig. 5, *lower*) where they
were abandoned apparently when the citadel was besieged. Unusual coarse,
apricot slipped jugs and jars, usually with one handle, were decorated with
painted vertical wavy bands or branchlike patterns in red or black. Some
large pithoi types were decorated with combined incised wavy bands or
branchlike painted patterns in red or black. Red-painted bowls and pot
covers with knobbed central vertical handles were numerous. The red-
painted style is reminiscent of the wares found at Byzantine Khirbet Kerak,
Palestine. They also recall the Hama wares published by Vagn Poulsen,
the dating uncertain but ascribed by him to about the 12th century (Riis et
al, 1957). At Samosata our dating is certain, as the ware was found *in situ*
together with datable 12th-13th century ceramic material.

Glass. The glass finds on the west and east areas of the east-west trench
of the plateau (fig. 5, *lower*) belong chronologically and culturally to the
same era as the ceramics, the 12th and 13th centuries, despite the difference in elevation. The enamel decorated and inscribed glass vessels, called
Syrian, are usually ascribed to the 14th century; in the Samosata complex
our fragments indicate a Seljuk 13th-century date. It is to be recalled that
the Seljuks were Turkish invaders from central Asia by way of Persia and

Fig. 8. Room 300, Level III (Early Byzantine Period), showing dressed limestone stairway and pavement.

Iraq. They defeated the Byzantine emperor Romanus Diogenes in 1071 at Manzikert, north of Lake Van, and began their western pressure toward and settlement of Anatolia (Turkey).

LEVEL II:

During 1967, digging down below the first or Seljuk level in the area of the 1964 excavation area, we reached two main lower levels in which the character of the ceramics changed. Level II produced many examples of plain light-slipped, plastic-decorated small and large jars of about the 9th-10 centuries A.D. belonging to the Arab Abbasid Period when the seat of the Caliphate was at Baghdad. Together with these we found numerous sherds, the so-called Abassid splashed-glaze Samarra ware resembling the Chinese T-ang type (fig. 7), as well as some Ommayad 7th-9th century mottle-glazed sherds of large plates; whether these finds were imported from Iraq or Syria or made locally is not yet known.

LEVEL III:

At 5 meters below the plateau surface on the eastern periphery we reached Level III with remains of a cut-stone paved floor, dressed limestone stairway, and other vestiges apparently of Byzantine occupation before the conquest of the region by the Moslem Arabs in the 7th century (fig. 8). This lower level, heavily overlaid with a fill of mixed debris, requires more extensive excavation and study. In the fill covering Level III there were masses of Roman ceramic roof-tiles plastically decorated with impressed Roman waves and X-es; also lumps of so-called "Greek Fire."

One of the welcome surprises of our excavations was finding a considerable mass composed of lumps of rusty-looking material resembling iron slag. The Turkish Metal Research Institute of Ankara *(Maden Tetkik ve Arama Enstitusu)* analyzed some specimens and informed us that the material was asphalt or mineral pitch. We know from Pliny the Elder *(Natural History,* II, 108, 235) that "in Samosata the capital of Commagene there is a marsh that produces an inflammable mud called mineral pitch. When this touches anything solid it sticks to it; also when people touch it, it actually follows them as they try to get away from it. By these means they defended the city walls when attacked by Lucullus (69 B.C.); the troops kept getting burnt by their own weapons. Water merely makes it burn more fiercely; experiments have shown that it can only be put out by earth." The formula for this mineral pitch has been lost, and it is therefore exciting and important to have found, on the fortification citadel of Samosata itself, this chemical weapon called by the ancients "Greek Fire," for which Commagene was famous (Pliny, *idem).* We have not yet located the source of this pitch in Samosata (see Partington, 1960).

City Walls of Samosata

Our second objective for 1967 was to conduct preliminary explorations of the Hellenistic-Roman and Byzantine-Arab periods by surveying the architectural remains of the encircling city walls of Samosata, which stretch for a considerable distance (about 4 kilometers) and height on the plain below the citadel-mound. The late surveyor Sabri Günenç began this field survey. Our present data provide an outline of the wall's circuit and its fragments. Unfortunately, this wall of limestone rubble with concrete joints was used later as a quarry, dismantled, and the stones carried off to build the later villages of Samosata, environs, and present-day Samsat (plan: fig. 2).

On the southeastern edge of Samosata, considerable fragments of the Late Hellenistic-Roman wall and Edessa gateway faced the Euphrates river-crossing, connecting with roads on the eastern shore leading to ancient Amida (modern Diyarbakir), Siverek, Edessa (modern Urfa), Harran, and Rakka (in Syria). The Edessa gateway remains are flanked by walls of rubble concrete standing to a considerable height (fig. 9); fragments of rooms in

FIG. 9.   Detail of Roman *opus reticulatum* building technique in the city fortification wall; facade at southeast side facing Euphrates River.

the wall most likely were casements for the legions who protected the river-crossing and western shores against the Parthians and Sassanians. One of the Roman techniques used for the construction of the walls' lower parts was the well-known, netlike *opus reticulatum* (fig. 9) (Mau, 1899). In Rome itself this Augustan technique continued to be used even later; it is crucial for giving precious comparative data for the Commagenian Hellenistic-Roman period to which the encircling city wall belonged.

Beginning from the neighboring village, Kilisyan Köy to the northeast, we followed this city wall along the clifflike second Euphrates bank for some distance south, paralleling the river; the wall disappeared at the edge of the gully along the north base of the citadel mound (plan: fig. 2). Along the line of the wall from Kilisyan Köy to the gully there are deep pits and scars showing where the wall foundations were plundered as a quarry. No vestige of the wall was found on the east base of the mound where there are two gushing springs of cold water. The limestone through which they emerge, below a conglomerate pebble deposit of the river, is part of the natural mound-base. It lies slightly higher than the silt-laden Euphrates, the present lowest bank. The stratified occupation layers of the mound lie above the conglomerate deposit.

At the southern end of the mound a path runs easterly at right angles toward the ferry crossing. The same path joins a deep depression suggesting a moat along the west base of the mound. The north side of the mound was bordered by a deep trench, which is not a moat but a modern canal carrying water to a proposed mill, not built because the project did not prove to be feasible. The Roman city-wall remnants appear on the heights above the south side of the ferry path. Only the wall's base, composed of rough courses of stone blocks fashioned out of cut-up classical fluted column shafts, friezes, and moldings, survives. This suggests a hasty repair or reconstruction in the Roman Imperial or possibly during the Persian wars in the early Byzantine period. The wall continued south along the edge of the heights on the east side of the city and finally reached the southeastern entrance or the Edessa gateway, whence it continued south and turned sharply north-westerly. Today, this western wall runs through and is obscured by modern houses, courtyards, and gardens (plan: fig. 2). Emerging into the open, it continues along the high east embankment of a wide natural gully bordering the western edge of the ancient city and modern town, then disappearing into the northerly hills. The gully separated the city from the fertile fields and hills to the southwest (plan: fig. 2). It is not to be identified as the River Marsyas, which joined the Euphrates near Samosata (Weissbach, 1920). On the southeast side of the city, the wall technique, Roman-Byzantine *opus mixtum,* also is of significance in constructing a chronology: It is composed of large light red-tan brick tiles with intermediate rubblestone layers.

To the west of the modern cemetery located within the circuit wall at the southwest of Samsat a dirt road leads to Sinan-Kantara and the villages to the southwest along the Euphrates shore. On the eastern gully bank, deep down, there is a huge stone and concrete block (plan: fig. 2) that suggests a tower foundation or the abutment of an ancient bridge that might have spanned it. No traces of a similar construction appear on the opposite western side of the gully. This dirt road also leads into the western surrounding hills, to the vineyards planted on their heights by the Samsat landowners, and it gives access to the heretofore unrecorded and unpublished ancient *necropoleis* of Samosata with its rock-cut chambers and natural caves (see below).

The western portion of the city wall proceeds northerly along the east rim of the gully embankment; it is the western boundary of Samosata's fertile fields, rough with the rubble of destroyed building materials and broken pottery. In a fragmentary condition, the wall then takes a sharp turn to the northeast — joining our starting-point at Kilisyan Köy. It forms a complete bow-shaped circuit about 5½ kilometers long around the ancient Roman city area (fig. 2).

The Necropoleis of Samosata

North of the northern line of the city wall, toward the fields of Kilisyan Köy, there is an upper flood beach or terrace facing the Euphrates. Hewn out of the mass of this terrace are rock-cut tomb chambers. It is rumored that the villagers of Samosata have removed stone sarcophagi from this area. During a visit to Samosata in 1951 I saw along the Samsat-Adiyaman road a colossal limestone sarcophagus decorated with carved swags of fruit and flowers resembling Roman monuments of the 2d-3d centuries A.D.; since then the sarcophagus has disappeared. Questioning of the villagers failed to produce knowledge of its present whereabouts. Probably it is being used by villagers as a storage bin or was chopped up for use as lintels, treads, jambs, or millstones. If undisturbed burials could be located in this necropolis, investigation of the skeletal remains might lead to information regarding the ethnic composition of the population of Samosata at the time of interment.

To the west (plan: fig. 2) of the western gully of Samosat, hills run parallel to the Euphrates and reach behind the next village, Sinan-Kantara Köy, where there is a private *kayik* (ferry) crossing the Euphrates toward the east, connecting with the Edessa, Harran, and Amida roads. This ridge is riddled with rock-cut tombs and (probably) natural caverns. The chamber tomb nearest to Samosata has been looted, and no sign of the sarcophagus remains. The heaped-up earth above on its exterior forms the apex of a burial mound. The ridge's summit levels out inland into a plateau covered with vineyards. I was informed by the landowner's children that while cultivating these heights they uncovered six colossal limestone sarcophagi (their covers missing), of which two are still standing along the road. A third is used as a storage bin in front of the home of the mayor of Samosata, Bahri Firat. I was told that in Sinan-Kantara rock-cut tombs have also been found with objects (which I have seen) of the Roman period. We have not examined these necropoleis in detail and therefore cannot date precisely the cave-tombs and the six sarcophagi. One of our objectives in future campaigns is to conduct thorough-going examinations of the necropoleis.

Problems of Identification of Samuha-Samosata

At the beginning of August 1967 an exploration trip by raft on the Euphrates was made by Col. (then Lt. Col.) John D. Yarbrough, myself, and Yarbrough's Turkish *kelikci* from Kemaliye, who constructed our raft *(kelik* in Turkish) composed of 26 inflated skins supporting an open grid platform of poplar trunks covered by leafy tree branches (fig. 10). Colonel Yarbrough had already navigated the entire river from its source near Erzincan, Turkey, to the Persian Gulf, in 1964 with the late Col. Robert Perry. I am deeply indebted to Colonel Yarbrough for use of his raft and guidance of our 1967 trip.

During my first visit to Nemrud Dagh in 1947, I learned that the fertile region below Nemrud Dagh, near the castle of Gerger (ancient Arsameia-on-the-Euphrates) on the west bank of the river, was now called Eski (old) Pütürge. In the Anti-Taurus Mountains to the north there is another town with a castle called Yeni (new) Pütürge, situated on the Shiro Chai, which flows into the Euphrates. The place name Pütürge could be equated with the Hittite place name Pittiyarik or Pittiyariga. The important Hittite cult-center Samuha occurs in the same context in a well-known Hittite text with a place called Pittiyariga on a river (KUB.XXXI, 79: Garstang and Gurney, 1959, p. 33, note 3). Some modern Hittitologists conjectured that Samuha might have been located on the middle Euphrates. The gist of the Hittite letter concerns navigation, saying that "ships brought the food supplies from Pittiyariga.... to Samuha." They argued whether Samuha and Hel-

FIG. 10. Raft constructed of animal skins, with superimposed poplar grid platform covered by leafy branches. Used in Euphrates exploration trip in 1967 to determine whether Samuha-Samosata can be equated. To right, Col. J. D. Yarbrough conversing with local shepherds.

lenistic-Roman Samosata could be equated as the same place. But not one of them had explored this disputed Euphrates area; they knew Samosata environs from maps on a very brief visit.

The purpose of our trip on the Euphrates was to cover the course of the river and shores between the area of Gerger (called Eski Pütürge today) and Samosata in order to judge at first hand, on topographical grounds, whether Samosata could be equated with Samuha, the seat of the Hittite goddess Hebat and the Weather-God Teshup.

Our river trip started from Yarmuluk Köy north of Gerger, near where the Euphrates emerges from the massif of the Anti-Taurus Mountains and begins its descending widening course to Samosata, to Apameia-Zeugma, and eventually to the Persian Gulf. I shall not record here the exact details of our observations. However, as a result of our three-day trip, I can state unequivocally that the region near Gerger cannot be equated with Hittite Pittiyarik. It is easy enough to go downstream by raft, but the waters of the Euphrates could not be navigated by barge or raft or pulled by rope in an upstream direction back from Samuha (? Samosata) to Pittiyariga (? Eski

Pütürge) because of geological and topographical obstacles. After discharging their loads, and selling the wooden raft beams, the boatmen would have to return that long distance over arduous paths by foot or animal. Besides, the area around the present-day Eski Pütürge is not extensive or fertile enough — and seasons are too short in that rocky pocket of the Anti-Taurus Mountains — to support cultivation of large crops and the transfer of grain to the outer world. However, the fields around Samosata, in the lower valley and the flanking plains of Adiyaman on the upper plateau (or ancient Euphrates terrace), are extremely vast and fertile for farming, and the growing season is long. Samuha (if=Samosata) would not have had to import supplies from the inner wilder rocky reaches of the river. Primarily for this reason, we can affirm that the place-name pairs Samuha-Samosata and Pittiyariga-Eski Pütürge of the Hittite text cannot be equated. These places must be sought somewhere in the "Upper Lands" or the modern Keban Dam region north of Malatya (Hittite Milid-Maldiya=Hellenistic Melitene) as suggested by Garstan. More recently, Dr. Hamit Kosay, former director of the Turkish Department of Museums and Antiquities, while excavating in the soon-to-be-flooded Keban area located a village called Samuka on the west side of the Euphrates. Since it meets the geographical requirements for ancient Samuha, he provisionally equates it with the latter. Dr. Koşay's conclusion awaits systematic excavations for a decisive identification. I am indebted to Dr. Koşay for showing me his new-found evidence (Koşay, 1972).

REFERENCES

[Additional references, to Classical and other early authorities, appear in the text]

BARNETT, RICHARD D., and FORMAN, W.
  1959. Assyrian palace reliefs and their influence on the sculpture of Babylonia and Persia, 36 pp., illus. Batchworth, London.

DÖRNER, FRIEDRICH KARL, and GOELL, THERESA
  1963. Arsameia am Nymphaios: Die Ausgrabungen im Hierothesion des Mithradates Kallinikos von 1953-1956, 340 pp., illus. Gebrüder Mann, Berlin.

DÖRNER, FRIEDRICH K., and NAUMANN, R.
  1939. Forschungen in Kommagene. Istanbuler Forschungen, Band 10, 114 pp., illus. Deutscher Archäologisches Institut (Istanbul), Berlin.

GARSTANG, JOHN, and GURNEY, O. R.
  1959. The geography of the Hittite Empire. Occ. Publ. Brit. Inst. Archaeol. in Ankara, no. 3, x + 133 pp., illus. London.

GOELL, THERESA
  1957. The excavation of the "Hierothesion" of Antiochus I of Commagene on Nemrud Dagh (1953-1956). Bull. Amer. Schools Oriental Res. (Jerusalem, Baghdad), no. 147, pp. 4-22, illus.
  1961. Throne above the Euphrates. Nat. Geogr. Mag., vol. 119, no. 3, pp. 390-405, illus.

1967. Samosata. Archaeol. Soc. Staten Island (A.I.A.) News Notes, vol. 1, no. 2, pp. 1-3.
1968. Geophysical survey of the Hierothesion and tomb of Antiochus I of Commagene, Turkey. Nat. Geogr. Soc. Res. Rpts., 1963 Projects, pp. 83-102, illus.
1969. The Nemrud Dagh (Turkey) geophysical surveys of 1964. Nat. Geogr. Soc. Res. Rpts., 1964 Projects, pp. 61-81, illus.

HONIGMANN, E.
1924. Kommagene. Cols. 978-990 *in* Pauly's Real-Encyclopädie, suppl. 4. Stuttgart.

HUMANN, KARL, and PUCHSTEIN, OTTO
1890. Reisen in Kleinasien und Nordsyrien, 2 vols. (vol. 1, 424 pp., illus., text; vol. 2, atlas). D. Reimer, Berlin.

KOŞAY, HAMIT
1972. Hitit Tapingi Samuha Nerededir? Bell. Türk Tarih Kurmu, vol. 36, no. 144, pp. 463-468, illus.

LE STRANGE, GUY
1890. Palestine under the Moslems: A description of Syria and the Holy Land from A.D. 650 to 1500, xxii + 604 pp., illus. Translated from medieval geographers. (Republished by Khayats, Beirut, 1965.)
1900. Baghdad during the Abassid Caliphate, xxxi + 381 pp., illus. Clarendon Press, Oxford.
1905. The Lands of the Eastern Caliphate, vii + 536 pp., illus. Cambridge University Press. (Republished by Frank Cass, London, 1966).

MAU, AUGUST
1899. Pompeii: Its life and art, xxii + 509 pp., illus. Macmillan Co., London. (Translated from the German by F. W. Kelsey.)

MOLTKE, HELMUT VON
1882. Briefe über Zustände und Begebenheiten in der Türkei aus den Jahren 1835 bis 1839, ed. 4, vi + 431 pp., illus. Mittler, Berlin.

PARTINGTON, J. R.
1960. A history of Greek Fire, xvi + 381 pp., illus. W. Heffer, Cambridge.

RAMSAY, WILLIAM MITCHELL
1890. The historical geography of Asia Minor. Roy. Geogr. Soc. Suppl. Papers, vol. 4, vi + 495 pp., illus. John Murray, London.

RICE, DAVID T.
1930. Byzantine glazed pottery, xii + 120 pp., illus. Clarendon Press, Oxford.

RICE, TAMARA T.
1961. The Seljuks in Asia Minor, 280 pp., illus. Thames & Hudson, London, and Frederick A. Praeger, New York.

RIIS, P. J.; POULSEN, VAGN; and HAMMERSHAIMB, E.
1957. Hama fouilles et recherches 1931-1938, IV, 2: Les verreries et poteries médiévales, viii + 316 pp., illus. Fondation Carlsberg, Copenhagen.

WEISSBACH, F. H.
1920. Samosata. Cols. 2220-2224 *in* Pauly's Real-Encyclopädie, ser. 2, vol. 1 bis. Stuttgart.

THERESA GOELL

An Archeological Survey in the West Cameroon

Principal Investigator: Donald D. Hartle, University of Nigeria, Nsukka, Nigeria.

Grant No. 653:   In support of archeological investigations in the Cameroon, Africa.

In the latter part of 1967, working under the above-named Society grant, I conducted a brief archeological survey of the Bamenda ringroad area of the West Cameroon. This expedition was called the "National Geographic Society—University of Nigeria Archeological Survey in the Cameroon." My aim was to obtain comparative data for stone tools excavated in Afikpo, Nigeria, in 1966. These excavations were made under the auspices of the University of Nigeria at Nsukka and further supported by a National Science Foundation grant in November 1964.

The Ezi Ukpa Rock Shelter in Afikpo was excavated in 1966. It contained pottery sherds and worked stone to a depth of nearly 13 feet. Nine radiocarbon dates determined by Geochron Laboratories, Inc., range from A.D. 15 to 2935 B.C. (Hartle, 1968). This is the earliest determined date for pottery thus far in the area. I believe that this date corroborates a date of 2555 ± 130 B.C. for the pottery at the Nsukka Farm site (Hartle, 1966). Some of the stone artifacts found in association with the pottery appear to be rare in West Africa. Details of the stone industry were presented at a meeting of West African archeologists in Freetown, Sierra Leone, in July 1966 (Shaw, 1966). *The Nigerian Field* published photographs of similar stone artifacts, surface finds, collected some years ago by M. D. W. Jeffreys in the Bamenda area of the Cameroon (Jeffreys, 1964). The lithic industry found during excavations at the Ezi Ukpa Rock Shelter in Afikpo and in surface finds along the escarpment north of Afikpo on the Afikpo-Abakaliki road suggested the possibility of similar tools extending from there to the Bamenda area. The proposed Cameroon survey originally formed a part of my extended plans for archeological research because eastern Nigeria and West Cameroon are in a common geographic area. Since the civil war made it impossible for me to return to Nsukka, it seemed an opportune time to investigate that phase of the research.

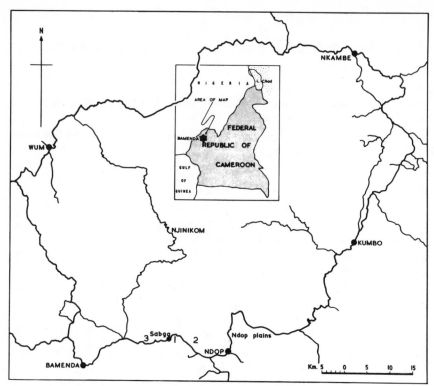

FIG. 1.   The ringroad, West Cameroon.

The initial survey was begun in Mamfe, but because of excessive rain and overgrown forest conditions I decided to move on to Bamenda, some 160 kilometers east and use that town as a base of operations. The Bamenda ringroad is located in the northern part of the West Cameroon, beginning in the west at Bamenda, east to Kumbo, north to Nkambe, west to Wum, and south to Bamenda again. Because of the weather I was unable to get either to Wum from Bamenda or north and west beyond Kumbo. Therefore my work was confined for the most part to the area between Bamenda and Kumbo, although we did attempt, without success, to survey some of the area northward toward Njinekom.

The comparative material for the Afikpo material was located east-ward and beyond the Ndop Plains in the grasslands. Although three specific sites were recorded (see map, fig. 1), I believe that these are an extension of a single area. Site no. 1 is 1 kilometer east of Sagba village and was located as a result of recent bulldozing operations for a new road. The rain also helped to expose many specimens here. Site 2 is near a small stream at the bottom of a hill 4 kilometers east of site 1. Site 3 is 4 kilometers west of Sabga village on both sides of the road. All finds were from the grasslands, along cow trails, at water holes, and at erosion areas; none came from forests. One informant, who had worked with Jeffreys many years ago, claimed that these were "grassland" tools and would not be found in the forest. However, Jeffreys apparently found these implements at every level of elevation from the grasslands to the rain forests (Jeffreys, 1951). This was not checked because, as stated earlier, I was unable to survey in the forest area. As I have indicated, these tools were surface finds and there was no indication of any habitation area. In fact, it appears that they might simply have been discarded or dropped in the grasslands. Most of the specimens at site 3 had been kicked out by cattle walking along a trail, and the tools had remained in the depression of the trail. These have not been compared with the Afikpo artifacts. Although the initial processing of the Afikpo materials had been completed, civil war interrupted the analysis of the artifacts.

Many of the tools collected by Jeffreys are in the Bamenda Museum, but at the time of independence the files were "relocated" and the data were lost. The material is without any provenience, although most of it apparently came from the ringroad or south of Sabga in the Nsi salt area (Jeffreys, 1951). I collected specimens from the museum that seemed to characterize or represent different "types" of the tools and included them with the artifacts collected during the survey.

I recovered some 65 artifacts in addition to 10 specimens from the Bamenda Museum. Most of them are made of a fine, sandy-textured basalt and are light gray in color. Some, however, are made from larger grained materials, which I could not identify. None of the tools was made of quartz or of a good siliceous material although such raw material was available in the area. Primary flaking is obvious, but because the tools are very well worn, weathered, and rolled it is difficult if not impossible to determine if secondary flaking is present. What polish is present, with one exception, appears to be the result of use rather than of intent.

Fifteen groups with some subdivisions were tentatively identified. I have purposely avoided the use of "type," since in some instances only one or two specimens represent a group. The final report is now in preparation, and some of the tools can be described as:

Large, heavy cores	Side-edge knives
Axes, some of which may have been hafted	Discoidal flakes

Blades, which may be axes	Picklike objects
Cleaverlike objects	Grubbing tools (?)
Cutting tools	Polishing tools (?)

Jeffreys believed his stone industry to be Neolithic because he found polished and unpolished tools associated. He further thought they were agricultural implements (Jeffreys, 1951). The tools from Afikpo would tend to bear this out since pottery was present throughout and many of the stone implements were polished.

One specimen that appears to be similar to my Group II was recovered from the lower levels of the Iwo Eleru site in the Western State of Nigeria (S. G. H. Daniels, personal communication). Davies (1967) also illustrates comparable materials from Ghana as well as some of those from Bamenda. These he calls "waisted axes." Thus indications are that these artifacts may be widespread throughout West Africa even though reported occurrences have been rare.

The Sabga area of the West Cameroon should be more intensively investigated so that a stratified site containing the various groups of tools might be located and excavated. This would provide us with a good control for a chronological yardstick.

Before I conducted this survey in West Cameroon I considered the possibility that these stone tools were derived from the south, perhaps the Congo area, and spread throughout the forest into West Africa. I still consider this a valid possibility that warrants future investigation. Jeffreys (1951) suggests that these implements made their way down the Cross River Valley. This too is a good possibility and could in fact complement my suggestion. I hope soon to conduct an intensive survey from Calabar to and beyond Afikpo not only to determine if these tools are present in the Cross River valley but also to locate other sites, similar to the Ezi Ukpa Rock Shelter in Afikpo, that would repay intensive excavation.

REFERENCES

DAVIES, OLIVER
    1967. West Africa before the Europeans, 364 pp., illus. Methuen & Co., London.
HARTLE, DONALD DEAN
    1966. Archaeology in eastern Nigeria. West Afr. Archaeol. Newsletter, no. 5, pp. 13-17.
    1968. An archaeological survey in the West Cameroon. West Afr. Archaeol. Newsletter, no. 11, pp. 35-39.

JEFFREYS, M. D. W.
   1951. Neolithic stone implements (Bamenda, British Cameroons). Bull. Inst. Franç. Afrique Noire, vol. 13, no. 4, pp. 1203-1217, illus.
   1964. Notes on the Neolithic Stone Age culture in Bamenda. Nigerian Field, vol. 29, no. 1, pp. 38-41, illus.
SHAW, THURSTAN, ed.
   1966. Report of conference of West African archaeologists at Freetown, 28th-30th June, 1966. West Afr. Archaeol. Newsletter, no. 5.

DONALD D. HARTLE

Prehistoric Desert Markings in Peru

Principal Investigator: Gerald S. Hawkins, Smithsonian Astrophysical Observatory, Cambridge, Massachusetts.

Grant No. 665:   To investigate the mysterious lines and figures in the vicinity of Nasca, Peru, to determine whether there is a relationship between astronomy and these prehistoric markings.

The lines and figures in the Peruvian desert have been described comprehensively by Dr. Maria Reiche (1949). They have also been discussed by Prof. Paul Kosok (1949), who saw the sun setting exactly over a narrow line on June 22, the solstice date. It led him to conjecture that this line was traced for the special purpose of marking this date. He calls the multitude of tracings a gigantic calendar and points to the fact that a reliable calendar was a vital necessity for an agricultural people like the ancient Nascans, whose economy was based on irrigation from rivers that carry water only during certain months of the year. If it was a calendar, the dates of the year would be marked by the rising and setting of the stars, sun, or moon along specific lines.

At the Smithsonian Astrophysical Observatory we decided to investigate the astronomical hypothesis. It had become firmly set in the popular literature, and the markings offered an opportunity to apply the principles of astroarcheology (Hawkins, 1968) to an ancient construction by preliterate people. We had available the computer program used for investigating Stonehenge in southern England (Hawkins, 1963, 1964, 1971) and also the catalogues of star positions in prehistory (Hawkins and Rosenthal, 1967). These mechanical advantages would largely overcome the difficulties of mathematical labor mentioned by Reiche. But there remained the difficulty of obtaining an accurate survey of the lines, the altitude of the distant horizon, and the date of construction of the lines. There was no definitive date for the making of the lines, except that it was thought the patterns were connected with the Nascan culture. One of the first criteria in astroarcheol-

117

ogy (Hawkins, 1968) is that "construction dates should not be determined from astronomical alignments." In the case of Stonehenge it was possible to compute alignments in the absence of an exact date because they were toward the sun and moon, whose positions change very slowly through the centuries. If the lines in the desert were built to point to the stars, as Reiche suggests, then considerable care had to be exercised because of the more rapid precessional movement of the stars. Because of this precessional motion, the configuration of the stars with respect to the lines changes markedly over a period of less than 100 years. However, several offsetting factors made this study seem worthwhile. If the lines were attributable to the Nascan culture, then the broad archeological period was known; also, there were many instances of one line cutting through another so that there existed a time sequence of construction in the pattern of the lines that would provide a detailed clue.

There are many localities in the flat, dry foothills of the Andes where ancient markings have been made. A typical area would occupy approximately 25 square kilometers and contain a few dozen lines and/or cleared surfaces in the form of triangles, rectangles, or figurative designs. I have visited one of these sites at Palpa, one near Ingenio, and two near Nasca. Other sites have been brought to my attention, in the Cantogrande Valley near Lima, in the desert at Tacna, and in a small area photographed from the air in the high Andes where the exact location was not given. It is impossible to make a reliable estimate of how many sites were originally laid out, because some have undoubtedly disappeared. For a site to survive it must have been constructed in an area free from wind-blown sand. Thus, there may be line sites beneath the ubiquitous drifting sand of the desert region. Other sites undoubtedly have disappeared because of modern construction. In particular, one of the sites north of Nasca was inspected by one of our expeditions in July 1968 but was nonexistent in December of that year because of a vast irrigation project that had commenced. With these factors in mind, one might estimate very approximately that 50 to 100 such sites existed at one time in Peru.

We concentrated our efforts on the location that contains the greatest number of features. This is in the Pampa de Jumana and Pampa Colorada near the village of Ingenio. The major concentration of lines is at long. 75°8′ W., lat. 14°42′ S., where the Pan American Highway climbs the southern edge of the Ingenio Valley. The greatest concentration of features occurs in an area approximately 15 by 10 kilometers, although other features were observed to extend over the flat mesa covering an area of approximately 30 by 15 kilometers. In addition, we investigated a subsidiary site approximately 8 kilometers north of Nasca at long. 74°59′ W., lat. 14°49′ S.

The pavement of the desert surface consists of small irregular stones, whose upper surfaces appear dark, sometimes black, and the undersurfaces reddish brown. Samples of the rock and subsoil were brought back to headquarters of the Smithsonian Astrophysical Observatory (SAO) for geological analysis by Dr. Ursula B. Marvin. She made the following conclusions:

No clue to the age of the Nasca lines can be deduced from the samples collected, and it is unlikely that dates could be derived from a study of the regional geomorphology.

The pebbles are partially coated with a thin film of desert varnish that may have begun to form, not when the Nasca people were active, but at some much earlier date in the late Pleistocene.

Desert varnish, formed by slow, *in situ* decomposition of rock and the deposition of oxides upon the surfaces by capillary action, is characteristic of outcrops and pebbles in warm, arid regions. The rate of formation varies from desert to desert but is everywhere very slow. Examples have been found in southern Nubia, where petroglyphs, probably at least 10,000 years old, were formed by the scraping away of desert varnish on cliff faces. The "fresh" surfaces have not been recoated with desert varnish. This suggests that, in that area, the varnish formed mainly in prepaleolithic times, when the climate may have been more humid. This occurrence demonstrates that although desert varnish may acquire archeological significance, it is of no use in the dating of given sites.

The desert area evokes varying reactions from different people; the spectrum of emotions ranges from ecstatic inspiration to incipient nausea. The flat mesa with its innumerable black pebbles stretches out endlessly like the maria on the moon. There are no landmarks except for the desert lines, which are indistinguishable one from another. There is no vegetation, no water, and no sign of animal or insect life. The distant hills do not change perceptibly as one walks, and the appearance of the hills resembles that of a distant coastline seen from an offshore vessel. To aid in relocating various areas in the desert, we utilized markers such as a cow's skull and a donkey skeleton.

On the surface the narrow lines show up remarkably clearly when one stands on them, but they usually become unnoticeable when one steps a few paces to the side. The lines are generally about 50 centimeters wide. The narrowest we found was the width of a boot, about 10 centimeters, and stretched into the desert from a low group of hills for a distance of about 12 kilometers. Other lines give the impression of cleared roadways, and wider features become almost rectangular cleared surfaces. The larger surfaces are difficult to comprehend *in situ*. One of the expedition staff asked where the large delineated rectangle was, only to find that he was standing in the center of it.

Reiche has described the markings and the manner of their construction. She refers to the pebbles with the black surface glaze and the pale-yellow color of the sand-clay-calcite substratum:

> This contrast made it possible to use the level surfaces as immense blackboards on which white designs could be produced on a dark background by simply removing the upper layer of black stones. These were disposed of by being heaped up on both sides of the cleaned surfaces. Around the larger fields, the accumulated stones form long, straight elevations. They are the black lines on the aerial photographs which run along the contours of the triangles and trapezoids, as if they had been outlined with black pencil.

On our expedition we cleared a small area some distance from the main site. By picking up the stones by hand a single worker was able to clear an area at the rate of 1 square meter in 3 minutes. This may be taken as a reasonable estimate of the amount of effort spent by the original constructors. With a wooden rake the process of clearing would proceed more quickly, although as the area cleared became larger more time would be required to carry the piles of stones to the edge of the delineated area. The clearing of the square mile as estimated by Dr. Reiche would therefore take 1.3×10^5 hours. That is to say, it could be accomplished by 1,000 workers in approximately 3 full weeks of work. Thus, although these markings are extensive, they do not represent a prodigious amount of labor.

As one walks over the surface he notices many pottery fragments, painted and unpainted. In some places a pile of fragments is found that is apparently the result of fracturing a single vessel. The fragments are certainly at least 1,000 years old and give the impression that nothing has been disturbed since the original fracture. It is possible that some of the breakage has occurred recently, but from erosional features of exposed surfaces and the relatively undamaged undersurfaces it is reasonable to conclude that some of these items were broken many centuries ago.

The pottery fragments are more numerous in the vicinity of the mounds. At the large mound at the west end of the main rectangle, I counted fragments from 10 different vessels. This was not an exhaustive count, nor was I the first person to look for pottery fragments at that spot. In the course of the various expeditions, many fragments were collected from the surface and were appraised by Profs. Dorothy Menzel and John H. Rowe of the Department of Anthropology at the University of California, Berkeley. An additional opinion was given by Prof. Gordon R. Willey, Department of Anthropology, Peabody Museum, Harvard University.

TABLE 1 – POTTERY SHERDS OF EXPEDITIONS 1-4

Period	Style	Fragments	Vessels	Notes
EIP 1	Nasca 1	0	0	
EIP 2	Nasca 2	1	1	
EIP 3	Nasca 3	21	12	
EIP 4	Nasca 4	38	3	
EIP 5	Nasca 5	2	1	
EIP 6	Nasca 6	0	0	
EIP 7	Nasca 7	29	2	
EIP 8	Nasca 8	1	1	
LIP 1	Carrizal 1	1	1	
LIP 2	Carrizal 2	0	0	
LIP 3	Carrizal 3	1	1	
LIP 4	Carrizal 4	0	0	
LIP 5	Poroma 5	2	2	
Late horizon	—	7	6	5 vessels near edge of mesa

The results of the analysis of pottery fragments are shown in table 1 and in figure 1. This analysis was fraught with difficulties and uncertainties because the identification was made solely from photographs of the sherds and many of the fragments were in poor condition. Meager though it is, table 1 is the only quantitative evidence in existence concerning the pottery artifacts on the Nasca desert pampas. The number of vessels represents the estimated number of complete objects necessary to produce the corresponding set of fragments. Where the patterns are distinct, this identification is certain, but in instances where there is a similarity of pattern we may have overestimated or underestimated the number of vessels. In two instances sufficient fragments were recovered to reconstruct the original artifact almost completely. One of these vessels was a bulbous vase of style Nasca 4; the other was a deep bowl of style Nasca 7. In addition to the identifications in table 1, there were 46 fragments representing approximately 13 different pottery vessels that were impossible to identify.

The style most commonly represented is that of Nasca within the early intermediate period. There are a few examples from the late intermediate

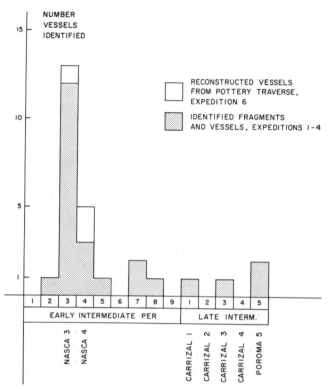

FIG. 1.   Analysis of pottery sherds.

period (LIP) and the late horizon. The most prolific style is Nasca 3 and 4, corresponding to the third and fourth decans of the early intermediate period (EIP). Most of the vessels of the late horizon were found at the edge of the mesa near the village of Ingenio, whereas the other fragments were found scattered over the larger area containing the lines and mounds. This conclusion was confirmed on the sixth expedition, when 29 fragments representing approximately 26 different vessels were collected and presented to Professor Rowe for comment. He wrote: "Only a few of the sherds you sent for identification are sufficiently well preserved and diagnostic for phase attribution; these are Nasca 3 and 4." On the sixth expedition sufficient fragments were collected to reconstruct three vessels partially. Of these, two were bulbous vases, type P, following the Gayton-Kroeber classification (Gayton, 1927), with a two-color flower and/or seed motif similar to the vessel identified on an earlier expedition as Nasca 4. The third reconstructed pot was a flared cup or bowl, type F. The motif on this last vessel was that of the jaguar, or feline deity, consistent with the style of Nasca 3.

We undertook a pottery traverse to determine the number of fragments per square kilometer. This was carried out on the sixth expedition, when three members of the staff walked from the Pan American Highway to the peak of the foothills, following the narrow extension of the main rectangle. The distance involved was approximately 2 kilometers, and each person surveyed a strip approximately 5 meters in width. Thus, the total area surveyed was approximately 30,000 square meters. There was no noticeable concentration of fragments on the cleared line from the main rectangle to the mountains. Fragments were found in isolated groups and individually scattered among the pebbles of the desert. (As it happened, the traverse chosen by the expedition did not contain many of the thick unpainted fragments that are noticeable in this area. These fragments are large, being derived from amphorae approximately 2 feet in height. This pottery is approximately 0.5 inch thick, with a light terra-cotta color, and shows internal signs of having been molded on a potter's wheel. It is designated as modern by the local Nascans. We showed photographs of these larger fragments to a staff member of the Peabody Museum, Harvard University. In his opinion one could not categorically rule out these fragments from the prehistoric era. However, they were not identifiable as any particular style, and in the absence of other evidence we have assumed that they were water jars, or containers for the popular Peruvian chicha beer.)

The traverse was chosen to be fairly representative of the area. It ran through an area where the concentration of lines was high but less than the degree of concentration farther to the north. It did not contain any focal feature such as the mounds in the main rectangle. The traverse gives a lower limit to the density of ceramic artifacts, because we cannot preclude the possibility that souvenir hunters may have visited the area previously; also, the traverse of the expedition was certainly not 100 percent efficient in locating these objects. The statistics indicate approximately 17,000 fragments per square kilometer, representing 1,500 pottery vessels per square kilometer.

It was my hope that the pottery fragments could be used as a means of obtaining a date for the construction of the desert markings. I fully agreed with the careful and well-measured warning of Prof. John H. Rowe (private communication, 1969): "Sherds collected on the desert surface do not date the desert markings. They show only that people were crossing the desert at the time indicated. If found on the surface of a desert marking they might

FIG. 2.   Plan view of the desert, sites 1 and 2.

indicate that the marking was older than the sherds, depending on the precise circumstances of the relation between the sherds and the markings."

Although it is far from conclusive, the evidence suggests a connection between the desert markings and the period relating to Nasca styles 3 and 4. Rowe and Menzel (1967) have discussed the difficulties of obtaining reliable dates for this particular phase. Part of the problem is caused by a discrepancy between radiocarbon dates obtained before 1962 and those obtained after 1962. This amounts to approximately 300 years, with the more recent determinations indicating a long time scale extending from 395 B.C. to A.D. 540 for the early intermediate period. Rowe and Menzel cite evidence in favor of this long time scale, according to which the approximate dates for Nasca 3 and 4 span the period 100 B.C. to A.D. 100. (The corresponding dates on the short time scale would be approximately A.D. 200 to A.D. 350.) We will adopt the birth of Christ as the probable date for the construction of the lines.

I was able to make a preliminary analysis of the lines in 1967 by using plans published by Reiche (1949) and aerial photographs. I discussed the preliminary results with Dr. Fred L. Whipple, Director of SAO, and he suggested an accurate site survey to the limits of available techniques. The surveys, expeditions, and subsequent computer analysis were supported by the National Geographic Society. We decided to extend the stereographic and standard photogrammetric method used at Stonehenge and Callanish in Britain. This method provides contours above mean sea level and a rapid and accurate mapping of all surface features. We cooperated with the Geophysical Institute of Peru and the Servicio Aerofotográfico Nacional (SAN) of the Peruvian Air Force.

On August 1, 1968, SAN obtained 30 overlapping, high-resolution photographs of the area. These were used to make a ground plan to the scale of 1:2000, so that 10 centimeters on the chart represented 200 meters on the ground. The four charts are reproduced here as figures 3-6. The general area is shown in figure 2. From a comparison with the plan and a visual inspection of the site, we conclude that lines wider than approximately 30 centimeters were recorded. This represents the majority of the features that exist at the present time at the desert site. The lines can be read with an accuracy of $\pm$ 0.5 centimeter, which corresponds to an error of $\pm$ 1 meter on the ground. For a 200-meter line this corresponds to an error of $\pm$ 0°.28. It was not feasible to measure the altitude of the skyline as viewed along each individual line. Several hundred linear features are shown on the four sheets of the aerial survey (figures 3-6), and individual measurements would have required several months of work. Instead, the skyline was recorded with a panoramic series of photographs at three different positions within the field of lines.

The linear features can be divided into elongated triangles, lines, and near-rectangular areas. For the triangles, a line was drawn along the center; for the wider lines, measurements were made along one side; for the rectangles, measurements were made along the borders or along a line connecting the central mounds. We divided the area into two portions, site 1 centered on the west mound of the main rectangle, and site 2 centered on the point referred to above at coordinates 8376750N, 487580E. The boundary between the two sites is approximately the line of the Pan American Highway. Altogether we measured 21 triangles and 72 linear features. Since each feature could be viewed along two directions, this gave a total of 186 directions for consideration.

In certain areas of the pampas, noticeably on the northern side of the large rectangle, there are sets of parallel lines. These occur in sets of two and three and sometimes up to as many as a dozen. Only one line from a set of parallel lines was measured for the reduction program. In the first place,

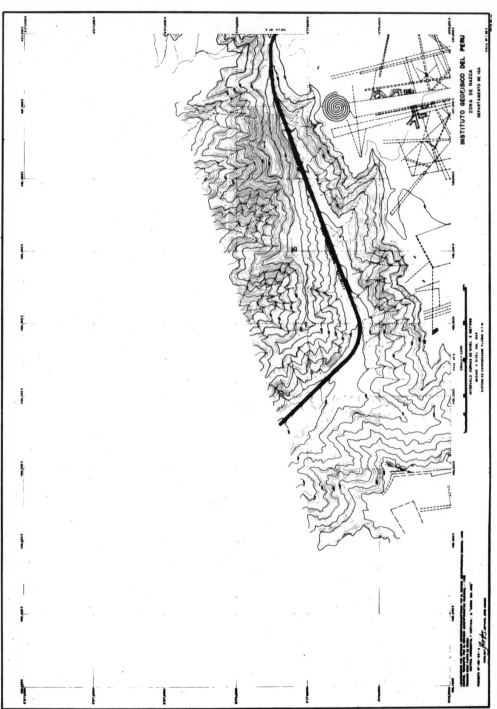

Fig. 3. SAN photogrammetric survey.

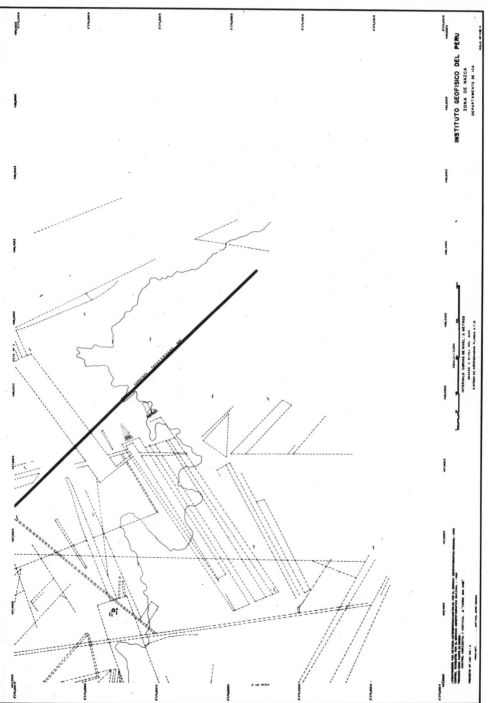

FIG. 4. SAN photogrammetric survey.

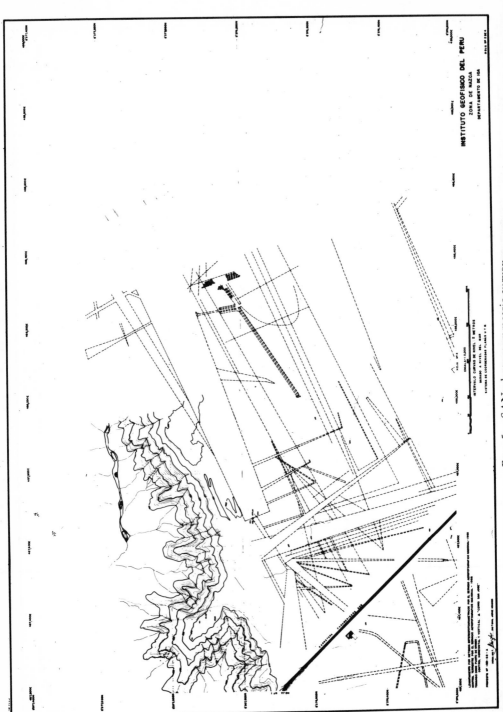

Fig. 5. SAN photogrammetric survey.

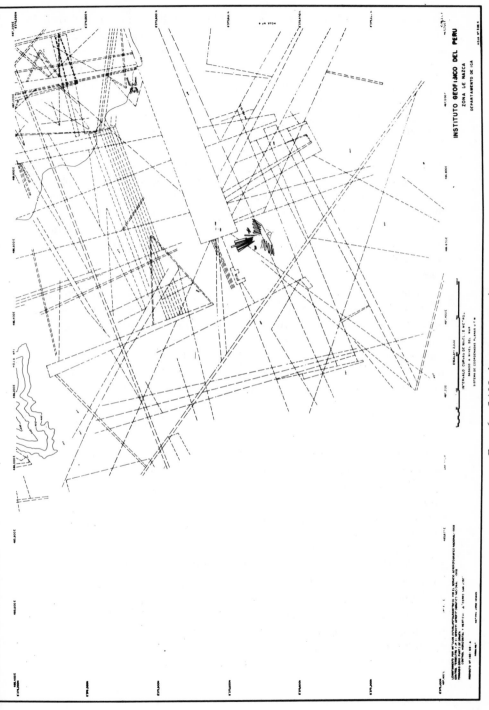

FIG. 6.　SAN photogrammetric survey.

the addition of parallel members would be redundant in the calculation. In the second place, these families of lines would weight the statistics unduly in favor of that particular direction. If in the ultimate analysis the chosen member of the parallel set showed astronomical significance, then the other members of the family of lines could readily be added to the statistics.

Three points were chosen along each line and coordinates read from the Peruvian national grid. Thus, two pairs of points were available for each line, and any slight bend in a line would show itself in the analysis. Four lines of a total of 72 had deviations that were quite large, ranging from $1°.5$ to $3°.9$; 75 percent of the lines had a deviation of less than $0°.3$, which is attributed to errors of measurement from the photogrammetric plans. It corresponds to an uncertainty in determining azimuth of $\pm 0°.15$. Thus, the majority of lines are straighter than the capabilities of measurement of this photogrammetric survey. The deviations may indeed approach the limits of resolution of the human eye, $\pm 0°.02$. Regarding the straightness of the lines, Maria Reiche quite rightly states that "we have to admire their technical perfection."

The method of analysis follows the principles of astroarcheology (Hawkins, 1968), and we used an adaptation of the computer program previously employed for a study of Stonehenge, Callanish, and other sites. At the commencement of the investigation, we set up a rational criterion for testing a particular hypothesis. We would expect to find all or a vast majority of the lines to be explained in terms of a particular type of astronomical alignment. That is to say, we would expect all the lines to be satisfied by some unified postulate such as the rising and setting of the sun and/or moon at key dates in the calendar, or the rising and setting of the brighter stars. It is possible, of course, that alignments might occur with sun, moon, and stars and possibly even planets, but the more "targets" that are included in this solution, the weaker the argument becomes. But no matter what hypothesis is finally adopted we must expect an almost total explanation for the lines; otherwise, we have the unsatisfactory situation of explaining only part of the construction work and leaving the "why?" for the remainder of the lines unanswered. This requirement of general plausibility is also forced by the mathematical nature of the problem. It is always possible that by chance a number of the lines will fit a chosen target. At a "halfway" point of credibility, one might be alert to the possibility of a particular subgroup fulfilling the alignment requirements. For example, all the triangles or all the rectangles might point to some astronomical target.

In the first instance, we chose the Stonehenge hypothesis: the targets might be the 12 solstice points on the horizon where the sun or moon reaches an extreme in azimuth, and the 6 intermediate equinoxal points. At Stonehenge, of course, I have shown that the majority of alignments from stone to stone and through the double archways fit these sun-moon turning points with an accuracy of about ± 1° in declination. Hoyle (1966) supports these astronomical findings and the overwhelming appeal of the fit between astronomy and the structure: "As Hawkins points out, some positions are especially relevant in relation to the geometrical regularities of Stonehenge, and it is these particular positions which show the main alignments."

The 186 directions at Nasca were tested, and 39 of these fitted with extrema of the sun or moon to an accuracy of ± 1° in declination. This leaves approximately 80 percent of the lines unexplained, and therefore one can categorically say that the lines were not built for the general purpose of marking the extremes of the sun and moon as was done at Stonehenge. A discrepancy of 1° in declination corresponds to approximately 1° in azimuth at the latitude of the desert lines. Since 18 targets cover 36° of the horizon and this is one-tenth of the full horizon, one might expect approximately 10 percent of the lines to fit the sun and moon targets by chance. On this basis, the expected number would be 19, whereas the actual number is 39. Some of the alignments are due to the symmetry of the rising and setting of sun and moon in which the winter solstice is approximately opposite the summer solstice, etc. Thus, of the 39 alignments, 8 are duplicates in which a single line matches both a summer and a winter position. A closer inspection of the computer output shows that only a few of the 39 sun-moon correlations are made with an obviously significant line. The lines that match are no different in character from the other lines that do not match with the sun and moon. A few, but not all, of the triangles are in the correlation.

With a negative result for the calendar points of the sun and moon, we turned to the stars. We used the catalogue of star positions in antiquity (Hawkins and Rosenthal, 1967). These positions are tabulated back to 10001 B.C., allowing for precession and proper motion of the stars. We used a high-speed digital computer, CDC 6400, and the programs were prepared by Shoshana K. Rosenthal.

Azimuths were computed from the line coordinates, and declination was found from azimuth and horizon elevation. The coordinates of 45 stars brighter than visual magnitude 2.0 and of Eta Tauri (mag. +2.9) were fed into the machine. These stars are the ones that might reasonably be expected to be visible when rising or setting over a low horizon. The additional star is the brightest in the Pleiades, included because of its acknowledged importance in pre-Columbian culture. The computer was programed to find and print out from the list those stars that could appear when rising or setting at the end of the line. Because of the slow drift in declination (amounting to approximately 0°.36 per century on the average), the machine was instructed to interpolate from the table and print out the exact date when the star would be so aligned. The possible archeological period is approximately the first century B.C. and the first century A.D.; however, only a few seconds had to be added to the running of the machine to probe a wider span of time. The computer was therefore permitted to search from 5000 B.C. to A.D. 1900.

Each of the 46 stars changes approximately 0°.36 in declination per century. Because of the circumpolar caps, the declination for a line is limited to ± 75°, a range of 150°. Thus, we would expect, by chance, approximately $46 \times 0.36/150$ stars per century along a given direction, or 0.11.

Is there any century in pre-Columbian history when a large number of lines matched with stars, and is there any exceptional number of alignments during the dates of archeological interest between A.D. −99 and +100?

We counted and printed out the number of alignments per century for the two contiguous sites. There is no apparent difference between the two sites. The data were then combined. The results are shown diagrammatically in figure 7. It can be seen that the maximum number of successes is in the 34th century B.C. We would expect approximately 20 stars per century for the total of 186 directions considered, and this is close to the mean value of 17.3 shown in figure 7. Even at the peak value of 31 stars we are still far short of finding at least one star for each of the 93 individual linear features. Even for the 34th century B.C. the number of unsatisfied lines is actually greater than 61, because several of the lines show two or more stars. Thus, at the best, less than 34 percent of the lines are satisfied. The dates of archeological interest are even less successful for the matching of lines and stars. This strongly indicates that the lines were not built at any time in this period subsequent to 5000 B.C. for the purpose of pointing to the rising and setting of the stars.

Maria Reiche (1949) previously computed the conditions for the large rectangle. She remarks on the set of lines that run parallel to this rectangle and states:

> It is possible that they were built pointing to the rising of the Pleiades, as it is known from history that great importance was given to this group of stars by ancient Peruvians. The years which saw this constellation rise in the above mentioned direction, were between 500 and 700 A.D. This is in accordance with actual estimates of the age of the Nazca culture, whose painted pottery has the same motifs as the gigantic figures traced on the ground. Other heavenly bodies whose rising or

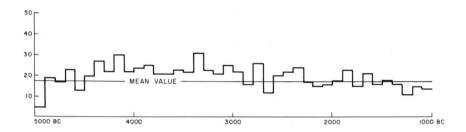

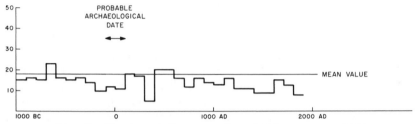

FIG. 7.   Number of alignments from 5000 B.C. to A.D. 1900.

setting took place in this direction, are the largest star in Scorpion, one star in Gemini and also the moon in a special position. If in the progress of the investigation a definite result should be reached, it may be possible to declare one of these stars or the moon as the guiding factor in these tracings.

This is the only identifiable feature for which an astronomical alignment had previously been computed. It is, of course, the largest rectangle in the area of the markings (approximately 100 × 800 meters), with two large mounds and a 2-kilometer extension laid out between the rectangle and the mountain.

We confirm her calculations. Eta Tauri, the brightest star in the Pleiades, rose along the line connecting the mounds in A.D. 610. But so did Regulus in A.D. 410. In the direction away from the mountain, west toward the coast, the feature aligns with Antares in Scorpio, as Reiche suggests for the year A.D. 210. There are also 16 other alignments for this rectangle over the complete period of the present study. Noticeably, there are no star alignments for the dates of Nasca 3 and 4, and yet many fragments of this period were found at the mounds. Reiche's statement that the alignment with the Pleiades occurs at the date of the Nasca culture must be discounted in the light of the redetermination of the radiocarbon dates and the fairly specific identification now made within the Nasca period. Thus, the alignments that she alludes to seem to be no more than a part of the series of chance alignments that must be expected with any feature.

The program also confirmed the moon alignment for the large rectangle, pointed out by Reiche. It is for declination 18°.5, the low extreme for the Peruvian winter solstice. However, as was noted previously, there is no evidence for a pattern of solstice alignments such as was found at Stonehenge. The low position at declination 18°.5 should logically be matched with a high position at +29°, and this is not indicated by any feature approaching the prominence of the large rectangle. At Stonehenge, the complete set of positions was marked, the two for the moon and the bisecting point for the sun, and the structure itself showed symmetry. The large rectangle, on the other hand, has scored a single hit on one part only of the lunar cycle, which requires 18.6 years for completion. Thus, this particular alignment does not seem to be significant.

Reiche (1949) states: "The considerable number of important tracings, all within a margin of 2° (of azimuth) and distributed over a vast area, cannot be casual. As there are only two ways of defining direction in the field, which are by compass or by the course of the heavenly bodies ... the similarity of the alignments can only be the result of their having been directed towards the rising or setting of the sun, the moon, or a star." This is an interesting suggestion and if true would indeed indicate some astronomical alignment even if the actual objects in the sky could not be positively identified. Since the site near Ingenio was divided into two portions, we compared the azimuths between these two portions. Admittedly, in the initial measurements I omitted parallel grids by measuring only one member of such a set. However, Reiche is talking of parallelism over "a vast area" where the second line cannot be seen from the first. The parallel grids are fairly obvious on the ground, could be made by the simple process of "pacing off," and do not require an astronomical marker for their construction.

Let us consider duplication of targets. Reiche talks of a "margin of 2°." We divided the horizon into intervals 1° wide; the results are shown in table 2. This is a narrower element than Reiche suggested, but not so narrow as to lose cognizance of the large-scale parallelism discussed by her. At site 1 the lines point to 89 out of a possible 360 targets in azimuth. The probability of finding a filled element is therefore 89/360. Thus, we would expect the 70 targets at site 2 to hit approximately 70 × 89/360, or 17 of the elements previously marked at site 1. Actually, there are 22 correlations in azimuth between the two sites, which is close to the expected value. There is therefore no clear evidence for deliberate parallelisms over the area of the most prolific site. A similar result was found by comparing the Ingenio site with the site 8 kilometers north of Nasca. The measurement inaccuracies at this latter site are greater than at the main site, but the general lack of parallelism, or duplicated directions, is evident.

TABLE 2 – AZIMUTHAL TARGET ELEMENTS (1° WIDE)

	Filled	Vacant	Maximum number hits	Maximum expected
Site 1	89	271	4	3
Site 2	70	290	3	2

TABLE 3 – DECLINATION TARGET ELEMENTS (1° WIDE)

	Filled	Vacant	Maximum number hits	Maximum expected
Site 1	72	80	6	4
Site 2	58	94	4	3

The above argument, based on azimuths, neglects the variation in the altitude of the horizon, which may have some significance in the discussion. It is more satisfactory to compare the declinations at two particular sites, because a correlation in declination is more indicative of the use of astronomical markers for setting out the lines. Again, target elements 1° wide were used. At Nasca, a line can point anywhere between declinations $-76°$ and $+76°$. There are therefore 152 target elements, although this number can vary slightly from site to site, depending on the exact nature of the skyline. From table 3 it can be seen that we expect, of the 82 directions at site 2, approximately $72 \times 58/152$, or 27 coincidences in declination targets by the process of chance. The actual number of coincident elements found is 33, which again indicates that there is no clear parallelism between the two sites that can be accounted for by deliberate alignments toward an astronomical marker.

Let us now consider concentration on particular targets. The maximum number of hits in declination was 6 for declination $+68$ at site 1. This was marginally significant when tested with the Poisson distribution. If the probability of m hits is Wm and the number of directions (2 per line) is n, then the expected maximum can be defined by $nWm = 1$. This number is approximately 4 for the case under consideration. Similarly, at site 2 there were two declinations with 4 hits each, $-23°$ and $+18°$. This concentration is again marginally significant. One could say that of the 186 directions measured 6 *might* point significantly to declination $+68°$, 4 to $-23°$, and 4 to $+18°$. Even so, this at the most is a total of only 14 out of 93 linear features and falls far short of a substantial explanation for the general field of markings.

In view of this lack of preferred declination we did not search in detail for alignments with the planets. These objects are confined to a band of azimuths within 30° on either side of the east-west line, and less than 50 percent of the lines fall within that band. Thus, planets could never satisfy any substantial proportion of the lines.

There are gigantic patterns and figures interspersed among the lines. Since they are made in the same manner as are the straight lines and most probably are related to them, we included them in our study. These patterns are too large to be seen effectively at ground level. Members of the expedition walked over many of those described here without recognizing them or indeed realizing that a figure existed. Reiche describes how Kosok traced out one of these features in 1941 with a compass and measuring tape. She herself continued this work and then resorted to the use of aerial photography. Reiche (1949) describes several figures, including a bird, a spider, spirals, and an ornamental pointer. These features were studied further by us, and we were fortunate enough to discover several others, including a monkey, a lizard (approximately 200 meters long), and what we call for want of a better phrase a "beaked creature."

Most of the figures have a distinctive artistic characteristic — they are single-line drawings. That is to say, the drawing commences at a certain spot, and then after many twists and turns the continuous line either returns to its starting point or ends as abruptly as it began. Reiche uses the term "ornamental pathway" to describe this, and indeed one can walk around the entire line that makes the figure. To my knowledge, this single-line drawing is not used on the Nascan-style pottery, particularly not on phase 3 and 4, though this difference in technique may be a natural result of transferring from the decorating of pottery to the decorating of a large expanse of desert. The line figures do bear a resemblance to the incised patterns that were used to decorate preceramic gourds. I possess a gourd, purported to be from Paracas, that is decorated by linear incisions, though not with a single-line technique.

The spider was photographed with infrared film from the air on one of

Fig. 8. Spider.

our expeditions (fig. 8). The four pairs of legs are obvious, as is also the pedipalpi at the head. It is a single-line figure and can be walked around by starting and finishing at the cleared area at the end of the third leg. (The parallel curved tracks are made by vehicles; the other features are ancient. The dark line above the spider is the northern edge of the large rectangle.)

This drawing is most remarkable from the biological point of view. Spiders in general have a unique sexual problem. To quote the *Encyclopedia Britannica* (1960): "It consists in a complete separation of the male copulatory apparatus from the reproductive system proper." The males overcome this difficulty by transferring the sperm mechanically, using blades of grass, the threads of a web, the pedipalpi, or other devices. "How such an arrangement could have originated remains a mystery." The order Ricinulei is found in the Amazon jungle and is unique among spiders—the end of the third leg is used for copulation.[1]

In the absence of a written record it is speculative to presume that the spider drawn in the desert has any bearing on this sexual peculiarity. However, in the absence of any other explanation, the original artists may have known of this Amazon spider, may have recognized its behavioral pattern, and may have represented this knowledge in the deliberate distortion of this figure. One might suggest even that some type of fertility rite may have been celebrated in the cleared triangle at the end of the third leg.

The bird in outstretched attitude is interesting for the biological detail of the enlarged knee-joints, and the claws. The mound is placed symmetrically in the center of the body and seems to be related to the figure. In front of the left wing tip is a small unidentifiable figure.

A discovery made on our sixth expedition is a figure that we identify as a spider monkey of the Amazon jungle. The anatomical details are of interest. The ears are conspicuous. The tail is emphasized so as to become a spiral. The continuous line that makes the figure enters and leaves in the vicinity of the reproductive organ. If one walked around the figure, he would first of all walk into the center of the spiral, and then the path would turn on itself so that one automatically came out again along the top of the

[1] Ricinulei is the rarest order of spider and probably also the rarest order of animal; for over 100 years no more than 32 specimens were known. It lives in the darkness of caves and in the humus of the jungle floor. Its reproductive pattern was not known to modern science until the mid-20th century. The spider is small, about 1/4 inch in length, and the copulatory device on the leg requires a microscope to be seen. Yet, the desert drawing is deliberately distorted, perhaps with meaning. Prof. A. G. Humes, a colleague of mine in biology, commented that for the ancient Peruvians to observe and record Ricinulei would be a remarkable achievement, as remarkable as if the lines had indeed pointed to the stars.

tail. We did not have sufficient time to locate this figure on the ground, but we estimate its length to be of the order of 100 meters. We have no doubt that the detailed figure would be totally unrecognized by a person who looked at normal viewing height.

The lizard, approximately 200 meters in length, has been partially destroyed by the construction of the Pan American Highway, and it is not possible to verify that it was drawn with a continuous line. We passed across this area on several occasions but did not recognize the feature. Nor was it noticed during the construction of the Pan American Highway. It was discovered by means of an aerial photograph.

There is what seems to be a 6-petaled flower extending on a stalk from the eastern end of the main rectangle. It is approximately 100 meters in length. Here, again, the figure is partially obliterated, and it is difficult to confirm the continuous-line technique. It seems that the stalk is a long pathway that turns at the base of the flower and returns to the rectangle. The flower itself is a separate figure, with possibly a small circle within the flower. There is a second pathway, or stalk, approaching the flower from the end of the rectangle. If this figure is a flower, then one might think of some fertility symbolism in walking up to the flower and then turning back to the rectangle, although this is of course an extreme speculation.

Another figure is what seems to be that of a walking bird, approximately 50 meters in maximum dimension. The artwork is somewhat crude and biologically inaccurate, with four appendages on one foot and five on the other.

We were unable to suggest an identification of the "beaked creature," maximum dimension 150 meters. There are two mounds at the end of the beak. The vertical wide line is the extension of the main rectangle.

What is the connection between the lines and the figures? Did the lines predate the figures, or vice versa? Or are they of the same period? In some instances (for example, the "beaked creature") a wide cleared surface seems to have been made subsequent to the figure. In other instances the figures seem to be placed by the side of a large cleared rectangle. Thus, one might conclude that figures were made in the desert at the same time that the system of lines and cleared surfaces was being developed. Mounds are common features both to the cleared rectangles and to the figures, and mounds are also found associated with the lines. The common sharing of mounds is therefore a further supportive argument for the contention that the figures and linear features are of the same period. However, this is a very weak supposition and does not agree with the seemingly different styles of the desert figures and the painted Nascan vessels.

The ancient lines in the desert near Nasca show no preference for the directions of the sun, moon, planets, or brighter stars. Nor do the lines show any deliberate alignment with a fixed but unidentifiable object in the sky, such as a nova or the center of some ancient pattern of stars. Thus, the pattern of lines as a whole cannot be explained as astronomical, nor are they calendric.

The negative result that is the outcome of this careful and seemingly exhaustive study takes away the most commonly accepted explanation for these lines. From the astronomical point of view, this conclusion is a reasonable one: that is to say, it agrees with other evidence at the site. The visibility at the site is not good by astronomical standards. If the dust haze and mist existed at the time of construction of the lines (and there seems to be no evidence of any dramatic climatic change over the past few millennia), then it is doubtful whether bright stars could have been seen with any clarity when situated on the low skylines. I found better conditions in Malaga, Spain, where I observed a series of risings of Sirius over a sea horizon on 14 occasions. Usually, the star was not visible until about $0°.5$ above the horizon, but on one occasion it was visible at $0°$ altitude. At rising, it was an extremely faint object scintillating to invisibility. Even under ideal theoretical conditions, a star on the horizon is dimmed by six magnitudes, which is more than a hundredfold reduction in brightness. In my opinion the conditions at Nasca are generally worse than those at Malaga, and Nasca would be most unsuitable for horizon observations. Toward the elevated mountains, conditions would be somewhat better, but there is no evidence of a pointing of the lines in this eastern direction, either from the lines themselves or from the star alignments computed.

Then again, a moment's reflection will show that the lines themselves are useless for marking the rising of a star. At night the lines are totally invisible. Without additional attachments, the lines would be of no avail for star marking. Admittedly, a line could be identified by small lamps set along its length, but none of the pottery fragments found were representative of lamps. Nor were wicks found, and it would be possible for these to have survived if they had been covered over by pottery fragments. Or fires could have been lit. Yet no remnants of any charcoal, wood, or other evidence of fires were found in the area. Also, bright fire would tend to obscure the faint rising of a star.

Thus, the astronomical result is negative and is corroborated by other factors that have a bearing on the problem. This is the end of my expertise, and it is not possible for me to comment with any authority beyond the astronomical possibilities. However, as an interested scholar with cognizance of the desert site and the local artifacts, I close with a few ideas that come to mind.

These lines are not roadways or footpaths because the track is perfectly straight within the limits of modern photogrammetric measurement techniques. The features jump across dry river beds and pick up the same direction on the other side, whereas the footpaths in the area show noticeable wandering and deviations that conform to surface features. On the other hand, after a line had been constructed it is most probable that it was the chosen area for walking. Although the feet of ancient Peruvians were undoubtedly tough, there must surely have been a preference for the cleared sandy surface in contrast to the rough angular pebbles. I therefore lean toward Reiche's suggestion of ornamental pathways.

There is no evidence of any burials on the desert plateau. It is well known that the Nascans (ancient) buried the dead in extensive graveyards in the desert immediately adjoining the cultivated areas. One might say, with no wish to be irreverent, that the mummified bodies were carried with efficiency the shortest distance required for preservation of the cultivated areas. It is well known that Nascans (modern) are equally efficient at un-burying the dead. But despite this efficiency, nothing has been found buried on the desert plateau. Thus, the area of the lines is not a cemetery.

Several investigators have suggested that the lines point to significant features on the skyline. In my opinion this is not an adequate explanation for the orientation of the lines. As with the stars, one must note that there are dozens of significant features on the horizon and there is a high possibility of alignment by chance. Also, from the point of view of plausibility, one must expect the vast majority of lines to be explainable on this hypothesis, whereas an inspection of the site shows that many of the lines do not fit horizon features. A typical narrow line may be viewed in both directions. To the south the line points to a flat, featureless skyline. To the north the line runs toward some low hills across the Ingenio Valley. But it cannot be said that the line points to any particular feature. It misses the peak of the small hill by a wide margin. Nor does it accurately mark the valley. Another example of "misfit" is the large rectangle itself. This rectangle points to a flat horizon in the western direction, and to the east it points to the foothills of the Andes. One photograph shows a vertical line that marks the azimuth of the eastern mound as viewed from the western mound on which the theodolite is placed. The line does not match a peak or a valley. There is a minute protuberance on the side of the valley in the direction of the line, but on investigation this proved to be a natural outcrop of rock indistinguishable from many others in the vicinity. Even if for the sake of argument we accept the alignment of the mounds with this small outcrop, the extension of the rectangle picks out several other directions along its various segments and these point to other equally indistinguishable parts of the mountain.

The decorations on Nascan pottery are concerned with life forms, such as birds, reptiles, fishes, flowers, and seeds. The tracings in the desert are of similar subject matter, although the style is somewhat different. The figures, particularly the spider and monkey discussed above, and with them the lines, might have been concerned with an interest in fertility and life. They might also have been of religious significance, and, since they are appreciated best from considerable height above the desert floor, it has been suggested that these drawings were made to be seen by the gods. The lines also might be considered to be large man-made signals to be seen by gods and spirits in the sky.

It is fairly easy to scrape off the pebbles and leave a pale-yellow indelible mark. One or two members of the expedition expressed a compulsion to mark out their names in gargantuan letters but were constrained not to do so. It is a tempting, seemingly unlimited markable surface, and the lines and figures themselves might be nothing more than a process of decorating the desert. As one member put it, "this is the world's largest scratch pad."

The most general explanation of the area to date places it in the category of a "waca." The early Spanish priests (Mason, 1964) have given us descriptions of ancient Inca customs that are probably representative of early pre-Columbian beliefs in Peru. The waca, transliterated huaca, was a spirit place "ranging from great temples to hills, springs and piles of stones. Each [place] was believed to be—or to harbor—a spirit which might be malevolent and which should be gratified or placated by some gift or sacrifice whenever it was neared. Each native knew only those in his vicinity. One of the chroniclers lists 350 within twenty miles of Cuzco.... The wacas of the Cuzco region were thought of as lying on lines radiating from the temple of the sun... there were from 4 to 15 wacas on each line. Naturally the lines were not perfectly straight.... Every person also had an individual fetish, the abode of his guardian spirit who was considered his twin brother or huauqui."

It is reasonable to suppose that this desert region was singled out as one associated with spirits. Certainly, the evidence points to the fact that the lines and pottery vessels are related. One may assume as the most probable conclusion on the basis of available evidence that the lines and figures were laid out by the people who placed the vessels in position. After visiting and studying the site, I believe that the vessels are more important than the lines. There are remains of more vessels per square kilometer than there are desert markings, and the vessels are richly painted and would have been valuable possessions even at the time of manufacture. The lines certainly helped one to find his way around the otherwise featureless surface, and, whether it was intended or not, the lines must have served as a unique grid for placing and subsequently relocating these pottery vessels.

Each pottery vessel—and they numbered in the thousands—was placed in the desert deliberately, and this deliberation is the closest that we can come to the idea of a purpose by our standards. The vessels were either a sacrifice, an offering, or a symbol. The vessels may have been placed there to house the guardian spirit of a person, his personal genie as per Aladdin. Or perhaps the vessel housed the spirit of a dead person. In numerous instances, we found fragments of vessels in the desert that matched almost exactly a vessel that had been dug from a grave by a huaquero. One might suggest that they buried the body in the grave and deposited the soul of the person in the vessel placed in the desert.

But these are nothing more than speculations. The lines were laid down by a nonliterate culture, and after successive conquests nothing concerning their beliefs remains in the present-day folklore. We are separated by an immense gulf of cognitive perception from this lost culture. When discovered in 1941, the markings were a mystery. Much work has been carried out in the intervening years, surveying and mapping the region and studying the artifacts. The six expeditions sponsored by the National Geographic Society have produced as a contribution to the problem a negative astronomical result. The markings are not astronomical. They remain an unsolved mystery in the desert.

REFERENCES

GAYTON, ANNA H.
   1927. The Uhle collections from Nievería. Univ. California Publ. Arch. and Ethnol., vol. 21, no. 8, pp. 305-329, illus.
HAWKINS, GERALD S.
   1963. Stonehenge decoded. Nature, vol. 200, pp. 306-308.
   1964. Stonehenge: A Neolithic computer. Nature, vol. 202, pp. 1258-1261, illus.
   1968. Astro-archaeology. Pp. 45-88 *in* "Vistas in Astronomy," vol. 10, 215 pp., illus. Pergamon Press, London.
   1971. Photogrammetric survey of Stonehenge and Callanish. Nat. Geogr. Soc. Res. Rpts., 1965 Projects, pp. 101-108, illus.
   1973. Beyond Stonehenge, 319 pp. Harper & Row, New York.

HAWKINS, GERALD S., and ROSENTHAL, SHOSHANA K.
    1967. 5000- and 10,000-year star catalogs.   Smithsonian Contr. Astrophys.,
        vol. 10, no. 2, pp. 141-179.
HOYLE, FRED
    1966. Stonehenge — an eclipse predictor.   Nature, vol. 211, pp. 454-456, illus.
KOSOK, PAUL, and REICHE, MARIA
    1949. Ancient drawings on the desert of Peru.   Archaeology, vol. 2, pp. 206-
        215, illus.
MASON, JOHN ALDEN
    1964. The ancient civilizations of Peru, 330 pp., illus.   Penguin Books,
        Baltimore.
REICHE, MARIA
    1949. Mystery on the desert, 24 pp., illus.   Privately published, Lima.
ROWE, JOHN H., and MENZEL, DOROTHY
    1967. Peruvian archaeology, 80 pp., illus.   Peek Publications, Palo Alto.

GERALD S. HAWKINS

Archeological Excavations at the Clovis Site at Murray Springs, Arizona, 1967

Principal Investigator: C. Vance Haynes, Jr., Southern Methodist University, Dallas, Texas.

Grant No. 639:   To continue archeological exploration of the mammoth-kill site near Murray Springs, Arizona.

The Murray Springs site is located 7 miles east of Sierra Vista in Cochise County, Arizona. Mammoth bones were discovered in Curry Draw by Peter J. Mehringer and myself in the spring of 1966. Because the stratigraphy there was similar to that at the famous Lehner Clovis site 10 miles to the south, correlation could readily be made, and the occurrences of mammoths at Murray Spring were at the proper stratigraphic position for Clovis man to have been responsible for their death.

Excavations sponsored by the National Geographic Society in 1966 led to the discovery at locality 1 of five flake artifacts, some showing edge grinding, near the dismembered carcass of a mammoth (Haynes, 1973). This evidence and a radiocarbon date of 9280 B.C., the same age as the Clovis level at Lehner, convinced me that we were at the edge of a Clovis site and that excavations should be continued the following year.

This proved to be a wise decision because, with the assistance of E. T. Hemmings, the 1967 excavations uncovered another, nearly complete, mammoth carcass at locality 1 along with associated flint and bone tools, which definitely proved the site to be a Clovis hunting site. The tool assemblage consisted of a flake knife from within the rib cage, a broken blade, a broken edge-ground biface, three whole or broken Clovis projectile points, and a bone shaft wrench that is unique to Early Man tools known from the New World. In addition nearly 3,000 flakes representing the chipping waste of Early Man were found, mostly in three distinct concentrations demarking the location of the flint knappers as they sharpened their butchering tools and repaired their projectiles. The skeletal remains of a large Pleistocene wolf, the dire wolf, were also found and added to the faunal assemblage of mammoth, horse, camel, and bison found so far at localities 1 and 2.

The scattered occurrences of burned bone and the heat fractures on some of the flint artifacts indicate that fire was used at the site, but the main hearth concentration has yet to be found. Charcoal from the stream channel along which the hunters camped has been identified as that of ash trees, which do not grow at Murray Springs today.

The geology at the site is significant not only for the accurate geochronology that is provided but also for the circumstances that allow each artifact, bone, or flake, regardless of size, to be found in the exact position in which it was left before being buried by a thin black organic clay very soon after the mammoth-hunting events took place. Because of this fortunate situation, as much as 8 feet of overburden can be mechanically removed and the "black mat" uncovered by hand. Then the very careful removal of the "black mat," piece by piece, exposes the "living floor" and all it contains *in situ,* including mammoth tracks. No other Early Man site has lent itself so well to the precise techniques of stratigraphic excavation. Because of this we will be able to reconstruct the activities of these ancient hunters with more precision and reliability than have ever been possible before, at least in the New World.

The stratigraphy of Murray Springs arroyo shows a nearly complete record of events for the past 40,000 years or more. Between 12,000 and 30,000 years ago a lake (unit D & E) occupied the valley, and between 11,000 and 12,000 years ago a small stream flowed across the flats left by the former lake and eroded a channel (unit F_1) along which Early Man and mammoth lived. A rising water table caused a black organic mat (unit F_2) to grow over the former channel and seal in the animal bones and artifacts approximately 11,000 years ago. Calcium carbonate and silt (unit F_3) accumulated over the valley after 11,000 years ago and reflect gradual drying conditions until a deep channel was cut (unit G_1) and removed part of the Clovis site shortly before 6,000 years ago. The channel filled with pond and alluvial sediments during a moist interval between 4,500 and 5,700 years ago, after which another channel (unit G_2) was cut and filled between 2,500 and 4,000 years ago. People of the Cochise culture occupied the valley during these cycles of arroyo cutting and filling. The valley was a broad grassy swale at the time the Murray family ranched there at the turn of the century. Modern arroyo cutting began shortly before World War I and is continuing today as the torrential summer showers erode away at the headcut and walls of the arroyo. Sometime after 1938 the site was exposed and partly removed by erosion because aerial photographs taken then show the headcut to be 300 feet down the valley from the site. If this headward extension of the arroyo and tributaries continues at this rate of 10 feet per year the site could be totally destroyed in less than 10 years.

The persistent association of mammoth bones with Clovis artifacts in the San Pedro Valley make it imperative that every mammoth skeleton found, even in older units, be scientifically excavated on the chance of discovering Clovis artifacts or some that may be ancestral to Clovis. Toward this end we excavated three additional mammoth skeletons in 1967 all within 3 miles of Murray Springs. At the Escapule site two Clovis points were found among the ribs of a young mammoth which, as at the Schaldack site, underlaid the black organic clay hence dating the sites as approximately 11,200 years old. No evidence of man was found at either the Schaldack site or the Hurley site where a mammoth skeleton occurred in lacustrine mudstone dated at approximately 30,000 or more years old.

By the end of the 1967 field season at Murray Springs it became apparent from our excavation maps that the camp site extends to the south and west of the present excavations. This has been further confirmed by the recent discovery of Clovis artifacts 200 feet south of the south wall in an area where the Clovis occupation surface rises to very near the present surface. In addition recent calving of the arroyo wall 200 feet west of the west wall has exposed more bone fragments beneath the black mat. Therefore during the 1968 field season we plan to extend the excavations to the exploratory backhoe trenches numbers 9 and 10 and simultaneously to test the areas farther out with test pits so that our efforts can be concentrated on the most favorable ground.

In conclusion I can state with complete confidence that the National Geographic Society sponsorship of the Murray Springs project has already yielded the most significant contributions to our knowledge of the Clovis hunters since the discovery of the Clovis type site in New Mexico because for the first time we have clearly defined the actual undisturbed ground surface upon which Clovis hunters lived.

REFERENCES

HAYNES, C. VANCE
    1973. Exploration of a mammoth-kill site in Arizona. Nat. Geogr. Soc. Res. Rpts., 1966 Projects, pp. 125-126.
HAYNES, C. VANCE, and HEMMINGS, E. THOMAS
    1968. Mammoth-bone shaft wrench from Murray Springs, Arizona. Science, vol. 159, pp. 186-187, illus.
HEMMINGS, E. THOMAS, and HAYNES, C. VANCE
    1969. The Escapule mammoth and associated projectile points, San Pedro Valley, Arizona. Journ. Arizona Acad. Sci., vol. 5, pp. 184-188, illus.

C. VANCE HAYNES, JR.

Charcoal Collecting at La Venta
for Radiocarbon Dating

Principal Investigators: Robert F. Heizer, University of California, Berkeley, California, and Philip Drucker, University of Kentucky, Lexington, Kentucky.

Grant No. 640:   To conduct excavations at the La Venta site for the purpose of collecting charcoal to verify chronological placement of the site.

In 1964 questions were raised (Coe and Stuckenrath, 1964) concerning the accuracy of the age of the archeological site of La Venta, Tabasco, which was based upon nine radiocarbon dates of charcoal collected in 1955 when we carried out extensive excavations in the site with the support of the National Geographic Society (Drucker, Heizer, and Squier, 1959). The La Venta site had gone through four building periods, which are referred to as Phases I-IV. Where possible, charcoal was collected in 1955 from layers that could be identified as to Phase. In 1964 the only possible way to check the accuracy of the nine radiocarbon dates that had been determined at the University of Michigan in 1957 was to submit to a radiocarbon laboratory for dating some of the carbon that had been collected in 1955. We were fortunate in recovering two samples of charcoal that had been collected in 1955 and turned over to the U. S. Geological Survey Radiocarbon Dating Laboratory in Washington but that had never been processed. These two samples were each half of a larger amount that had been dated in 1957 (M-531, M-533), and so the results of the 1964 determinations were expected to indicate whether the 1957 age determinations were accurate or not. The two 1964 dates determined by the radiocarbon laboratory at the University of California at Los Angeles through the kindness of Dr. Willard F. Libby and Dr. Rainer Berger proved to be a few centuries older than the determinations made in 1957. The results are given in the table at the top of page 150.

These two check dates suggested that the 1957 Michigan age determinations were too young, or at least gave the impression of being too young. It will be noted that the plus-minus error of 300 years gave a 600-year span within which the probable true or exact date fell, while the 1964 Los

Sample No.	Age, B.P.	Range, B.P.	B.C. Date
UCLA-902	2940 ± 80	3020-2860	990
M-531	2560 ± 300	2860-2260	610
UCLA-903	2460 ± 80	2540-2380	510
M-533	2130 ± 300	2430-1830	180

Comparison of two age determinations of the same sample. B.P. means "Before Present," present being A.D. 1950. "Range" is calculated by adding and subtracting the plus-or-minus error from the median-age figure. Conversion to the Christian calendar is calculated by subtracting 1950 years, which is the mathematical "present," from the median age. Sample numbers are prefixed with the code initial of the laboratory (M, Michigan; UCLA, University of California at Los Angeles). All ages shown here are based on the radiocarbon half life of 5,568 ± 30 years.

Angeles age determinations were more precise in having a plus-minus error of 80 years or a 160-year span within which the probable true date fell.

The hint that the La Venta site could now be dated with greater precision and was probably older than had been believed was of considerable interest. We then proceeded to secure from Prof. James B. Griffin, University of Michigan, the untreated remainder of the charcoal samples that had been sent to him in 1957. The UCLA radiocarbon laboratory in 1967, again through the kindness of Drs. Libby and Berger, made age determinations of those charcoal samples whose quantity was sufficient. In some cases two UCLA check dates were determined. A comparison of the 1957 Michigan dates and the 1964 and 1967 UCLA dates are given in the table at the top of page 151.

The conclusions based upon these more precise age determinations are that Phase I at La Venta dates from 1000 B.C. and that abandonment of the site occurred about 600 B.C. La Venta was, in short, built about 200 years earlier and abandoned about 200 years earlier than had been believed in 1957. This dating for the La Venta site fits fairly well with the recent radiocarbon chronology of the San Lorenzo site, another large Olmec center about 50 miles distant, which is in many respects very similar to the La Venta site (Coe, Diehl, and Stuiver, 1967; Coe, 1968).

In July 1967 with support provided by the National Geographic Society we spent two weeks digging test pits at La Venta and collecting charcoal from the construction layers. This collection seemed desirable not only because the La Venta site is being rapidly covered with houses but also because it would provide a "bank" of datable carbon for future reference. A

Sample No.	Age, B.P.	Phase	Remarks
M-531	2560 ± 300	I	M younger by 380
UCLA-902	2940 ± 80		years than UCLA
M-532	2560 ± 300	I	M younger by 170
UCLA-1285	2820 ± 60		years than UCLA
M-534	2670 ± 300	I	M younger by 330
UCLA-1286	3000 ± 60		years than UCLA
M-530	2760 ± 300	II	M older by 210 and
UCLA-1284A	2550 ± 60		190 years than UCLA
UCLA-1284B	2530 ± 60		
M-528	2400 ± 250	Post IV	M and UCLA same
UCLA-1283	2380 ± 60		
M-533	2130 ± 300	Post IV	M younger by 285
UCLA-1287	2415 ± 60		years than UCLA
UCLA-903	2460 ± 80		

published report (Heizer, Drucker, and Graham, 1968) provides the details of our findings as well as a catalogue of 35 samples that were collected. Radiocarbon dating of these samples is not completed.

Not the least important of our observations made in July 1967 was that the great clay mound at La Venta, referred to as the pyramid, was not, as we had earlier proposed, a construction with a rectangular base, with flat sloping sides, but rather had a round base and was in the form of a cone whose outer surface consisted of a series of 10 alternating ridges and valleys. A preliminary survey of the base of the La Venta pyramid was made, and the correction of the earlier and erroneous plan of the pyramid was published shortly afterward (Heizer and Drucker, 1968). In 1968 a contour map of the pyramid was made, and this bears out fully the preliminary announcement of the unusual conical "pyramid" of La Venta (Heizer, Graham, and Napton, 1968).

REFERENCES

BERGER, RAINER; HEIZER, ROBERT F.; and GRAHAM, JOHN A.
1967. A reconsideration of the age of the La Venta site. Contr. Univ. California Archaeol. Res. Facility, no. 3, paper no. 1, pp. 1-24. Berkeley.
COE, MICHAEL D.
1968. San Lorenzo and the Olmec civilization. Dumbarton Oaks Conference

on the Olmec, October 28 and 29, 1967, pp. 41-78. Dumbarton Oaks
   Research Library and Collection, Washington.
COE, MICHAEL D.; DIEHL, RICHARD A.; and STUIVER, MINZE
   1967. Olmec civilization, Veracruz, Mexico: Dating of the San Lorenzo Phase.
   Science, vol. 155, pp. 1399-1401, illus.
COE, W. R., and STUCKENRATH, ROBERT
   1964. A review of La Venta, Tabasco, and its relevance to the Olmec problem.
   Kroeber Anthrop. Soc. Papers, no. 31, pp. 1-44. Berkeley.
DRUCKER, PHILIP; HEIZER, ROBERT F.; and SQUIER, ROBERT J.
   1957. Radiocarbon dates from La Venta, Tabasco.   Science, vol. 126, pp. 72-73.
   1959. Excavations at La Venta, Tabasco, 1955.   Bur. Amer. Ethnol. Bull. 170,
   312 pp., illus. Washington.
HEIZER, ROBERT F., and DRUCKER, PHILIP
   1968. The La Venta fluted pyramid.   Antiquity, vol. 42, pp. 52-56, illus.
HEIZER, ROBERT F.; DRUCKER, PHILIP; and GRAHAM, JOHN A.
   1968. Investigations at La Venta, 1967.   Contr. Univ. California Archaeol. Res.
   Facility, no. 5, paper no. 1, pp. 1-33. Berkeley.
HEIZER, ROBERT F.; GRAHAM, JOHN A.; and NAPTON, L. K.
   1968. The 1968 investigations at La Venta.   Contr. Univ. California Archaeol.
   Res. Facility, no. 5, paper no. 7, pp. 127-154. Berkeley.

ROBERT F. HEIZER

Olmec Colossal Stone Heads, Mexico

Principal Investigators: Robert F. Heizer and John A. Graham, University of California, Berkeley, California.

Grant Nos. 629, 663: For detailed study of the 12 colossal stone heads of the Olmec culture and to support publication of the monograph prepared on the basis of this research.

During the University of California, Berkeley, Winter Quarter of 1967, we directed a group of four graduate students in a study of Mesoamerican archeology, focusing primarily on the civilization and sculptural art of the ancient Olmecs of southeastern Mexico. The project represented a continuation of research activities in the Olmec area that have been supported by the National Geographic Society. The actual scientific discovery of Olmec civilization resulted from the Society-supported work of Dr. Matthew W. Stirling. The initial archeological explorations of the sites of La Venta, Tres Zapotes, and San Lorenzo by Stirling and Drucker have been followed by intensive archeological excavations at the La Venta site in 1955 (Drucker, Heizer, and Squier, 1959), in 1967 (Heizer, Drucker, and Graham, 1968a), and in 1968 (Heizer, Graham, and Napton, 1968; Heizer, Drucker, and Graham, 1968b); studies of identification and source location of stone used by the Olmecs in their sculptures (Heizer, Smith, and Williams, 1965; Williams and Heizer, 1965); and radiocarbon dating of the La Venta site (Berger, Graham, and Heizer, 1967).

Located in southern Veracruz and adjacent Tabasco states of southern Mexico, the ancient Olmecs were responsible for one of the earliest and finest major sculptural traditions of the prehispanic New World. Now dated (see below) at about 1000-600 B.C., the Olmecs have been credited by many students as creating the first Indian civilization of the New World and upon which the later and better-known classical civilizations were nurtured. In view of the important role of the Olmecs, considerable study of their civilization has been carried out during the past 30 years since their discovery by archeology. Nevertheless, speculation and theorizing have generally outpaced basic analytical studies of the fundamental material of Olmec archeology with respect to many realms of Olmec culture. Until a sufficient number of such basic studies are carried out, much interpretation must remain tentative and founded upon an inadequate groundwork. As part of our study of Olmec archeology, we hoped to contribute to the goal of full analytical description and study by carrying out a comprehensive survey and analysis of one category of Olmec monumental sculpture, namely, the famous "Cabezas colosales."

We began our project in Berkeley with an intensive briefing seminar. In addition to providing a general framework for Olmec archeology, the seminar was intended to enable the students to learn as much as was known about the colossal heads. As well as indicating what information was lacking in the scientific record, the seminar outlined possible research leads to be followed in the field work. As one result, a checklist of missing or incomplete data was drawn up, and this proved to be a useful tool in the field for making most efficient use of time available as well as insuring that as much significant data as feasible would be recorded.

Upon completion of the two-week seminar in Berkeley, our party departed by air for Mexico City, the first stop in our research schedule. We spent two days at Mexico City's Museo Nacional de Antropología, studying the archeological collections. The first colossal head to be examined at first hand (San Lorenzo Colossal Head no. 2) was studied here, and the techniques of measurement and routine of study for the heads were worked out.

From Mexico City we flew to the port of Veracruz where we embarked by bus for Jalapa, the capital city of the state of Veracruz. The Museo del Estado at Jalapa possesses an extraordinarily fine collection of Olmec and Olmec-related stone sculptures from a large number of archeological sites within the state of Veracruz. Four of the Olmec colossal heads from the site of San Lorenzo are now preserved at Jalapa, and these were photographed and recorded as well as compared to other Olmec monumental sculpture in the Museum's collection. At Jalapa our field party was joined by Dr. Philip Drucker, then residing at San Andrés Tuxtla, Veracruz. Dr. Drucker's extensive knowledge of Olmec archeology and his practical experience from many seasons of research in the Olmec region were of enormous benefit to our field party and contributed significantly to the success of our project.

Proceeding from Jalapa by bus, our group next traveled to San Andrés Tuxtla, Veracruz. Situated centrally in the miniature volcanic highlands known as "Las Tuxtlas," San Andrés was the logical base of operations for our work of the following two weeks. First, the colossal head removed many years ago to the plaza of the neighboring settlement of Santiago Tuxtla was studied and recorded. Next, we visited the ruins of Tres Zapotes, situated on the western flanks of the Tuxtla highlands, to record the colossal head still located at the site of original discovery. While working at Tres Zapotes we had the good fortune to discover, with the aid of local villagers, the area of the original location of the colossal head we had just finished recording at Santiago Tuxtla. This head, previously referred to the Tres Zapotes ruins proper, can now be more accurately termed the Nestepe Head no. 1 after its true original provenience.

The Tuxtla Mountains are the major source of volcanic stone in the Olmec region, and from our field base at San Andrés we made a series of reconnaissance trips through the highlands to search out exposures of basalt deposits that could have served the ancient Olmec sculptors. Previous field work (Williams and Heizer, 1965) had successfully identified major Olmec stone sources in the Tuxtlas, and we were hopeful of locating the source of the basaltic columns so prized by the Olmecs of the La Venta ruins. Dr. Howel Williams, Department of Earth Sciences, University of California, Berkeley, joined our field group at this point to provide expert field identification of geological specimens and to make comparisons with the stones used in Olmec sculptures.

Although our efforts led to the discovery of several deposits of columnar basalt in the Tuxtlas, unfortunately none of these proved to be of the same type as that found in the La Venta site. We held our greater hopes with respect to a rather remotely situated exposure which had been spotted from the air by Williams and Heizer in 1961. This was an islet, seemingly composed of columnar basalt, just off the Punta Roca Partida on the Gulf coast of the Tuxtla highlands. From the islet basaltic columns could have been rafted along the coastline to the La Venta site locality, and, accordingly, this seemed an especially promising deposit. Thanks to the loan of a 4-wheel-drive truck and a capable driver from Petroleos Mexicanos, we were able to make a difficult trip through the Tuxtlas to the coast at the Roca Partida. Despite the rough sea and a canoe that inspired little confidence, we eventually reached the islet and examined the columnar basalt. Unfortunately, like the other exposures we had located, this too proved not to be of the La Venta type. The source of the basalt columns used by the builders of the La Venta site is surely somewhere in the Tuxtla Mountains, but the precise location remains to be found by future field workers.

Our final expedition out from San Andrés was an overnight trip up the Coatzacoalcos River to the important Olmec ruins at San Lorenzo. A field party from Yale University under the direction of Dr. Michael D. Coe was currently engaged in archeological excavations, and we were able to examine a number of only recently unearthed Olmec sculptures. With Dr. Coe's cooperation we were able to study, and to include in our project, the sixth colossal head to be found at San Lorenzo; this sculpture still lay half-buried in the ravine where it had been found in 1965.

Upon completion of our research in southern Veracruz, we departed our San Andrés base and made our way next to Villahermosa, capital of the neighboring state of Tabasco. Here, in the Tabascan counterpart to the state museum at Jalapa, Veracruz, a rich and valuable collection of Olmec sculpture has been assembled under the direction of Don Carlos Pellicer and his assistant Carlos Sebastian Hernández, Conservador del Museo. In addition to the collections of the Museo del Estado, most of the large stone sculptures discovered by Stirling in the earlier explorations at the La Venta site are now displayed in the local museum-park known as the Parque La Venta. Several days were required to record fully the four La Venta colossal heads and other unpublished Olmec stone sculptures. Also, while at Villahermosa, we made an excursion to the La Venta ruins to examine the present condition of the site. During our inspection of the site an exposure of charcoal was discovered; samples were collected and their radiocarbon age determination has contributed to our recent revision of the dating of the La Venta site contained in a paper already published (Berger, Graham, and Heizer, 1967).

With completion of our studies at Villahermosa and La Venta, the group proceeded to Yucatán, visiting the archeological museums at Campeche and Mérida and the archeological ruins in their vicinities. From Yucatán the party returned to the U.S.A. via central Mexico where brief excursions were made to the ruins of Monte Alban, Mitla, Teotihuacán, and Tula. These studies of additional archeological sites served useful comparative purposes and led to the preparation of research reports by the students.

Upon return to Berkeley we devoted the remainder of the Winter Quarter to study and analysis of the data collected during the expedition. Examination of the data revealed that a number of hitherto unnoticed features of the colossal heads had been recorded. Probably the most important conclusion to emerge from the study, and one that was made possible by a detailed comparison of all features of each head, was that the dozen colossal heads were essentially contemporaneous. The probable explanation for the stylistic similarities in the 12 heads collected at four sites is that there were local groups ("schools") of sculptors which observed the same stylistic canons. This conclusion, strongly supported by the detailed data collected, contradicts the views of some writers who have seen a lengthy sequence of development in the head series.

With completion of the research a detailed monograph reporting the data collected during the trip and the conclusions reached from their analysis was prepared. This monograph (Clewlow, Cowan, O'Connell, and Benemann, 1967) has now appeared thanks to support for publication by an additional National Geographic Society grant (no. 629).

REFERENCES

BERGER, RAINER; GRAHAM, JOHN A.; and HEIZER, ROBERT F.
  1967. A reconsideration of the age of the La Venta site. Contr. Univ. California Archaeol. Res. Facility, no. 3, paper no. 1, pp. 1-24. Berkeley.
CLEWLOW, C. WILLIAM; COWAN, RICHARD A.; O'CONNELL, JAMES F.; and BENEMANN, CARLOS
  1967. Colossal heads of the Olmec culture. Contr. Univ. California Archaeol. Res. Facility, no. 4, 170 pp., illus. Berkeley.
DRUCKER, PHILIP; HEIZER, ROBERT F.; and SQUIER, ROBERT J.
  1959. Excavations at La Venta, Tabasco, 1955. Bur. Amer. Ethnol. Bull. 170, 312 pp., illus. Washington.
HEIZER, ROBERT F.; DRUCKER, PHILIP; and GRAHAM, JOHN A.
  1968a. Investigations at La Venta, 1967. Contr. Univ. California Archaeol. Res. Facility, no. 5, pp. 1-34. Berkeley.
  1968b. Investigaciones de 1967 y 1968 en La Venta. Inst. Nac. Anthrop. e Hist. Bol. 33, pp. 21-28. Mexico.
HEIZER, ROBERT F.; GRAHAM, JOHN A.; and NAPTON, L. K.
  1968. The 1968 investigations at La Venta. Contr. Univ. California Archaeol. Res. Facility, no. 5, pp. 127-154. Berkeley.
HEIZER, ROBERT F.; SMITH, T.; and WILLIAMS, HOWEL
  1965. Notes on Colossal Head no. 2 from Tres Zapotes. Amer. Antiq., vol. 31, no. 1, pp. 102-104.
WILLIAMS, HOWEL, and HEIZER, ROBERT F.
  1965. Sources of rocks used in Olmec stone monuments. Contr. Univ. California Archaeol. Res. Facility, no. 1, pp. 1-40. Berkeley.

ROBERT F. HEIZER
JOHN A. GRAHAM

Australian Meteorite Expedition, 1967

Principal Investigators: Edward P. Henderson and Brian H. Mason, Smithsonian Institution, Washington, D. C.

Grant No. 621: For continuation of a search for and study of meteorites and tektites in Australia.

The purpose of the 1967 expedition was to follow up and further explore significant problems pertaining to the distribution of Australian meteorites and tektites (see Mason and Henderson, 1968). Some of these questions were the outgrowth of our former expeditions, while some emanated from the field searches of others. The finding of tektites in a new area is always of interest, but it is not as important as being able to date the tektite-bearing beds. Dating these will resolve the existing discrepancies between the potassium-argon ages (about 700,000 years) and the ages estimated by geologic methods (about 10,000 years).

On our 1963 visit to Wolf Creek Crater, in north Western Australia, we collected quantities of altered meteoritic material that we assumed was the meteorite responsible for making the crater. A revisit to that crater was necessary because an Australian geologist, who examined it a few months before we did, published an account suggesting that it was volcanic in origin. To reach the Wolf Creek locality required driving across the entire Australian Continent, but such a trip would permit us to revisit several important tektite and meteorite localities as well as to do some original prospecting. The return trip from Wolf Creek would give us another opportunity to look for tektites north of the upper limits of the known Australian tektite areas.

We left Sydney on May 26, 1967, in out tested Land Rover for the Lake Torrens-Lake Eyre tektite areas in South Australia. For several years Dr. and Mrs. Gregory of Leigh Creek, South Australia, assisted us by obtaining important information about new areas to search, and so it was important to see them and to go to those places. Also, we wanted to revisit some of the localities in that area where we had prospected. Each time we searched these localities we recovered fewer tektites than we had on our search of the previous season. This steady decrease in number of tektites recovered convinced us that on our first visit we were collecting the accumulation after many years of an erosional process that exposed these specimens.

In 1967, although a few additional tektites were found, most of our efforts went into the search for field evidence that would help date the beds from which these tektites were coming. On this visit we convinced ourselves that the tektites came from a bed of Late Pleistocene or Recent age. Also we confirmed our impression that the tektite shower, which extended over a vast area in this part of Australia, was a rather spotty one; e.g., more tektites fell in some places than at others. Although we worked these localities four times we cannot prove that we ever found a tektite where it originally fell. But we believe that many of our tektites came from a level within a meter of the elevation on which it fell. These Lake Torrens tektites have not moved down drainage more than a few feet.

A considerable percentage of the tektites from the Lake Torrens area are flanged buttons, but without exception all of them are etched. We believe this etching results from their exposure to saline waters. Lake Torrens, which is a few miles to the west, is usually a dry salt basin where incoming drainage collects and evaporates. The wind blowing over that flat carries the dry saline material for miles out over the surrounding country where it again starts its return trip toward this basin. The occasional rains dissolve some of the salts and carry them into the sandhills. We believe the extent of the etching on these tektites is about what could happen to a tektite buried in these sands for a few hundred years and occasionally wetted in this fashion.

We have observed a process that disperses these tektites over the area of an inter-dune pan. Because the floors of most of these pans are rather impervious to water, the occasional heavy rains, which can fall even in these areas of low rainfall, sometimes flood the pan. The water rises very slowly, first collecting in low places; then these local ponds expand until they form a sheet of water over most of the inter-dune pan. The surface tension of the slowly rising water floats the small tektites and also some of the larger rather flat buttonlike ones.

A floating tektite can be moved by the wind until it is stranded on the other shore or beached on a protruding sand mound. Floating tektites drifting against the occasional brush that rises above the water sink when they hit the stems, because that gentle impact is enough to break the surface tension of the water. We have found localized concentrations of tektites near bushes or isolated sand mounds.

On our 1967 excursion we hoped to find some charcoal or other associated carbon-bearing materials that would be useful in getting a carbon-

FIG. 1. Brian Mason examining a shatter cone on one of the circular hills at Gosses Bluff, Northern Territory, Australia.

14 age. No charcoal was found in these beds, but lime concretions were abundant; some of these were collected and sent for study to the Carbon-14 Laboratory of the Australian National University, which found that they ranged in age from 6,000 to 16,000 years. These results support the younger age of tektites, but lime concretions may not be the most desirable specimens to use in estimating carbon-14 ages. Some day we hope a "Tektite Rosetta Stone" will be found.

Following our search around Lake Torrens-Lake Eyre we went to Adelaide to confer with mineralogists at the South Australian Museum and the University of Adelaide about Australian meteorites and tektites. While there we examined the 6-ton Mundrabilla iron meteorite, discovered by an oil prospecting party in 1966 on the Nullarbor Plain, not far from where we were working in 1965.

In mid-June we rendezvoused with Keith Quartermain and William Cleverly of the Kalgoorlie School of Mines. The date of this meeting was set before we departed from the United States, and after we traveled halfway around the world both parties arrived in Cocklebiddy, a small place on the Eyre Highway, on the appointed day within two hours of each other.

Immediately we drove north, in our two vehicles, toward Rawlinna, a small station on the Trans-Australian Railway, and then farther north on the Nullarbor Plain.

We wanted to recover more specimens of a stony meteorite that had recently been found on this vast treeless plain. A rabbiter, while tending his traps, found what he suspected was a meteorite and gave it to our associates, along with instructions for relocating the discovery point. For this man to see a small stony meteorite, no larger than a hen's egg, while riding over this terrain on a motor bike, was a remarkable feat in itself. To describe a definite point on such a featureless plain is difficult, but to take another person's description and to relocate that point also require considerable skill.

This rabbiter recorded both the mileage and the compass directions that he traveled from the discovery point to some other landmark, and continued doing that from landmark to landmark until he reached a rather well-marked trail, some 80 miles away. Our job was to follow his instructions but in reverse order. Actually we ran a compass course over the Nullarbor Plain, navigating our vehicles as one would a boat at sea. When we got close to the desired spot we spread out and started our search on foot. Late in the afternoon of the first day of search we found two small stones. The next day each of us found another stone. These six meteorites averaged about the size of a large hen's egg.

Two meteorites we collected on the Nullarbor Plain turned out to be ureilites, a rare type. Another specimen, on being studied in our laboratory, was found to contain two new minerals, ringwoodite and majorite, both named after staff members of the Australian National University.

After our successful Nullarbor exploration we went to Kalgoorlie to examine the extensive meteorite and tektite collections at the Kalgoorlie School of Mines. While there arrangements were made to send the 200-pound Mount Padbury meteorite to Washington for cutting. From Kalgoorlie we drove 325 miles west to Perth, where we conferred with staff members at both the Western Australian Museum and the University. Here we examined and photographed the larger of the two Mundrabilla irons. This 12-ton iron, displayed in the Western Australian Museum, is the largest meteorite thus far found in Australia.

From Perth we drove north, intending to spend two days at the Dalgaranga meteorite crater. We reached there about two hours before sundown and after looking the crater over and finding a few rather unimportant specimens bedded down for the night. Before dawn we heard an occasional raindrop hit our sleeping bags, but when it was light enough to

FIG. 2. When the Mount Egerton meteorite fell among these rocks it broke into pieces smaller than the average rocks shown here. Only a shrewd prospector would have spotted a stony meteorite among these rocks. Mount Clere Station, Western Australia.

see it was raining harder and the dark-gray sky indicated that this rain could continue all day. Since the road to this crater is passable only in dry weather, we decided to get out before we became bogged down, for perhaps a week or more. Our skiddy drive to Mount Magnet was made in a cold steady rain. The next morning we proceeded north and slightly east past the town of Wiluna to the Earaheedy Station, a large cattle property near the western edge of the Gibson Desert in central Western Australia.

Our information about this locality came from Keith Quartermain of the Kalgoorlie School of Mines. The station manager and his wife, Mr. and Mrs. C. Smith, were of great help during our stay. They not only guided us to a remote corner of that large station, where they said we would find surface features that we had described to them as favorable places to find tektites, but also spent the day with us picking up tektites.

Mr. Smith then took us to another place where a few tektites had been found. There we spotted a tektite partly buried in the sand on a gentle slope to a shallow lake. Only a fraction of it was exposed, and so we chan-

FIG. 3.   William H. Cleverly, of the Kalgoorlie School of Mines, and Brian Mason, Smithsonian Institution, each pointing to two specimens of the Coorara meteorite. North of Rawlinna, Western Australia, on the Nullarbor Plain.

neled the sand several inches away from the tektite and tenderly lifted out the entire block. This was carefully packed and carried back to Washington. Since this part of Australia has little topographic relief, it is unlikely that this tektite was transported very far from where it fell. Furthermore, nearby we picked up other tektites from an elevation only a few inches below that of the partly buried tektite. We cannot prove that this tektite fell where we found it, nor can anybody prove that it was transported to that spot. As interesting as this specimen is, it does not resolve the question about the age of the Australian tektites. However, this find, like some of the other occurrences we have seen, makes it more difficult to accept the potassium-argon age for tektites (about 700,000 years).

From the Earaheedy Station we headed north to hunt for more of the Mount Egerton meteorite. This stony meteorite was identified from a small sample a prospector sent to the Government Laboratory in 1941. It was found to belong to the enstatite-achondrite group, of which only a few examples are known. No one believed that more of this particular meteorite would ever be found. However, Alan Bain, owner of the Mount Clere Station, became interested in this problem and after considerable effort

FIG. 4. This sink hole was found in the road just as we started from our camp one morning on the Nullarbor Plain. Had the party driven a few meters farther on the preceding night both vehicles and gear might have been lost in this remote place. Between Cocklebiddy and Rawlinna, Western Australia.

located the native who was with the prospector when this meteorite was discovered some 25 years earlier. Finding the native improved the chances of getting more of the meteorite because aboriginal people have an uncanny ability of being able to return to a place they once visited. Sometime in 1966 Mr. Bain with the native relocated the spot on a steep hillside and recovered about 30 pounds of the Mount Egerton meteorite. Some of the Mount Clere Station hands directed us to the locality, and in one day we collected about 8 pounds more of the Mount Egerton meteorite. Unless another piece of this stone is discovered we are sure that nobody will find it worthwhile to rework where we searched. We prospected until the chips we picked up became smaller than the thickness of a needle and shorter than half an inch.

As we approached Mount Clere Station we happened to notice a sign indicating a road to the Yarlarweelor Station. Realizing we were in an area where two meteorites, Mount Egerton and Mount Padbury, had been found, we turned in to familiarize the folks with meteorites. Usually when you inform people you are on a meteorite recovery search, they tell you they either have one or saw one fall nearby. True to form, the Yarlarweelor people said they had a meteorite. Immediately we expressed a desire to see it, expecting them to come forward with a strange rock but not a meteorite. To our surprise they produced a 2-kilogram mass of the Mount Padbury meteorite. As we were leaving Mr. and Mrs. Forrester kindly donated their specimen to the Smithsonian Institution.

Our next important stop was the Wold Creek Crater, in north Western Australia. Here we had to confirm our original impressions about this crater or explain how we failed properly to evaluate it. At the time we collected our first samples we were satisfied that what we had were pieces of a highly altered iron meteorite, but perhaps we were hasty in assuming it was their fall that made this crater. On this last visit we found many pieces of the weathered meteorite both within the crater and on the outside slopes of the crater walls. Nowhere either within or around the crater were we able to find any volcanic rocks or evidence of volcanic activity. At the top and outside of the upturned crater rim we saw very large overturned blocks that had been tossed out and had flipped over. The findings of lateritic surfaces on the underside of several of these blocks, and the other evidence mentioned above, proved this to be an impact crater.

Incidental to our examination of the meteorites collected at Wolf Creek Crater, the new mineral pecoraite, a nickel silicate analogous to the terrestrial mineral serpentine, has been described in collaboration with Dr. George T. Faust and other scientists of the U. S. Geological Survey (Faust et al., 1969).

From Wolf Creek we would be driving across a long trail through the unsettled Australian outback toward Alice Springs, Northern Territory. This distance, when measured in a straight line on our road map, was about 600 miles, but as we would make side excursions whenever conditions looked promising, we had to be prepared for an additional 300-500 miles of driving. As all this distance was north of the probable limits of the Australian tektite strewnfield, it was quite possible that we might happen upon some important new tektite finds.

The tektites from the areas south of this Trans-Australian Tektite line usually are found where the drainage and weathering processes have removed the fine-grained material and concentrated all the residual material, which is slightly heavier than the sand. Our exploration, north of this line, showed us that most of that country is silted over. If tektites are present, they are under the silt. Therefore it will take a lot of searching, plus a bit of luck, to find tektites in the northern areas. However, our contacts with the natives along the routes we traveled indicated that few of them knew a tektite and most of the natives who have heard of them have not seen them. The few tektites that some of these natives had could have been acquired by barter with natives living farther south.

As we approached Alice Springs we decided to visit Gosses Bluff. This unusual feature consists of a series of circular cliffs rising abruptly to a height of about 1,000 feet from the surrounding flat country. Our visit came at a fortunate time because Gosses Bluff was being cooperatively investigated by the U. S. Geological Survey and the Commonwealth Bureau of Mineral Industries. Although the bluff was formed by an impact of a large extraterrestrial body, this structure is different from Wolf Creek Crater. It is an astrobleme, and many well-formed shatter cones occur in these rocks. None of the impacting material has been found, because this collision occurred so long ago that all the incoming material plus hundreds of feet of the surface rocks have been eroded away. The broken, upturned, and shocked rocks in these circular hills were deep below the surface and around the zero point of the impact.

After driving another 200 miles or so we arrived in Alice Springs and called upon Douglas Boerner, with whom we prospected the meteorite craters near Alice Springs in 1963. He gave us several important leads that took us north and east of Alice Springs for about 200 miles. After collecting some geological material from these places we headed back toward Sydney, via the Lake Torrens region.

On our last visit to the area west of Leigh Creek we collected some additional material for the carbon-14-dating investigation and also obtained the loan of an important and sizable lot of tektites collected from a place just south of there. After we delivered the last of our samples for carbon dating to the Department of Geophysics at the Australian National University in Canberra, we drove on to Sydney.

Our arrival in Sydney, on August 10, completed our fourth Australian trip and added another 11,600 miles to our impressive total mileage in the Commonwealth. Almost all our travel had been in what some people call the Dead Heart of Australia but which we regard as Australia's Wonderland.

REFERENCES

FAUST, GEORGE T.; FAHEY, JOSEPH J.; MASON, BRIAN; and DWORNIK, EDWARD J. 1969. Pecoraite, $Ni_6Si_4O_{10}(OH)_8$, nickel analog of clinochrysolite, formed in the Wolf Creek meteorite. Science, vol. 165, pp. 59-60, illus.

MASON, BRIAN H., and HENDERSON, EDWARD P.
  1968. Australian meteorite expeditions. Nat. Geogr. Soc. Res. Rpts., 1963 Projects, pp. 189-201.
McCALL, G. J. H.
  1965. Possible meteorite craters—Wolf Creek, Australia and analogs. Ann. New York Acad. Sci., vol. 123, pp. 970-98, illus.
McCALL, G. J. H., and CLEVERLY, W. H.
  1968. New stony meteorite finds including two ureilites from the Nullarbor Plain, Western Australia. Min. Mag., vol. 36, pp. 691-716, illus.
SMITH, J. V., and MASON, BRIAN
  1970. Pyroxene-garnet transformation in Coorara meteorite. Science, vol. 168, pp. 832-3.

EDWARD P. HENDERSON
BRIAN H. MASON

Orientation of Migrating Pink Shrimp

Principal Investigator: David A. Hughes, Institute of Marine and Atmospheric
Sciences, University of Miami, Miami, Florida.

Grant No. 641:   In further support of a study of the life history of migrating
pink shrimp.

The objective of this investigation was to elucidate the mechanisms underlying the migrations carried out by pink shrimp, *Penaeus duorarum*. The larval and postlarval stages move from spawning sites at sea to inshore "nursery grounds," where they remain for approximately 6 months before returning to sea as subadults.

Most attention has thus far been focused on the method whereby the shrimp carry out movements within inshore waters where the influence of ebb and flood tides is present. Sampling showed that postlarvae utilize flood tides and the juveniles (subadults) ebb tides to effect their respective inshore and offshore movements. From the experiments conducted during the 1967 season it was concluded that the shrimps' ability to discriminate between and to utilize one or other tide for their displacement is probably based on the respective responses of postlarvae and juveniles to salinity changes occurring with the change in tide (Hughes, in press).

A "current chamber," constructed from plexiglas, consisted of two cylinders placed one within the other in such a manner that a channel, approximately 6 inches wide, was formed between the inner and outer cylinder. A current of water was produced within the channel by means of four paddles attached to a central axis, which was driven by a variable speed motor. By using this apparatus it was shown that juvenile shrimp within a current of water usually swim in an upstream direction; however, when exposed to a salinity decrease they turn about and swim downstream. Postlarvae, usually active within the water column, will, following a reduction in salinity, drop to the substrate and remain there. These responses if elicited in nature would, during the ebb tides when the salinity is reduced, result in the active offshore swimming of juveniles, whereas the postlarvae would evade displacement by remaining on the substrate. When the tide floods and salinity again increases the juveniles swim against the current, thereby evading inshore displacement; conversely the postlarvae are not capable of very strong swimming and are readily displaced shoreward.

The extent of the ability of postlarvae to perceive salinity differences was examined by testing their responses at a discontinuity barrier between waters of different salinity. These experiments indicated that they were reluctant to penetrate the barrier even when the salinity difference between the two bodies of water was as small as 1 ‰.

Further experiments are necessary to determine whether salinity is the only factor, changing with change in tide, to which the shrimp will respond. Some other aspect of water quality may well elicit similar responses that would be equally adaptive.

The investigation of biological rhythms has been continued, and a study of the factors that confine activity to the hours of darkness was completed (Hughes, 1968). In each series of experiments 70 to 80 juveniles were used. These were housed in ten 15-gallon aquarium tanks maintained within the laboratory in a light-tight enclosure in which light-dark cycles could readily be altered while other factors were kept constant. This study confirmed that emergence and subsequent activity were under rhythmic control and indicated that the light-to-dark transition occurring at sunset was the principal factor synchronizing the internal rhythm of the shrimp with the day-night cycle. A 24-hour feeding rhythm was indicated by the emergence from the substrate and subsequent food searching, even during the day, of shrimp that had been fed 24 hours previously. Feeding always occurs immediately after emergence of the shrimp from the substrate; it is therefore probable that this timing mechanism serves to reinforce the influence of the circadian rhythm controlling emergence and activity.

In another study (Hughes, in press) juvenile shrimp were exposed in the current chambers to a constant current of water for a day or two after their collection from nature. Records of their swimming showed that its "pattern" throughout the night is basically similar in all shrimp collected together from nature. Also the pattern differed predictably in shrimp collected at different stages of the tidal cycle. The evidence indicates that both the direction of swimming with respect to the current and the intensity of swimming are endogenously controlled. The pattern followed appears to be entrained by some aspect of the tidal cycle to which the animals were exposed prior to collection. This evidence further supports the contention (Hughes, 1967) that cohesion of aggregations of migrating shrimp is largely maintained through the synchrony of all their activities by biological rhythms and timing mechanisms. Maintenance of these aggregations may have survival value with regard to predators and will be clearly advantageous at times of mating and spawning when groups at a similar developmental stage will arrive at suitable spawning sites together.

REFERENCES

HUGHES, DAVID A.

1967. Two papers delivered at FAO World Scientific Conference on the Biology and Culture of Shrimps and Prawns, Mexico City: "Factors Controlling the Time of Emergence of Pink Shrimp, *Penaeus duorarum*" and "On the Mechanisms Underlying Tide Associated Movements of *Penaeus duorarum* Burkenroad."

1968. Factors controlling emergence of pink shrimp *(Penaeus duorarum)* from the substrate. Biol. Bull., vol. 134, no. 1, pp. 48-59.

1969. Responses to salinity change as a tidal transport mechanism of pink shrimp, *Penaeus duorarum*. Biol. Bull., vol. 136, pp. 43-53.

1972. On the endogenous control of tide-associated displacements of pink shrimp, *Penaeus duorarum* Burkenroad. Biol. Bull., vol. 142, pp. 271-280, illus.

[Accounts of previous phases of these investigations, supported by National Geographic Society grants, have appeared in these Reports as follows: 1964 Projects, 1965 Projects, and 1966 Projects.]

DAVID A. HUGHES

Comparative Behavior and Ecology of Asian Storks

Principal Investigator: M. Philip Kahl, Naples, Florida.

Grant No. 655:   In support of the Asian portion of a continuing study of the storks of the world.

These studies, encompassing the storks of India, southeast Asia, and Japan, are a continuation of those conducted in Africa (Kahl, 1973). In field observations at active breeding sites emphasis was placed on comparing the various species and tracing differences that have evolved in homologous behavior patterns and on studying ecological factors related to the breeding season.

The Asian Storks

PAINTED STORK *(Ibis leucocephalus)*

One of the world's four species of wood storks, the painted is also one of the most beautiful of all the stork family. In its breeding behavior and ecology it is very similar to the other wood storks, which I suggest should all be combined in the genus *Mycteria*.

The largest known breeding colony of painted storks is located near Bharatpur, Rajasthan, India, where several thousand pairs gather to nest in years of adequate monsoon rains. In August and September, after the rains have flooded their feeding areas and made fish available in the shallow water, painted storks commence building their nest platforms in low acacia trees. Here they nest in close association with openbill storks (see below), several species of herons, ibises, spoonbills, and cormorants.

MILKY STORK *(Ibis cinereus)*

The southeast Asian counterpart of the painted stork, the milky stork, occurs in the Malay Peninsula, Sumatra, Java, and Cambodia. In Cambodia it is sympatric with the painted stork. Although it has not yet been recorded, the milky stork may sometimes occur in Thailand. The breeding colony that I studied was one of approximately 25 pairs on Pulau Dua, a small mangrove island off the northwest coast of Java, Indonesia.

Except for a stronger preference for coastal areas, the milky stork closely resembles, in behavior and ecology, the other species of wood storks in Asia, Africa, and the Americas. All four species of wood storks possess a remarkably uniform "greeting" display, given to the partner at the nest. In the American wood stork the bill is held vertically upward and gaped open, and a hollow, hissing sound is uttered as the head and bill are moved downward. The yellow-billed stork in Africa gives a similar "greeting" display, except that a few single snaps of the bill are given as the head is lowered. The painted stork also gives a similar display but incorporates a number of single, double, and triple bill-snaps. And the milky stork carries the process one step further by including many multiple bill-snaps in its "greeting" display.

These differences in the "greeting" display shown by the wood storks are species-specific and presumably are genetically controlled. They are perhaps similar to stages that have led to the evolution of homologous "greeting" displays in other storks (e.g., European white stork) that include loud and prolonged clattering of the bill.

ASIAN OPENBILL STORK *(Anastomus oscitans)*

This species resembles the African openbill in most respects other than the plumage, which is predominantly white with black flight feathers. The behavior of the two species at the nest is similar. Like its African cousin, the Asian openbill feeds largely on large fresh-water snails of the genus *Pila,* which it commonly extracts from the shell without crushing (Kahl, 1971).

Breeding colonies of the Asian species were studied at Bharatpur, India, in August-October 1966 and 1967, at Wilpattu National Park, Ceylon, in December 1967, and near Bangkok, Thailand, in February 1968.

WOOLLY-NECKED STORK *(Dissoura episcopus)*

Populations of this species range across the Old World tropics from Africa to the Philippines. Observations of nesting birds were made in Uttar Pradesh, Rajasthan, and Kerala, India, and further observations of non-breeding individuals were made in India and Cambodia. In the Dehiwela Zoo, Colombo, Ceylon, I was able to observe the "greeting" display in a captive pair at close range. The form of the display and the accompanying vocalizations were remarkably similar to those of the Abdim's stork *(Sphenorhynchus abdimii)* of Africa (details to be published elsewhere).

BLACK-NECKED STORK *(Xenorhynchus asiaticus)*

Uncommon to rare over most of its range, the black-necked stork was found in numbers only at Bharatpur, India, where it was studied between August and October in 1966 and 1967. I found two active nests in 1966 and four in 1967 in this area. In morphology, general behavior, and ecology the black-necked stork closely resembles the saddle-billed stork *(Ephippiorhynchus senegalensis)* of Africa, and I believe that the two species should be combined in the genus *Ephippiorhynchus.*

The spectacular "greeting" display of the black-necked stork consists of both birds standing erect and facing each other, opening their wings fully and fluttering them rapidly, while they clatter their bills. (The homologous display has not been described for the saddlebill, but it will probably prove similar.)

GREATER ADJUTANT STORK *(Leptoptilos dubius)*

A single nest of this, the most massive of the Asian storks, was found at Kaziranga Wildlife Sanctuary, Assam, India, in November 1967. Other nonbreeding individuals were observed in Assam and near New Delhi, India, and in the New Delhi and Calcutta Zoos.

In many respects of morphology and behavior the greater adjutant resembles its African cousin, the marabou stork *(Leptoptilos crumeniferus).* However, these two species differ in an important aspect of their behavior. In the marabou's "greeting" display the head is first thrown upward — with the bill near the vertical — and a squealing vocalization is given; then the head is lowered and the bill pointed *downward* and clattered loudly (Kahl, 1966). In the greater adjutant, however, the clattering in the homologous display is done with the bill pointed *upward.* Such a basic difference in a display of paramount importance to courtship and pair formation would probably serve as an effective isolating mechanism to prevent interbreeding under natural conditions (should the ranges of the two species overlap). Therefore, I feel that it is biologically sound to consider *L. dubius* and *L. crumeniferus* valid and separate species.

LESSER ADJUTANT STORK *(Leptoptilos javanicus)*

A number of nests of the lesser adjutant were found near Nowgong, Assam, India, in November 1967. Further observations of nonbreeding birds were made in Assam, India, Malaysia, and Cambodia.

The lesser adjutant differs in several respects from the greater adjutant, with which it is sympatric over part of its range. The lesser adjutant is a smaller bird, with a thinner and slightly recurved bill, more feathering on the head and neck, a naked, whitish forehead, and white (as opposed to sooty-gray in the greater) under tail coverts. The lesser lacks the large inflatable throat sac of the greater and the light-gray band of greater secondary coverts; it has, instead, a series of oval copper-colored spots on the median secondary coverts.

The social behavior of the two species of adjutants is similar, and both clatter upward during their "greeting" display. Since they are sympatric in some areas — and are said to breed together in large mixed colonies in parts of Burma (Smythies, 1953) — their morphological differences are apparently sufficient to prevent interbreeding.

EASTERN WHITE STORK *(Ciconia ciconia boyciana)*

During April and May 1968 I visited Japan in the hope of obtaining information on the displays of the eastern population of the white stork *(C. c. ciconia),* which will be reported in the third report of this series. However, this bird is nearly extinct in Japan, and I was unable to make the necessary observations. Therefore, pending further investigation, I would favor the retention of *boyciana* as a subspecies of *C. ciconia.* Studies might be possible on the Asian mainland (Manchuria and Khabarovsk, U.S.S.R.) where *boyciana* is said still to occur in some numbers (Dementiev and Gladkov, 1951; Cheng, 1964).

REFERENCES

CHENG, TSO-HSIN, ed.
1964. China's economic fauna: Birds, 946 pp. Joint Publication Research Service, U. S. Department of Commerce, Washington, D. C. (Mimeographed.)
DEMENTIEV, G. P., and GLADKOV, N. A.
1951. Ptitsy Sovetskogo Soyuza [Birds of the Soviet Union], vol. 2, 480 pp. Moscow.
KAHL, M. PHILIP
1966. Comparative ethology of the Ciconiidae, pt. 1: The marabou stork, *Leptoptilos crumeniferus* (Lesson). Behaviour, vol. 27, no. 1-2, pp. 76-106, illus.
1971a. Food and feeding behavior of openbill storks. Journ. für Orn., vol. 112, no. 1, pp. 21-35, illus.
1971b. Social behavior and taxonomic relationships of the storks. Living Bird, vol. 10, pp. 151-170.
1973. Comparative behavior and ecology of African storks. Nat. Geogr. Soc. Res. Rpts., 1966 Projects, pp. 137-141.
SMITHIES, B. E.
1953. Birds of Burma, 712 pp. Oliver & Boyd, Edinburgh.

M. PHILIP KAHL

Cyprus Underwater Archeological Search, 1967

Principal Investigator: Michael L. Katzev, University Museum, University of Pennsylvania, Philadelphia, Pennsylvania.

Grant No. 634:   In support of a search for ancient shipwrecks off the coast of Cyprus.

This archeological expedition of the University Museum surveyed the coast of Cyprus for ancient shipwrecks between September 20 and October 25, 1967, using modern electronic techniques and equipment. Five shipwrecks were found — four in water less than 75 feet in depth and one deeperwater wreck of considerable archeological interest inasmuch as it dates to the Classical period and lies in a condition perfect for future excavation. The vessel used in the search was the *Copper Queen,* a 45-foot motor yacht owned by John D. Burgess, general manager of the Cyprus Mines Corporation's operation on Cyprus, who kindly placed the boat at the disposal of the expedition. The season's results are presented here in chronological order.

Off the western coast of the Akamas Peninsula, near Koppo Island, a wreck of the Late Hellenistic Period was found by snorkeling. It lies in 8-10 feet of water on a rocky bottom, northeast of a marble bollard. The wreck has been badly broken up by wave action, making it unsuitable for excavation. However, it was noted that four different types of amphorae made up its cargo and that the predominant type was Late Hellenistic Rhodian. Broken pieces of coarse-ware cooking pottery, the rim of the ship's water jar, and a fragment of a molded glass bowl were observed in close proximity and suggest the location of the galley.

An area approximately 2 square miles to the southeast of Moulia Rocks, near Paphos, was next surveyed. Divers holding an "aquaplane" were towed at depth behind a rubber dinghy propelled by an outboard motor. Buoys were laid out in overlapping squares to insure a systematic search. Though carried out over a 5-day period the program failed to yield any evidence of shipwrecks.

The expedition then proceeded to Cape Andreas, where three shallowwater wrecks were found. The first of these lies off a submerged reef to the

FIG. 1. The visible portion of the wreck off Kyrenia. The amphora mound was found at a depth of 90 feet.

FIG. 2. Diver places the proton magnetometer over amphora mound during survey.

northwest of Table Rock. It was found by using the underwater magnetometer of Dr. E. T. Hall, director of the Research Laboratory for Archeology and the History of Art, Oxford (fig. 2). The wreck is in water 35 feet deep and is scattered into the crevices of the rocky bottom. Owing to the shallow conditions, the cargo of amphorae was so badly broken and cemented together that the amphora types could not be distinguished. However, the fragments of kylikes dating to the 4th century B.C. indicate a date for the ship's destruction. A bell-shaped stone anchor with a single hole lies amid the debris.

The second and third wrecks at Cape Andreas lie to the north of the second outlying island off the peninsula. The first of these was found by snorkeling and is widely scattered. The depth is 25-35 feet over a sloping rock bottom. The amphorae are hourglass in shape and of the Early Byzantine Period. Three triangular stone anchors were observed — two of a one-holed type and one with three holes.

The second of the wrecks off this island is the most interesting of the Cape Andreas group. It was located with the "aquaplane." The debris of

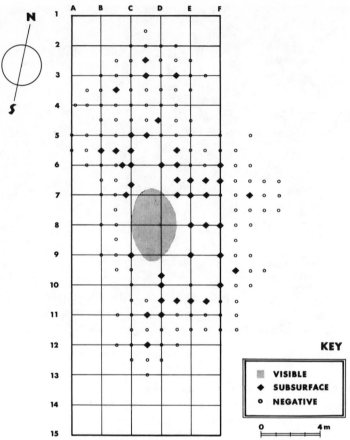

FIG. 3.   The extent of the Kyrenia shipwreck beneath the sand as determined by probing with metal rods.

the wreck has lodged in crevices of the sharply sloping rock at a depth between 35 and 75 feet. The amphorae of the wreck are again of the Early Byzantine hourglass type. However, a part of the cargo was composed of terra-cotta boxes without lids. These may have been a type of small sarcophagi. A one-holed triangular anchor was observed within the confines of this wreck. Although the ship is poorly preserved, salvage of one of the terra-cotta boxes might well be of archeological value.

The survey off Cape Andreas was cut short because we learned that Andreas Cariolou of Kyrenia had recently relocated a deep-water wreck. Mr. Cariolou was kind enough to take us to this wreck, located three-

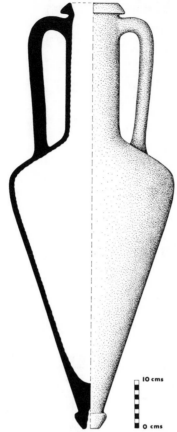

FIG. 4. The predominant type of amphora from the Kyrenia shipwreck. This jar was made on Rhodes during the second half of the 4th century B.C.

quarters of a mile east of Kyrenia and half a mile offshore. The depth is 90-95 feet, and the bottom is flat and composed of sandy mud, overgrown with *Poseidon maritima*.

The visible portion of the wreck (fig. 1) extends 3 by 5 meters. Its cargo comprises three different types of amphorae dating to the 4th century B.C. Miss Virginia Grace, of the American School of Classical Studies at Athens, Agora Excavation, who is an expert in amphora styles, believes that the most predominant type (fig. 4) from this wreck was produced on Rhodes. It seems, indeed, to be of the earliest known style of wine amphorae produced by this island. The other two amphora types from the wreck are at

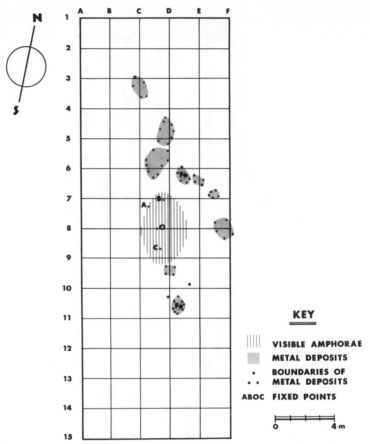

FIG. 5. A survey of the Kyrenia wreck site using a metal detector accurately
located the concentrations of metal beneath the sand.

present unknown to her.

Realizing the importance of the find, we immediately began a program
to survey the wreck without moving or removing any objects. We laid out
a simple cord grid, 10 by 28 meters, divided into 2-meter squares to serve
as orientation. Using a metal rod, we probed the soft bottom to determine
roughly the extent of the wreck beneath the sand. It was found that the
total dimension of the amphora cargo is approximately 10 by 19 meters
(fig. 3).

A survey was next begun using a metal detector developed by Jeremy

Green of Oxford. The instrument pinpointed nine metal concentrations beneath the sand. The positions of these deposits were then triangulated, using three fixed points (A, B, C) on the visible mound, and the result of this study is reproduced in figure 5.

Finally, using Dr. Hall's magnetometer, we identified two of the metal deposits as ferrous material, approximately 3 feet below the sand (fig. 2). It is conjectured that these iron concentrations represent the ship's anchors.

This survey in its three aspects represents a new approach toward inspecting a wreck site preliminary to excavation. It has provided clues to approaching the wreck that will eliminate much of the initial guesswork usually required. As an example, a system of permanent reference grids is normally laid over a wreck site before excavation begins. Hitherto, the placement of such grids has followed the axis of the visible cargo, often leading to an incomplete coverage. Our probe and metal surveys show quite clearly that the real axis of the Kyrenia ship and its cargo runs at a considerable angle to the apparent axis suggested by the amphora mound. In addition, the survey provides us with the approximate dimensions of the wreck as it lies beneath the sand. Thus, with the axis and dimensions of the site already known, one can design and position a grid system which will cover the entire wreck and require no later repositioning.

This development of a system for surveying wrecks is a side product of the Cyprus search program, but it is a procedure that should now become standard for all wreck sites preliminary to excavation.

The significance of the Kyrenia wreck cannot be overemphasized. It is, to date, the finest preserved ship of the Classical Period of Greek civilization ever found. Very little evidence comes to us from antiquity concerning the construction or shape of Greek merchant vessels. In fact, there are no material remains of merchant ships surviving from the 4th century B.C., nor are there any significant representations of them in art. The fact that this wreck lies on a muddy bottom suggests that the wood of the hull remains well preserved. For this reason the excavation of this ship should prove a milestone in the history of maritime architecture. In historical terms the ship will provide a hitherto unrevealed insight into the early phases of the wine trade in the Mediterranean world. Furthermore, it is hoped that, in addition to the cargo of amphorae, other implements and objects of the Classical Period will be uncovered, which will contribute significantly to our collection of artifacts of the time.

Because of the danger that the wreck may be plundered by amateur divers, it is most urgent that a full-scale excavation on it begin as soon as possible.

The final few days of the expedition were devoted to surveying off the jetty of the Cyprus Mines Corporation at Karavostasi. Although visibility was less than 4 inches, an attempt to locate objects with the metal detector was carried out. Time there being limited, we failed to locate anything of archeological value.

I wish to express my gratitude to our sponsors who so generously made possible this search and its rewarding results. They are the University of Pennsylvania Museum, the Cyprus Mines Corporation of Los Angeles, whose offices on Cyprus provided us with considerable assistance in technical, mechanical, and medical problems, the National Geographic Society, the Dietrich Foundation, Inc., and the Houghton-Carpenter Foundation.

The search handsomely achieved its objective in discovering a wreck of extreme archeological importance. It was our hope to begin excavation of this Classical ship in the spring of 1968.

Michael L. Katzev

Study of the Giant Pied-billed Grebe

Principal Investigator: Anne LaBastille (formerly Bowes), West of the Wind Publications, Big Moose, New York.[1]

Grant Nos. 620, 671: In support of research on the life history, ecology, conservation, and management of the giant pied-billed grebe *(Podilymbus gigas)* of Lake Atitlán, Guatemala.

The giant pied-billed, or Atitlán, grebe *(Podilymbus gigas* Griscom) is a flightless water bird endemic to Lake Atitlán in the Guatemalan Highlands. Until this investigation began virtually nothing was known of the species' life history, ethology, and ecology. Field research was conducted into these matters between 1960 and 1968 at Lake Atitlán, Guatemala, under grant support from the National Geographic Society, the Smithsonian Institution, the International Council for Preservation of Birds, and the World Wildlife Fund.

During the early 1960's, following introduction of large-mouth bass *(Micropterus salmoides),* the numbers of this grebe dropped to approximately 80 individuals, and the bird appeared to be in danger of extinction. The species may be considered one of the rarest water birds in the Western Hemisphere. In 1965, a cooperative conservation and management program, entitled "Operation Protection of the Poc," [2] was started in collaboration with the Guatemalan Ministry of Agriculture and Natural Resources.

The aims of the research were threefold: to investigate the life history, ethology, and ecology of the Atitlán grebe; to develop a conservation and management program that would preserve and protect the species and its habitat; to introduce conservation education to local inhabitants and bring an awareness of the necessity and rationale of managing Guatemala's natural resources to the people.

---

[1] Collaborators in the project in Guatemala were: Division of Fauna (Mario Saavedra, former chief; José Ovidio, present chief), Ministry of Agriculture and National Resources; Museum of Natural History (Jorge Ibarra, director), Parque La Aurora; and former Governor Julio C. Monterosa, Department of Sololá. Assisting personnel included Manuel Crespo, honorary game warden, and Edgar Bauer, regular game warden, and a small staff of Indian laborers.

[2] Indian (Tzutuhil) name for Atitlán grebe.

Field work was performed with a small boat and outboard engine along dense reed and cat-tail stands bordering the lake's 65-mile shoreline. Several censuses were run on the Atitlán grebe by day and by night. Observations were made on basic life history and behavior, the validity of the species' flightlessness, and population dynamics. Measurements and ecological analysis were made of the shoreline and aquatic habitats utilized by grebes. Surveys were taken of local Indian fishermen and skin- and scuba-divers to ascertain current and past fish and crab populations and effects of introduced bass and crappies.

Management techniques included surveys of other Guatemalan lakes in hopes of finding possible emergency refuges or new habitat; construction of a grebe refuge and visitors' center; capture and marking of four grebes for release in the refuge; stocking of the refuge as a potential fish hatchery.

Results

The carrying capacity, given sufficient food supply, was estimated at 280 giant pied-billed grebes; however, owing to the establishment of predacious bass and crappies, the population will probably stabilize around 200 birds. As of April 1973 the species numbered about 210 individuals. Limiting and mortality factors found include competition for food and probable predation on young grebe chicks by introduced large-mouth bass; naturally limited shoreline habitat (only 16 miles are vegetated) further reduced through cutting for a cottage industry by Indians; poaching, hunting, and egg-stealing; and the increasing recreational development of shoreline real-estate and water property by Guatemalans. A multimillion-dollar hydroelectric plant is also proposed for Lake Atitlán, which could seriously affect the aquatic ecosystem and reduce the grebes' chances for survival.

Concern over the declining status of the species and the evident need for conservation resulted in the establishment as a law-enforcement measure, through the Division of Fauna, of a year-round game-warden and patrol-boat service at Lake Atitlán. A new fiberglass boat and motor were donated by the World Wildlife Fund in 1972. A Presidential decree was issued to protect reed and cat-tail beds during part of the critical time of grebe reproduction. On visits made to the lake's 12 villages (total population about 50,000) conservation-education talks and lectures were given and posters erected.

Efforts were made to stimulate interest among Guatemalans in this unique wildlife resource. It was found that conservation could best be justified to the people in this developing Latin American country only through the motives of economic gain and national pride. Publicity for tourism and Guatemalan arts and crafts has wide appeal. In 1970 a series of three colored airmail stamps picturing the giant grebes and stressing conservation were issued in Guatemala.

REFERENCES

BOWES, ANNE LABASTILLE
1964. Ecological investigation of the giant pied-billed grebe of Guatemala. Res. Rpt. no. 5, Pan-Amer. Sect., Int. Comm. Bird Preserv., 6 pp. (Mimeographed.)
1965. Ecological investigation of the giant pied-billed grebe. Bull. Brit. Orn. Club, vol. 85, no. 1, pp. 14-19, illus.
1970. The life history, ecology, and management of the giant pied-billed grebe *(Podilymbus gigas)*, Lake Atitlán, Guatemala. Ph.D. thesis, Cornell University, dated September 1969. Dissertation Abstracts International, vol. 31, no. 1, 267 pp.
BOWES, ANNE LABASTILLE, and BOWES, C. V., JR.
1962. Recent census and observations of the giant pied-billed grebe of Guatemala. Auk, vol. 79, no. 4, pp. 707-709.
BOWES, ANNE LABASTILLE, and POWERS, J. E.
1967. Elimination of the fish in the giant grebe refuge using fish toxicant, antimycin. Trans. Amer. Fish. Soc., vol. 96, no. 2, pp. 210-213, illus.
HAMILTON, L. B.
1970. More on the giant pied-billed grebe of Lake Atitlán, Guatemala. Biol. Conserv., vol. 2, no. 2, pp. 142-143, illus.
LABASTILLE, ANNE
1972. How fares the poc? Audubon Mag., vol. 74, no. 2, pp. 36-43, illus.
1973. Census in April 1972 of the Atitlán grebe *(Podilymbus gigas)*, Guatemala. Biol. Conservation, vol. 5, no. 1, 2 pp.
LIDMAN, DAVID
1970. A year for conservation. New York Times (stamp column), Sunday, June 14.

ANNE LABASTILLE

Archeological and Paleontological Investigations in East Africa, 1967

Principal Investigators: Louis S. B. Leakey [1] and Mary D. Leakey, National Centre for Prehistory and Palaeontology, Nairobi, Kenya.

Grant Nos. 601, 610-619, 644-646. For continuation of the Leakeys' archeological excavations at East African sites and research on the artifacts collected, supported by the Society since 1959.

Fort Ternan. Work was resumed at the Fort Ternan site during February, March, April, and May 1967. Part of this was in the interests of protection — huts for staff, protection trenches, and fencing of the whole area that had been handed over by the Kenya Government. These operations were successfully carried out, and two permanent guards were installed.

Excavation work — cutting back into the cliff — was started, but it proved to be very much slower and more expensive than had been estimated. Consequently, the level of the fossil beds was not reached before the funds ran out.

Olduvai Gorge. Funds were awarded this year for protection and maintenance of the important Olduvai sites. This was accomplished by putting up about 20 miles of thornbush fence, isolating the important sites from other areas so that the Masai cattle could be kept from the sites when on their way to water, without doing damage.

Also during the period under review a grant was made available for capital works at Olduvai. The most important project was the erection of a stone building to provide a museum at the entrance to the Gorge, for the benefit of visitors to the sites. The Tanzania Government had promised to contribute money for the fittings and cabinets in the museum, provided funds were obtained elsewhere for the erection of a solid stone building. Richard Leakey undertook the main planning and supervision of the erection of this museum. Eventually a very satisfactory building was completed housing a magnificent exhibit dealing with the Gorge and the artifacts and fossils that have been found there.

---

[1] Dr. Leakey died on October 1, 1972.

A special grant made possible the purchase of a new lorry and a Land-Rover for use in the work, replacing vehicles that had become dilapidated.

During the latter part of the year, when it was clear that Mary Leakey would be unable to resume work at Olduvai, on the excavations at site DK and elsewhere, we sent our senior African worker, Heselon Mukiri, to a site in Bed I where parts of a fossil elephant skeleton had been located. We had expected and hoped that this elephant skeleton might have been surrounded by stone tools used by hominids scavenging for its flesh, but only three such tools were recovered.

The National Geographic Society also granted funds for special research to be carried out by Dr. Alan Gentry and Mrs. Shirley Coryndon in connection with important studies of fossil mammal remains from Olduvai, which they were undertaking in London. This work was not completed during 1967, and both paleontologists worked again the following year. Mrs. Coryndon made a specialized study of hippopotamuses and Dr. Gentry one of *Pelorovis*.

Another grant enabled Prof. R. Lavocat, engaged in a study of something like 100,000 jaws of fossil rodents from Olduvai, to hire an assistant to help in measuring and classifying the specimens. Thus it was possible to advance the work much more rapidly, but it is still not yet completed at the time of writing (1972).

Omo Research. A grant was made available for Richard Leakey to join an international research team working at the Omo site in southwest Ethiopia. The other members of the team were Prof. Clark Howell, then of the University of Chicago, and his assistants; and the late Prof. C. Arambourg of Paris, with his assistant, Yves Coppens. Scientists from Addis Ababa also made occasional visits to the site.

Richard Leakey was in charge of the over-all logistics for the whole expedition and was selected to explore the terrain, on the east bank of the Omo River on the north side of the river's bend. He gave a great deal of thought to the planning of this part of the work and had the valuable help of Allen O'Brien of Los Angeles in constructing a raft to get the vehicles and equipment across the fast-flowing, crocodile-infested river. When this crossing had been successfully achieved, Richard and his wife, Margaret, accompanied by a number of specially trained African workers, together with Dr. Paul Abel of Rhode Island University, explored the area. They had a very successful initial season and located two hominid skulls in the Middle-Pleistocene deposits of the Kibish formation, as well as several other fragments of hominid material. They also located the earliest fossiliferous deposits so far known in the Omo basin.

We made trips by plane to Richard's camp and also visited the French and United States camps. Accompanied by Richard we made some exploratory expeditions by helicopter. The season was an extremely successful one, far exceeding expectations.

LOUIS S. B. LEAKEY
MARY D. LEAKEY

Behavioral Aspects of the Rut in American Bison

Principal Investigator: Dale F. Lott, University of California, Davis, California.

Grant No. 662:   In support of a behavioral study of the American bison, in particular the aggressive interactions of breeding bulls.

The objective of this research was to increase knowledge about the social behavior of American bison, with principal emphasis focused on the animal's aggressive and sexual behavior, and the study has been so far largely confined to the rut.

There have been a number of popular, anectodal descriptions of bison behavior, but few serious efforts by trained students of behavior. The few scientific reports (e.g., Fuller, 1960; McHugh, 1958) are often sophisticated studies but are basically surveys that leave the description of a number of behaviors and social relationships in a preliminary stage. Still this limited scientific literature demonstrates convincingly that the popular accounts range somewhere between largely and completely wrong. Bison are such a tremendous biological success that an accurate description of their behavior seems certain to be valuable not only for itself but also for insights it might offer us into the range and nature of behavioral adaptations in grazing animals in general.

The observations were made during the rut on the National Bison Range at Moiese, Montana, during the summer of 1968. Total observation time was about 150 hours. Most observations were recorded in the form of field notes dictated on a portable tape recorder at the time and later transcribed verbatim for data analysis. These notes were supplemented by some hundreds of 35-millimeter slides, some tape recordings of vocalizations, and 2,000 feet of 16-millimeter motion pictures. The subjects were a herd of about 200 animals, of which 25 were mature breeding bulls. A tour road passes through the range, and so the bison are often exposed to slowly moving or parked cars with people in or near them. Probably as a consequence the animals are undisturbed by automobiles and observations are easily made in almost any part of the range from a 4-wheel-drive vehicle.

The primary focus of research during this period was on the aggressive interactions of breeding bulls. These interactions are dramatic, and no observer of bison ever fails to comment on them. Nonetheless, reports to date have tended to be brief and incomplete in several respects.

During most of the year the basic social group in American bison numbers some 20-50 cows, calves, and young bulls. The breeding bulls are generally outside the groups, spending their time either alone or in small temporary groups. During the three to four weeks of the breeding season the cow groups combine into a large herd and the bulls move into the herd where they compete for cows. Since there is nothing resembling a territorial mechanism that would reduce conflict by physically spacing the bulls, they must rely upon dominance and submission to avoid fights and to terminate fights without damage. Clearly the high level of competition combined with the absence of a territorial mechanism requires effective signaling. A major gap in the understanding of these relationships has been virtually complete absence of a discussion of the submissive signal or signals by which mature bulls yield to one another. The search for such submissive signals was a major focus in this summer's research.

Bulls may encounter one another in a variety of circumstances within the herd, and they come into conflict in several of them. In order to see which signal or signals indicate submission it is essential to identify submitting animals. For the sake of having an objective determination of winning and submitting, I chose to confine my analysis to situations in which one bull was standing with a cow (in a "tending" relationship) and another bull displacing or attempting to displace him. Since the cow was the object of the dispute, the bull that ended up without the cow could be regarded as submitting. Any signal characteristically given by bulls in this situation could be regarded as a submission signal.

In this particular interaction a relatively simple signaling system operates. Challenges to the tending bull take the form of behavior that is preliminary to a fight. There is a good deal of bellowing, and occasionally one or both of the bulls wallow, but always the challenging bull approaches the tending bull in a head-on, fighting orientation, and the tending bull responds with the same orientation. Sometimes these interactions lead to fights. At other times the fight is averted by one of the two bulls submitting. Submission takes the form of turning at least the head and neck, and sometimes the entire body, broadside to the challenging animal.

When fights occur a broadside submission signal is about the only behavior that can end them. A bull that retreats, however rapidly, without shifting from its head-on orientation toward the antagonist is usually pursued until it turns broadside. This made it appear that a very simple signaling system is operating in the species in which threat consists in the preliminary movements to a fight (particularly the head-on approach) and sub-mission consists in turning broadside, an action that might be thought of as the preliminary movement to retreat and withdrawal.

It seemed at first that this description might fit all the aggressive inter-actions of bison bulls, but this now seems quite doubtful. It now appears more likely that this is an accurate description of the relatively special case of interactions between tending bulls and their challengers. The aggressive interactions that occur in other contexts often seem to involve other sig-nals. This hypothesis is being tested by further research.

REFERENCES

FULLER, W. A.
    1960. Behavior and social organization of the wild bison of Wood Buffalo Na-tional Park, Canada.   Arctic, vol. 13, pp. 3-19.
McHUGH, T.
    1958. Social behavior of the American buffalo *(Bison bison bison)*.   Zoologica, vol. 43, pp. 1-40.

DALE F. LOTT

Alaskan Glacier Commemorative Project, Phase IV: Pleistocene-Holocene Sequences in the Alaska-Canada Boundary Range

Principal Investigator: Maynard M. Miller, Michigan State University, East Lansing, Michigan, and Foundation for Glacier and Environmental Research, Seattle, Washington. (Palynology analyses by James H. Anderson, Institute of Arctic Biology, University of Alaska, Fairbanks.)

Grant No. 649:   In support of the fourth year (1967) of a continuing program to study changes in glaciers and the causes of glaciation along the southern Alaskan coast since the Society's Tarr and Martin investigations early in the century.

In Phase IV of the Alaskan Glacier Commemorative Project special attention was given to the problem of out-of-phase glacioclimatic fluctuations in the maritime versus continental sectors of this cordilleran region, within the framework of secular trends over the past 11,000 years.

Investigations continued during the summer field season of 1967 with emphasis on the Alaska-Canada Coast Mountains (fig. 1). The main research was in the Boundary Range, particularly the northern sector in the Taku and Atlin Districts, lying between the Taku River Valley, which crosses the British Columbia-Alaska border at about lat. 58° 30' N. and the British Columbia-Yukon border at 60° N. (fig. 2). In recent years this area has served as a prototype for field studies of Pleistocene and Holocene glaciation emphasizing the dynamics of glacial, hydrological, and atmospheric processes, the fluctuations of existing ice masses, and the problems associated with simultaneous advance and retreat of adjoining valley glaciers during the past four centuries (i.e., the Alaska Little Ice Age) (Beschel and Egan, 1965; Miller, 1970).

The Phase IV program on the Juneau Icefield concentrated on glaciological and hydrological aspects of the region relating to short- and long-term variations. Emphasis was placed also on continuum mechanics and the processes of glacial erosion and deposition, including the evolution of recessional and washboard moraines associated with ice retreat (fig. 3) and the development of bold push moraines relating to vigorously advancing glaciers (fig. 4). The results of these aspects of the 1967 work are reported in

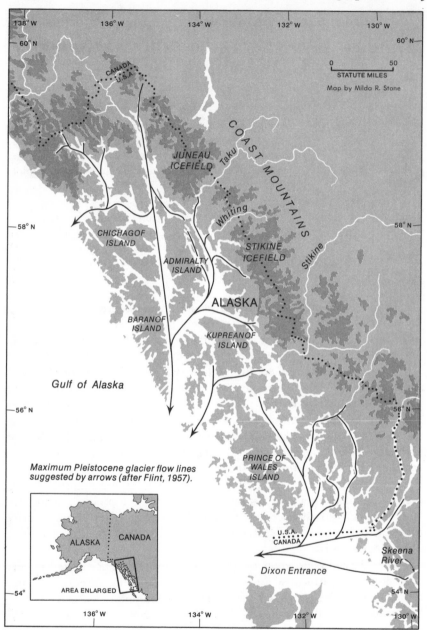

FIG. 1.   Map of southeastern Alaska, showing location and areas of the Stikine and
Juneau Icefields.

separate papers (Pinchak, 1972; Miller, 1972 a, b; Zenone et al., 1972; Pinchak and Lokey, 1972).

As all the processes involved are important in the interpretation of landform sequences in the peripherally deglaciated sectors, increased attention has been paid to the chronology of the Pleistocene and Holocene in this region. Thus research was conducted on the character and development of bog stratigraphy in the marginal areas affected by Wisconsinan glaciation. Correspondingly, the sequence of deglaciation features relating to the downwasting and retreat of Wisconsinan ice has been investigated. Some of the results of the glacial geological and geobotanical studies are reported here, with reference to an example of our mapping of existing ice masses as a basis for comparison with conditions and positions in the past, and, of course, the future. The bog stratigraphy particularly enlarges our understanding of secular climatic trends and the glacioclimatic character of this region since the beginning of Holocene time.

Neoglaciation and the Holocene

The main glacierized sectors of the Boundary Range include the Stikine Icefield (north and west of the Stikine River) and the Juneau Icefield (northwest of the Taku River), as noted in figure 1. Several hundred miles northwest of the Juneau Icefield extends the much larger St. Elias Icefield where, in the Yakutat Bay sector, Tarr and Martin (1914) initiated their pioneering glaciological studies for the National Geographic Society some 60 years ago. These three large icefields are Neoglacial in age, each expanding to its presently configurated form about 2,000 years BP. Thus, they are not relicts from earlier Pleistocene time. Their areas include respectively about 1600, 1700, and 8000 square miles of névés and outflowing glacier tongues, typified by the receding Llewellyn Glacier (fig. 3), which drains north from the Juneau Icefield into the dry interior of northern British Columbia, and the advancing Taku Glacier (fig. 4), which flows south to a tidal terminus from the same crestal névé. Our 1965-67 map of the advancing Taku Glacier and its complex terminal moraine, surveyed by terrestrial phototheodolite means, is reproduced in figure 5. This excellent map has been produced through the expertise and fine cooperation of our Canadian research affiliates in the Department of Surveying Engineering, University of New Brunswick, Fredericton, New Brunswick (Konecny, Gloss, and Knasovicky, 1972). Dr. Konecny conducted the field surveys; Professor Gloss carried out the plotting; and Dr. Knasovicky the cartography.

Today's glacial positions are close to and in some cases almost precisely parallel those of the early Neoglacial maximum of some 2,000 years BP.

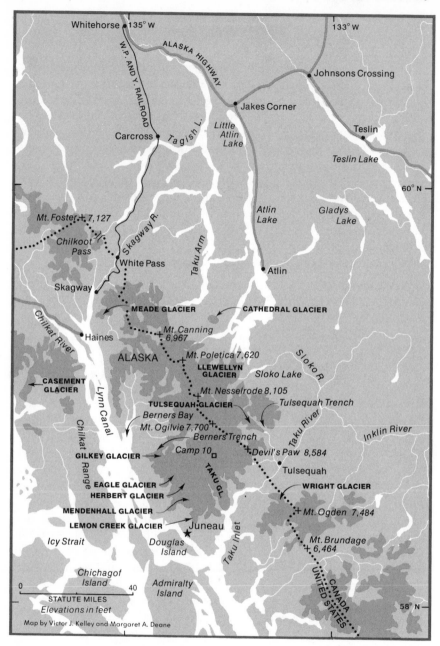

FIG. 2.   The Northern Boundary Range and the Juneau Icefield, in the Taku and
Atlin Districts.

This has been evidenced by lake varve studies and radiocarbon dating of ice-buried forest remains (Hanson, 1932; Kulp et al, 1951; Cross, 1968; Miller, 1956, 1967; Miller, Egan, and Beschel, 1968). These modern positions have, in fact, in some valleys been demonstrated to represent the most extensive glacial advance of the Holocene, that is, since the end of the late Wisconsinan Maximum about 10,000 years BP. Evidence for this lies in radiocarbon dating of peat material in muskegs in the peripheral sectors (Heusser, 1952, 1953, 1960, 1965; Heusser and Marcus, 1964), and the dendrochronologic investigation of old spruce and hemlock forests invaded by Taku ice during the Little Ice Age advances (Lawrence, 1950; Lawrence and Elson, 1953). Thus on the margin of these icefields and from study of the intervening zone between these features (which were formed at the periphery of late Wisconsinan glaciation) and the present glacial position, the character of the Holocene has been recorded. Some key measurements and interpretations from this research are reported below, including a suggested Holocene chronology and consideration of changes in the glacio-climatological characteristics of the region over the past 10,000 years.

Glacial and Bioclimatological Stratigraphy

Between 1965 and 1967, a new dimension in our stratigraphic study of glacial deposits was initiated through a systematic consideration of the palynology of Holocene bogs in the Atlin region. The palynological analyses were conducted by J. H. Anderson (1970). The purpose has been to compare sequences with those interpreted from muskeg bogs on the Alaskan side of the Juneau Icefield studied in our earlier programs by Heusser (1952). A typical low-elevation bog (Mile 16) and a high-level bog (in Upper Fourth of July Creek Valley) are illustrated in figure 6. The locations of the six key bog sites are shown in figure 7. In figures 8 and 9, pollen and spore diagrams are shown representing bog profiles at Mile 16 near the British Columbia-Yukon border on the Atlin road and at Jasper Creek, about 25 miles northeast of the Llewellyn Glacier terminus. From these and other pollen profiles obtained at the other sites noted in figure 7, a tentative Holocene glacial-geobotanical-climatological chronology has been prepared (fig. 10). In this chronology, certain comparisons are also made with respect to Heusser's sequence on the maritime side of the Boundary Range.

It is to be noted in figures 8 and 9 that there are three distinct zones representing major vegetation changes in the Atlin area at two key levels, in every case well revealed by the form of the pollen profiles. Radiocarbon dates show that these levels of boundaries between zones are not necessarily contemporaneous from one bog to another, although the zonations are

Fig. 3. (See opposite page for legend).

significant. The lowest zone is the *shrub zone,* characterized by alder and birch, plus willow, grass, *Artemisia* spp., and other Compositae. The significant aspect here is the low frequency of tree pollen and the dominance of shrub pollen. In the Mile 47, Jasper Creek, and Wilson Creek bogs, this zone begins at the base and extends well up into blue-gray clay sediments, where there are generally low pollen counts. It is assumed that these assemblages reveal the nature of contemporaneous vegetation.

The next or intermediate interval is the *spruce zone,* characterized by a rapid increase of white-spruce pollen percentages. Here the pollen counts of principal shrubs (willow, alder, and birch) decrease to levels intermediate between those of the shrub zone and the overlying pine zone. The *pine zone* is the third and uppermost one and is characterized by high percentages of pine pollen and relatively lower spruce-pollen percentages. Some alpine fir grains also occur here, but less so in the younger stratigraphy near the surface.

Anderson (1970) suggests that the scarcity of aspen and poplar pollen in the bog sediments is due to its low preservability, in the alkaline environment of this limestone region. Today aspen is a prominent constituent of the vegetation of the Atlin region.

Seven bog-sediment samples for radiocarbon dating were obtained in conjunction with palynological sampling. In Mile 16 bog samples were obtained at the somewhat arbitrary levels of 150 and 635 centimenters (fig. 8). In Mile 47, Mile 52, and Wilson Creek bogs radiocarbon samples were obtained at or near boundaries between major sediment types. Two samples were obtained from Mile 47 bog, one of which was divided into organic and inorganic fractions, and one sample each was obtained from Mile 52 and Wilson Creek bog. Dated samples permitted the calculation of possible sediment accumulation rates and thus the extrapolation of tentative dates to other levels. Cross correlations between bogs of pollen profiles served

---

FIG. 3. Receding Llewellyn Glacier, 1917-68, showing downwasting since maximum advance in 1920's: *Upper left,* Llewellyn Glacier in midsummer 1917, showing position of central sector close to its 20th-century maximum reached about 1925; the ice front has downwasted and receded approximately 1 mile since and is still experiencing negative regime (photo by L. C. Reed). *Upper right,* Llewellyn Glacier showing 1967-69 position of western sector and terminal lake formed by downwasting and 1-mile retreat since 1917-25 (photo by M. M. Miller). *Lower left,* View from col above Llewellyn Inlet, early summer 1920, showing maximum advance of early 1920's, (photo Provincial Archives, Victoria, British Columbia). *Lower right,* View from col above Llewellyn Inlet, summer 1968, showing recession since the 1920's (photo by J. H. Anderson).

further to establish the chronologic framework for the sedimentary sequences. In figure 9, the dates in parentheses are based on such correlations. Here, Jasper Creek bog profiles were correlated with those of the nearby Wilson Creek bog, to which a chronology based on radiocarbon dating was applied.

Although extrapolation of this kind introduces errors, it at least provides an estimate of the age and development of the bogs and from this a tentative Holocene chronology. For example, on this basis the age of the bottom sediments in the Mile 16 bog section is approximately 8,000 years BP. The oldest sediments, as determined by such extrapolation in the Jasper Creek profile, were deposited at least 11,000 years BP. Details of the interpretation have been defended in a comprehensive treatment by Anderson (1970).

Thus we have some indication of the earliest dates of deglaciation of the southern end of the Atlin Valley. These dates are commensurate with the C-14 dates of bog development since deglaciation in the adjoining highland valleys some 20 miles northeast of Atlin Village (see Fourth of July Creek Valley indicated in fig. 7). From this it is concluded that by no later than 9,500 years BP most of the Atlin Valley was deglaciated for some 70 miles south of the late-Wisconsinan moraines at the northern end of Little Atlin Lake, and hence that most of this region was deglaciated by the beginning of the Holocene. The final retreatal position of ice in this late-Glacial warming was presumably close to the location of subsequently developed Neoglacial moraines which are not far from the present periphery of the Juneau Icefield.

Chronological Subdivision of the Holocene and Relationship to Storm-Track Shifts

The time sequence of Holocene climatological and glaciological environments for the Taku-Atlin region is represented by a provisional geobotanical chronology comprising nine discrete intervals or time zones as shown in the chart of figure 10. Each time interval is described, working backward from the youngest to the oldest (i.e., from the present to Valders time about 11,000 years BP). Related changes in general storm-track positions, idealized in figure 11, are also considered. In this figure the shifts in position are related to solar-climatic considerations as discussed in our Phase III report (Miller, 1973).

Time Interval I, from the present to about 750 years BP. This interval essentially embraces the "Little Ice Age" and includes minor fluctuations in

FIG. 4.   Receding Norris Glacier (*left*) and advancing Taku Glacier (*right*), Juneau Icefield, Alaska; view from photogrammetric station on ridge south of Taku Fiord in mid-July 1965 (P-30 photo by G. Konecny and A. Chrzanowski, J.I.R.P.). Also see map, figure 5.

206

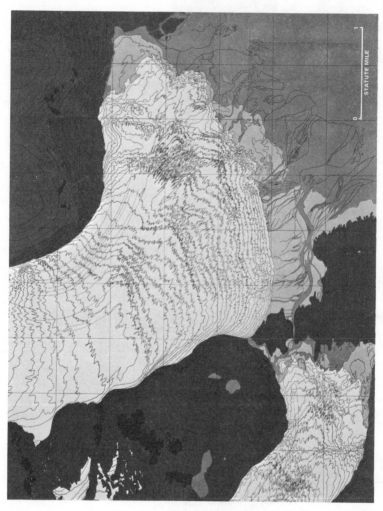

Fig. 5. Photogrammetric map of advancing Taku Glacier (*right* and *top*) and receding Norris Glacier (*left*), Juneau Icefield, Alaska, showing nature of topography and terminal moraine as of summer 1965. After surveys by Drs. Gottfried Konecny and Adam Chrzanowski, University of New Brunswick, Canada, in cooperation with the Foundation for Glacier and Environmental Research. Plotted by Gerhard Gloss, UNB (1967); cartography by Dr. Lazlo Knasovicky, UNB (1971).

late Neoglacial climate and glacier behavior during the most recent time of increased glaciation. This glacioclimatic pattern has been described in the 1961 to 1966 Alaskan Glacier Commemorative Project reports published by the National Geographic Society (Miller, 1969, 1970, 1971, 1973). The palynological method is not sensitive enough to reveal the complex, short-term climatic pulsations affecting this region during the Little Ice Age. This method is more applicable to the elucidation of regional vegetation and associated climatic changes over longer periods of time. Further research in dendrochronology, lichenometry, glacial geology, glaciology, and glacio-meteorology and more detailed short-term analyses of sedimentation, including lake-bottom sedimentology, can be significant in working out a more refined chronology.

That there has been a two- to threefold warming and cooling pattern (including the distinct cooling since the 1940's) superimposed on a general warming trend from the mid-1700's to present is well documented for the period following return to colder conditions around A.D. 1200. Further-more, there is evidence in the bogs of an increase in precipitation during these recent centuries and a rejuvenation and growth of subsurface ice in frost mounds (palsas) in the higher elevation bogs (fig. 6, *lower*) of the Atlin area (Anderson and Miller, 1972; Tallman, 1972). This has also been allied with a substantial build-up of glacial ice at higher elevations on the Juneau Icefield. In fact, all the glaciers of the icefield have responded sensitively to late Neoglacial climatic perturbations (Miller, 1973), supporting the con-tention that the Arctic Front [1] throughout the Holocene shifted back and forth across a linear belt in the axial zone of the Boundary Range shared by the Taku and Atlin Districts. In today's generally warm-moist situation, the storm tracks have a strongly maritime orientation with freezing levels considerably more raised than in the preceding interval considered below. Associated with this has been well-documented downwasting, general retreat and, in some cases, disappearance of glaciers with low névés and a notable thickening and advance of glaciers with high névés.

Time Interval II: ca. 2,500-750 BP. In this period the palynological records suggest cooler and drier conditions than at present, a situation in which the average position of the Arctic Front and associated storm tracks shifted inland with increased dominance of the maritime pressure cell and, of course, lowered freezing levels. The result was decreased storminess and less precipitation in the inland areas with a correspondingly cooler and

---

[1] The line of demarcation between the generally high pressure anticyclonic continental weather conditions and the low-pressure cyclonic maritime conditions on the coast.

FIG. 6. *Upper,* Mile 16 bog in the Atlin Region. *Lower,* Fourth of July Creek bog, showing palsa development at 3,400 feet elevation. (Photos by M. M. Miller.)

wetter situation pertaining in the coastal part of the Taku district. Associated with these climatic changes were Neoglacial advances in the lower névé glaciers and retreat of high névé glaciers in the Boundary Range. Documented early Neoglacial advances in the northern Boundary Range reflect conditions of lowered temperature and increased maritimity across the range; but decreased storminess is also indicated by the increase in dry climate vegetation in the interior Atlin region revealed by our bog pollen profiles. Anderson (1970) suggested that a greater proportion of pine in the Atlin valley forests reflects a higher frequency of forest fires resulting from these drier conditions. It is stressed that the relatively cool-dry climate of the Atlin valley at that time was quite out-of-phase with the climatic character of the Alaskan coast, a significant relationship first suggested by Miller (1956, p. 512) to explain divergences in the climatic environment of muskeg areas at low elevation and glacioclimatic trends at high elevation on the Juneau Icefield. The late Holocene Time II condition is also considered comparable to that of the beginning of the Holocene, depicted in Time Intervals VI and VIII in figure 10.

Time Interval III, 3,250 to 2,500 years BP. The appearance of alpine fir in the Atlin spruce forest connotes continuing wetness during the growing season, but decreasing temperatures, lowered freezing levels, and reduced storminess. At the end of this interval, mean July temperatures probably decreased to the present level, about 54° F. This was the end of the Thermal Maximum and may be compared to the sub-Boreal. Anderson's interpretation is that it ended about 1,000 years later in the Atlin area than in the Taku District as reported by Heusser (1952), making it contemporaneous with the sub-Boreal of other regions. At the end of this interval, the Arctic Front shifted inland with the approach of Neoglacial time. The return to less stormy and cooler conditions lowered freezing levels and presaged resurgence of many of the large Juneau Icefield glaciers in the late Holocene, about the beginning of the Christian Era (Neoglacial).

Time Interval IV, 5,500 to 3,250 years BP. Holocene temperatures and precipitation reached their maximum, with mean July temperatures probably as high at 56° F. and precipitation as great as at present. Relatively warmer and wetter conditions meant higher freezing levels, increased storminess, and dominant spruce forests with alder. During this interval the low névé Coast Range glaciers (Juneau and Stikine Icefields) shrank to their post-Wisconsinan minima, with some thickening of the highest elevation cirque glaciers and the very highest crestal névés. The result was that the main trunk glaciers in the Atlin valley receded well up into the Boundary Range, some miles south of the present position of the Llewellyn Glacier (fig. 3). Similarly, on the Alaskan coast, forests grew far up into the present ice-covered valleys of the Mendenhall, Herbert, and other maritime glaciers. Because of maximum downwasting of all but the highest Juneau Icefield névés, this culminated the progressive deglaciation trend that had begun some 6,000 years earlier (i.e., in Time VII, fig. 10).

With more extensive and luxuriant vegetation characterizing the apex of this interval, it is compared to the Atlantic period of other regions and to the late Hypsithermal (Thermal Maximum) identified by Heusser in studies of muskeg-bog stratigraphy in the Alaskan Panhandle. The mean position of the Arctic Front was then positioned much nearer the coast and sufficiently west of the Juneau Icefield that even the maritime Taku Glacier had a terminus some 12 to 14 miles up-valley compared to its subsequent Neo-glacial (and present) maximum. With such increased temperatures there were also increased atmospheric turbulence and storminess, responsible for the continuing wetter conditions.

Time Interval V, 8,000 to 5,500 years BP. At the outset regional temperatures in the Atlin sector approached present levels, thus marking the beginning of the Thermal Maximum. Including its waxing and waning phases, this warm interval extended over at least 5,000 years, about half of the Holocene. Precipitation in the Atlin area was at today's level (11-12 inches per year) or somewhat higher. In an absolute sense, the Atlin area was semiarid, but in comparison with the previous time interval it was relatively wet,[2] promoting widespread development of spruce-forest vegetation.

At the beginning of Thermal Maximum time, glacier regimes in the highlands were oscillating, with changes taking place rapidly. The over-all trend was thinning and retreat of low-névé glaciers and still-stands and some advance of the highest névé glaciers compared to regimes in the previous interval (VI). All this reflected an associated rise in mean freezing levels. At the end of the interval, the terminus of the Llewellyn Glacier may have reached a position not far from its present location.

Time Interval V correlates with the Boreal of other areas. In the Atlin sector this relatively warm-wet period began at the same time as the warm-dry Boreal of the Alaska Panhandle, recognized on palynological grounds by Heusser. This suggests that the mean position of the Arctic Front had shifted even closer to the Alaskan coast. Temperatures were higher than

---

[2] It is re-emphasized that use of the term "wet" is only to designate a precipitation regime which was wet relative to the drier and more continental conditions characterizing the preceding cool and dry spruce woodland and cooler and drier tundra vegetation of Time Intervals VI, VII, VIII, and IX.

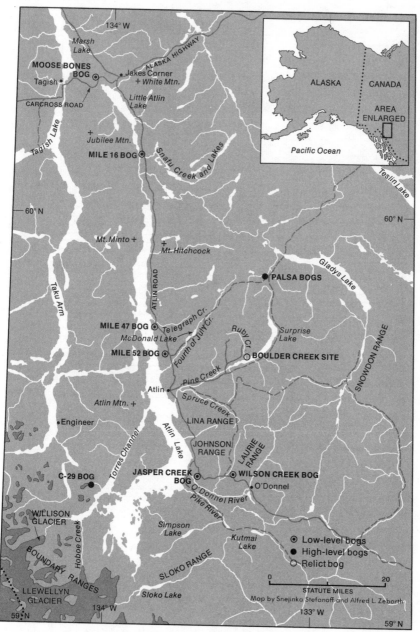

FIG. 7. Map of the Atlin Region showing sampling sites.

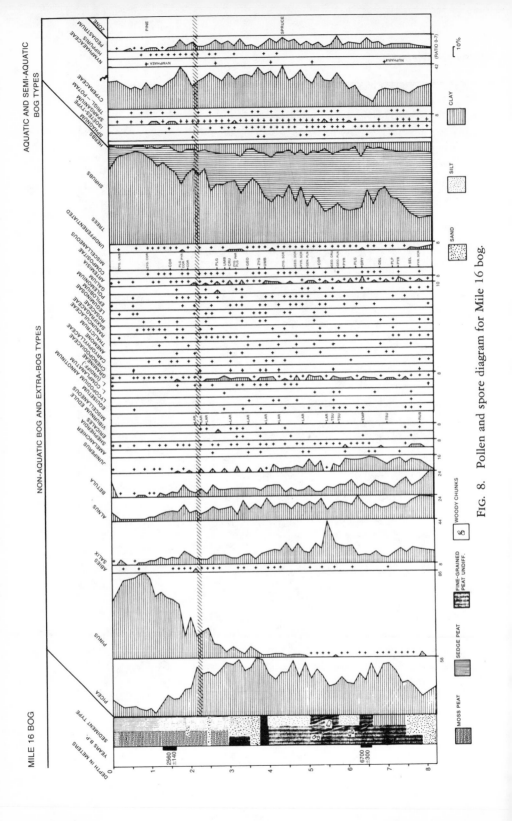

FIG. 8.   Pollen and spore diagram for Mile 16 bog.

in any earlier interval of the Holocene, including the warm incursion of Time VIII (fig. 10) which is also presumed to have brought an increased storminess and increased wetness during the annual melt season, especially in the spring and autumn months.

Time Interval VI, ca. 9,000 to 8,000 years BP. A significant and intermittent downwasting and retreat of the main Atlin Valley glacier occurred during this interval, probably resulting in formation of the series of compact recessional moraines and kame deltas found at the northern end of Atlin Lake. Ameliorating climatic conditions leading into the Thermal Maximum meant a change to somewhat warmer and moister conditions from the relatively cold and dry conditions of the preceding interval, promoting growth of spruce woodland in the southern sector. The Mile 47 and Mile 52 bog areas (fig. 7) were exposed as was probably the Mile 16 bog site, although ice cores in the ground moraine had presumably not yet melted out to create the kettle in which the latter bog developed.

Time Interval VI is considered by Anderson (1970) as a "third and final subdivision of a period comparable to the pre-Boreal in other regions or the contemporaneous Early Postglacial recognized by Heusser in Southern Alaska."

By extrapolation, the mean position of the Arctic Front was again moved toward the coast in response to dominance of the Polar continental anticyclone. This resulted in decreasing storminess and raised freezing levels compared to the preceding interval and apparently cool-dry climatic conditions in the Atlin area compared to the cool-moist (cool-humid) conditions described by Heusser for this time on the coastal flank of the Boundary Range. In accordance with our studies of Juneau Icefield glacier patterns (Miller, 1956, 1963, 1971, 1973), we interpret the consequence of this climatic trend to be increasing retreat of those inland glaciers with low névés. In turn, there was intermittent growth and advance of higher névé glaciers on the coast and intermittent decrease and retreat of higher névé glaciers inland. The glacial regime situation was comparable to that characterizing Interval II in the first half of the Neoglacial.

Time Interval VII, ca. 10,000 to 9,000 years BP. A shrub tundra vegetation characterized this period, with herbaceous tundra in the northern sector of the Atlin region. The cooler and drier climatic conditions represented the coldest part of the Holocene. With less energy in the atmosphere, storminess was also lessened. Correspondingly, according to Heusser's palynological interpretations, cooler and moister conditions prevailed along the Alaskan coast. It can be inferred that there was inland orientation of storm tracks and depressed freezing levels. The main valley glaciers on the

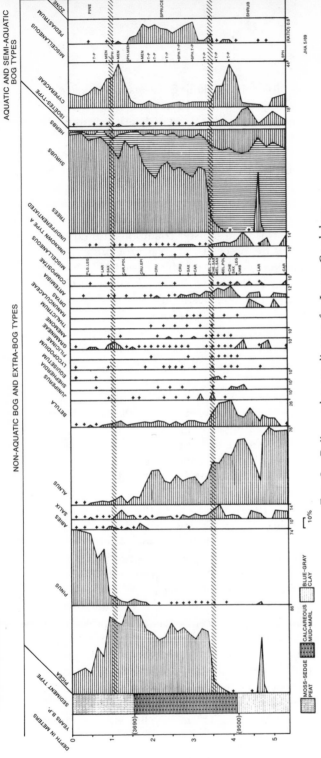

FIG. 9.   Pollen and spore diagram for Jasper Creek bog.

coast would respond by crowding forward as would low-névé inland glaciers, including the trunk glacier down the Atlin Valley. With chilling arctic conditions, highland glaciers would also become thermally polar to subpolar with lessened flow rates resulting in still-stands, if not advances. Extensive kame terraces on each flank of the Atlin Valley in its northern sector corroborate this interpretation. With low temperatures, the mean Arctic Front would again be shifted well inland and probably for long periods lay over the southern part of the Atlin region. The regional glaciation associated here would likely be in the Lesser Mountain Ice Sheet Phase of Miller (1964).

This Time Interval is pre-Boreal, or Early Postglacial according to Heusser's interpretation. It represents glacio-climatic oscillation not generally delineated elsewhere, although in the mid-continent chronology (Great Lakes region) there is evidence of a minor post-Valders (Valders II) resurgence. It also may correlate with the Sumas Stade of southwest British Columbia and the Sittakanay stage in the Taku Valley of northwest British Columbia (Miller, 1956).

Time Interval VIII, ca. 10,500 to 10,000 years BP. This interval represents a short oscillation, slightly warmer and possibly slightly colder than the preceding and subsequent intervals. During this time, the main Atlin Valley trunk glaciers of Wisconsinan age appeared to suffer a remarkably rapid 15-20 mile retreat from the maximum late-Wisconsinan position at the embankment moraines near the Alaska Highway (fig. 2) to a still-stand in the vicinity of what is now Mile 24 on the Atlin Road. The vegetation in the Jasper Creek-Wilson Creek bog areas changed from a shrub tundra to a spruce woodland type similar to but drier than the present vegetation found at 4,200 to 4,500 feet in the Atlin District.

Mean July temperatures are suggested to have been above 50° F., and precipitation rose to perhaps as high as 8-10 inches per year. With the mean position of the Arctic Front somewhat farther inland than in Time VII, yet closer to the coast than in Time IX, it was probably well south of the Atlin region. This would result in the passage of increased ice from higher névé glaciers into the main fiords on the coast at the onset of this period. But they would degrade into retreat as freezing levels lowered and storminess decreased at the end.

Anderson suggests that this interval could possibly be the first distinct subdivision of the Holocene Epoch, although the principal investigator suggests it is more appropriately referenced as a Valders equivalent (Bothnian in Scandinavia). Thus Time Interval VIII would then correlate with the Tulsequah stage in the Taku Valley, British Columbia, and with the

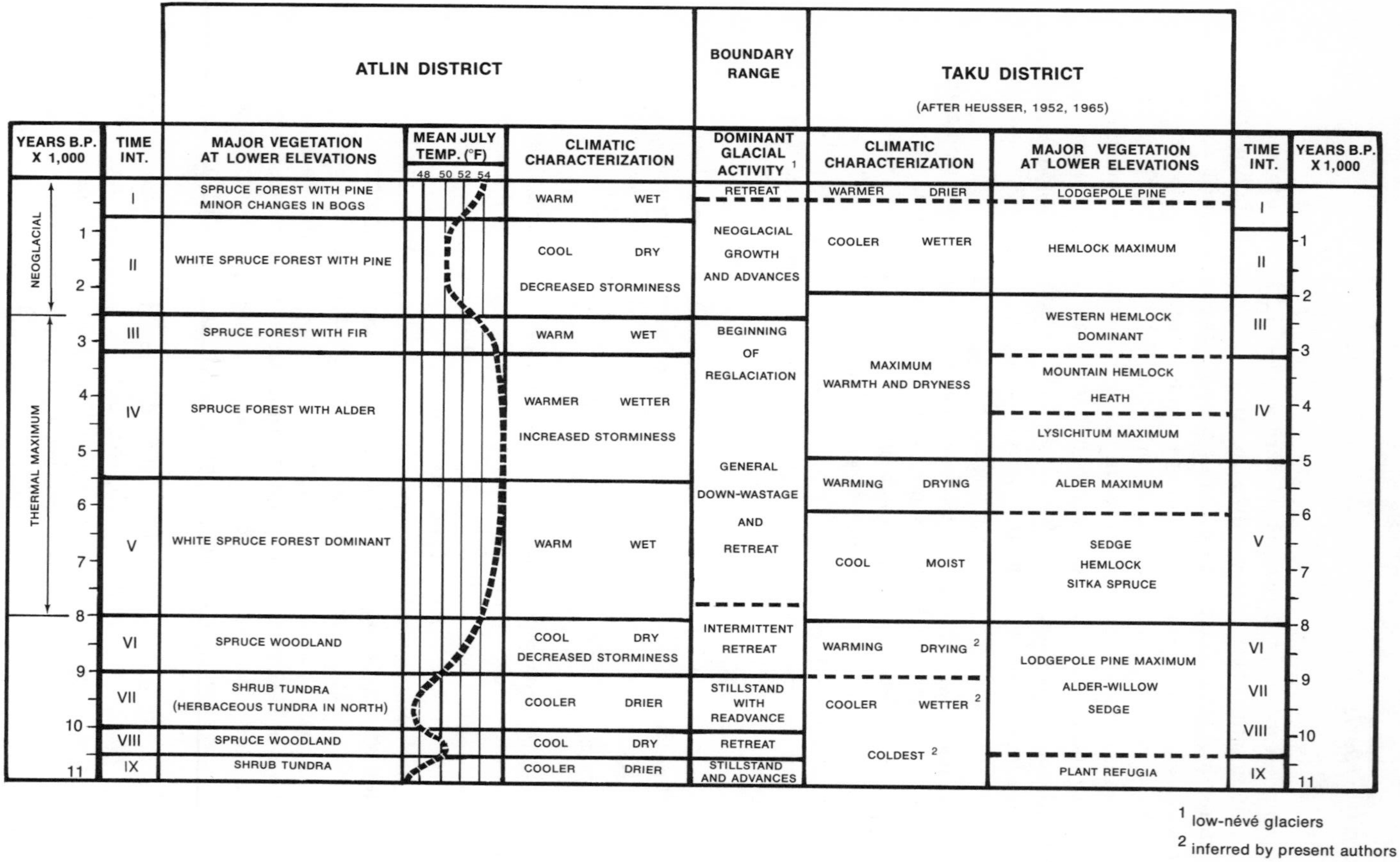

FIG. 10. Late Wisconsinan and Holocene glaciobotanical chronology in the Atlin and Taku Districts, Canada-Alaska.

upper blue-gray till in the Juneau area (Miller, 1956). In terms of Anderson's interpretation, the lower Holocene-Wisconsinan boundary would rest at or before 10,500 years BP and represent the beginning of pre-Boreal or Early Postglacial time. With Miller's interpretation, this boundary would more precisely rest at 9,500 to 10,000 years BP. More recent radiocarbon dates in the Atlin region may favor the latter view. For example, the broad upland glaciers at the head of tributary valleys in the region between Gladys, Surprise, and MacDonald Lakes (fig. 2) are now known to have begun major downwasting and retreating some 9,000 to 10,000 years ago. This is shown in bogs well within areas of late-Wisconsinan ice cover at the 3,000 to 3,500-foot level where peat was developing as early as 9,800 to 8,800 years BP. The best evidence is radiocarbon dating of heath twigs from the base of frost mounds and palsas in bogs of the upper Fourth of July Creek Valley (figs. 6b and 7), which gives dates of $8,050 \pm 430$ C-14 years BP and $9,315 \pm 540$ C-14 years BP (Geochron, 1972).

In this the Holocene is considered to represent only that time since onset of the final major deglaciation, at least in a formerly glaciated region. In a periglacial or nonglacial region this definition would include the interval since culmination of the last large-scale fluvial or pluvial change. This interpretation of the Holocene can imply different lengths of time for some regions, but it would appear to be more significant as a regional chronological unit than the somewhat arbitrary time span of 14,500-14,000 years BP considered by Mercer (1972) as comprising post-Wisconsinan time "since global temperature began to rise toward interglacial levels."

Time Interval IX, ca. 11,000 to 10,500 years BP. This interval represents the final stage of large-scale Wisconsinan glaciation in the Taku-Atlin region, establishing the major outermost moraine complexes within the peripheral distributary valleys of the Coast Range. In the Atlin sector, presumably this was the end-stage at the embankment moraines which today are crossed by the Alaska Highway at the northern end of Little Atlin Lake (fig. 2). In the Taku District, it was represented by the final laying down of older surface tills in Gastineau Channel and Lynn Canal (fig. 1). Where these tills lie above the highest marine terraces they are somewhat stained and slightly weathered. Where exposed in the lower fiord areas, just above present sea level, they are overlain by thin unweathered blue-gray till (Valders ?) which was laid down probably in Time Interval VIII, as discussed above.

In the Atlin area, the pitted outwash of the Moose Bones Bog area (fig. 7) and the knob and kettle topography and gravel terraces in the White Mountain-Squanga Lake region were formed at this time. The Mile 16,

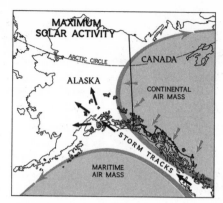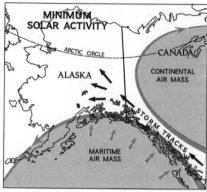

FIG. 11. Idealized storm-track relationships, showing shifted positions of the Arctic Front between opposing pressure cells on the North Pacific Coast at times of maximum versus minimum solar energy (after Miller, 1973).

Mile 47, and Mile 52 bog sites were still covered by ice, but the Wilson Creek and Jasper Creek bog locations had become exposed by glacial thinning during this transition time into the Holocene.

As the palynological record shows, vegetation in the vicinity of these bogs was shrub tundra, indicating mean July temperatures of 46° to 48° F. and a mean annual precipitation of probably less than 8 inches per year. The climatic character was cooler and drier than in any subsequent interval (although a short comparable interval also developed during period VII as previously noted). There was a cooler and moister counterpart along the Alaskan coast, at which time the inland fiords, including Lynn Canal, were largely filled with ice. The morphogenetic character of this glaciation would be equivalent to the Intermediate Mountain Ice Sheet Phase (Miller, 1964). From this and the evidence of glaciated cirques within 300 feet of present sea level (Miller, 1961), it is concluded that freezing levels were right down at tide water and that the Arctic Front had dominant inland orientation. At this time its mean position likely oscillated well over into the Atlin region.

Interval IX as depicted in figure 10 is also presumed to represent only part of a larger interval extending back into the Wisconsinan Age of the Pleistocene Epoch. It may be comparable to the tail end of the Port Huron maximum of the American mid-continent chronology and to the younger Dryas (Pollen Zone 1c) of the European chronology. Distinct evidence of an ameliorated Two Creeks (Allerod) intraglacial following this stage in the Atlin area, with corresponding milder conditions in the Taku (coastal) areas, is not clear, although this may be represented by the conditions cited for Time Interval VIII. Therefore, assuming Interval IX to represent only the last 500 years or so of a final major Wisconsinan glaciation, it could be related to the Late Glacial Phase III suggested by Heusser in his palyno-

logical study of the North Pacific maritime region and to the Inklin stage
of late Wisconsinan glaciation delineated by Miller (1956, 1972a) from
studies of the Pleistocene stratigraphy in the Taku District.

Discussion

The general sequence of biogeoclimatological subdivisions of the late
Wisconsinan and Holocene Epochs for the North Pacific region, which has
been described, shares some similarity to sequences interpreted from other
regions in the Pacific Cordillera. The best synchroneity is found in specific
time intervals of this chronology when it is applied solely to maritime regions west and southwest of the coast mountains and as far south as Washington State (Heusser, 1965). It differs, however, in interpretation of the
climatic character in corresponding time intervals between coastal and inland sectors in this study, specifically between the maritime and continental
flanks of the Alaska-Canada Boundary Range. Although in some cases the
subdivision boundaries are more or less contemporaneous, in others they
are not. Further understanding of these differences will come from more
detailed comparative studies of Pleistocene and Holocene stratigraphy on
both flanks of this broad across-range region. These studies should be supplemented by further bog profiles using the palynological method, including high elevation bogs in tributary valleys in each district.

The key to these regional interpretations and to the development of
more precise teleconnectional evidence lies in an important fact brought
forth by the investigations to date. This is that the development of cool and
moist conditions in the Alaskan coastal zone were paralleled by development of approximately contemporaneous cool and slightly drier climatic
conditions in the Northern British Columbia-Yukon interior. Similarly, the
development of warm and relatively drier oceanic climatic conditions on
the coast appear to have prevailed at times when the interior areas experienced a trend toward relatively warmer and wetter climates.

The explanation of these paradoxical secular trends lies in detailed
comparison of the behavior of existing glaciers on opposite flanks of the
range. The following conclusions derived from our study of glaciological
regimes covering the past several centuries on the Juneau Icefield are noted
for clarification.

The chief factors causing the fluctuations of modern glaciers on the
Boundary Range are: (1) The cyclic changes in level of maximum snowfall;
(2) the periodic shifting of storm tracks; and (3) the possible effects of
changing temperature conditions within the ice. Taken in conjunction with

known meteorological trends at weather stations on the north Pacific Coast, these interpretations are in agreement with the usual conditions associated with deglaciation in high latitudes, i.e., "warmer and wetter" conditions (v. fig. 10, Time Interval I) accompanying a rise in temperature and "warmer and drier" conditions typifying the middle latitudes (v. Willett in Shapley, 1953, p. 63). In contrast, conditions causing intense glaciation are generally colder and wetter (again v. fig. 10, Time Intervals VII and IX). Thus over the past two centuries the general tendency in the Boundary Range has been toward deglaciation in the high latitude sense.

A pattern of "warmer and drier" conditions in the last 200 years, and "cooler and wetter" conditions in the preceding 1,700 years, has been suggested by the pollen studies of Heusser (1952) in muskeg peat bogs of southeastern Alaska. Such is the condition expected in middle latitudes. In broad consideration, this apparent difference between sea-level areas and the presently glaciated sectors of the highland as well as in the interior region is probably intimately connected with secular shifts in storm belts. (The problem as to whether more or less precipitation occurs at any one locality is, of course, a matter for special study and one which must always be integrated into the regional picture.) We recognize the difficulties involved in a theoretical discussion without use of regional aerological data and also that there are other likely climatological aspects which have not been considered. Nevertheless, the general trend of changes indicated does agree with the field data we have been gathering concerning ice fluctuations in the névé areas.

Thus it is believed that the explanation of differences shown in the climatological characterization in the chronology of deglaciated terrain on opposite flanks of the Boundary Range relates to sensitive shifts of the Arctic Front across the range during late Pleistocene and Holocene time and to concomitant vertical changes in freezing levels (levels of maximum snowfall). The nature of short-term shifts has been considered in our glaciological reports to involve 80- and possibly 180-, 940-, and 2,400-2,600-year recurrences (Miller, 1973), p. 182). But the geological and palynological techniques and evidence upon which the chronology in figure 10 is based are too imprecise to permit defensible interpretation of such "cyclicity" in this chart. Although there is a hint of approximately 1,000- and 2,500-year interval spacings and a further implication that the pre-Neoglacial part of the Holocene might represent an 8,000 to 10,000 year "interglacial," this aspect is too tenuous for further evaluation at this time.

The interpretation of opposing climatic characteristics and their explanation still finds validity when referenced to the regime changes of modern glaciers in the transitional zone of the Juneau Icefield during the Little Ice Age. The results of our glaciological research in this region have, therefore, served usefully to guide interpretation of the complex paleo-climatic correlations in the deglaciated sectors discussed. Pertinent glaciological investigations supported by the National Geographic Society have also been documented in preceding reports of the Alaskan Glacier Commemorative Project presented in this research series.

REFERENCES

ANDERSON, JAMES H.
[1970]. A geobotanical study in the Atlin region in northwestern British Columbia and south central Yukon Territory, 380 pp. (Unpublished Ph.D. thesis, Michigan State University.)

ANDERSON, JAMES H., and MILLER, MAYNARD M.
[1972]. Palynological and glaciological interpretations of Holocene climatic environments on the continental flank of the Northern Boundary Range. Proc. Arctic and Mountain Environments Symposium, Michigan State University, April 1972. (In press.)

BESCHEL, ROLAND E., and EGAN, CHRISTOPHER P.
1965. Geobotanical investigations of a 16th-century moraine on the Bucher Glacier, Juneau Icefield, Alaska. Proc. 16th Alaska Sci. Conf., AAAS, pp. 114-115.

CROSS, AUREAL T.
1968. Mendenhall Glacier buried forest, Alaska. 19th Alaska Sci. Conf., AAAS, Whitehorse, Yukon Territory, August 1968. (Abstract.)

GEOCHRON
1972. Radiocarbon dates on upper Fourth of July Creek, British Columbia. Palsa samples nos. GX2694 and GX2695, August 1972.

HANSON, GEORGE
1932. Varved clays of Tide Lake, British Columbia. Trans. Roy. Soc. Canada, vol. 26, sect. 4, pp. 335-339.

HEUSSER, CALVIN J.
1952. Pollen profiles from southeast Alaska. Ecol. Monogr., vol. 22, pp. 331-352.
1953. Radiocarbon dating of the Thermal Maximum in S.E. Alaska. Ecology, vol. 34, no. 3, pp. 637-640.
1960. Late-Pleistocene environments of North Pacific North America. Amer. Geogr. Soc. Spec. Publ. no. 35, 308 pp., illus.
1965. A Pleistocene phytogeographical sketch of the Pacific Northwest and Alaska. Pp. 469-483 *in* "The Quaternary of the United States," 922 pp., illus. H. E. Wright, Jr., and David G. Frey, eds. Princeton University Press.

HEUSSER, CALVIN J., and MARCUS, MELVIN G.
    1964. Historical variations of Lemon Creek Glacier, Alaska, and their relation-
        ship to the climatic record.   Journ. Glaciol., vol. 5, no. 37, pp. 77-86,
        illus.
KONECNY, GOTTFRIED; GLOSS, GERHARD; and KNASOVICKY, LAZLO
    [1972]. A new large-scale terrestrial photogrammetric map of the Taku Glacier.
        Proc. Arctic and Mountain Environments Symposium, Michigan State
        University, April 1972. (In press.)
KULP, J. LAURENCE; FEELY, HERBERT W.; and TRYON, LANSING E.
    1951. Lamont natural carbon measurements, I.   Science, vol. 114, no. 2970,
        pp. 565-568.
LAWRENCE, DONALD B.
    1950. Glacier fluctuation for six centuries in southeastern Alaska and its re-
        lation to solar activity.   Geogr. Rev., vol. 40, no. 2, pp. 191-223, illus.
LAWRENCE, DONALD B., and ELSON, JOHN A.
    1953. Periodicity of deglaciation in North America since the Late Wisconsin
        maximum.   Geogr. Annaler, vol. 35, pp. 83-104, illus.
MERCER, JOHN H.
    1972. The Lower Boundary of the Holocene.   Quaternary Res., vol. 2, no. 1,
        pp. 15-24.
MILLER, MAYNARD M.
    1956. Contributions to the glacial geology and glaciology of the Juneau Ice-
        field, S.E. Alaska, 800 pp., illus.   U. S. Office of Naval Research Re-
        port, Project ONR-83001. (Ph.D. thesis, University of Cambridge,
        England.)
    1961. A distribution study of abandoned cirques in the Alaska-Canada Boun-
        dary Range.   Pp. 831-847 *in* "Geology of the Arctic." University of
        Toronto Press.
    1963. Taku Glacier evaluation study (some engineering implications of gla-
        ciology), 200 pp., illus.   State of Alaska Department of Highways and
        U. S. Department of Commerce, Bureau of Public Roads.
    1964. Morphogenetic classification of Pleistocene glaciations in the Alaska-
        Canada Boundary Range.   Proc. Amer. Philos. Soc., vol. 108, no. 3,
        pp. 247-256.
    1967. Alaska's mighty rivers of ice.   Nat. Geogr. Mag., vol. 131, no. 2, pp.
        195-217, illus.
    1969. The Alaska Glacier Commemorative Project, Phase I.   Nat. Geogr. Soc.
        Res. Rpts., 1964 Projects, pp. 135-152, illus.
    1970. 1946-1962 survey of the regional pattern of Alaska glacier variations.
        Nat. Geogr. Soc. Res. Rpts., 1961-1962 Projects, pp. 167-189, illus.
    1971. The Alaskan Glacier Commemorative Project, Phase II.   Nat. Geogr.
        Soc. Res. Rpts., 1965 Projects, pp. 181-194, illus.
    1972a. Pleistocene stratigraphy of the Taku-Atlin District, Alaska-Canada
        Boundary Range.   Michigan Acad. Sci., Arts, Letters, March 1972.
    1972b. A principles study of factors affecting the hydrological balance of the
        Lemon Glacier system and adjacent sectors of the Juneau Icefield, S.E.

Alaska, 1965-69, 210 pp. illus.   U. S. Office of Water Resources Report (Project B-002-Mich.).   Tech. Rpt. 33, Institute of Water Research, Michigan State University, in cooperation with the Foundation for Glacier and Environmental Research.

1973. Alaskan Glacier Commemorative Project, Phase III, 1966: A total systems study of climate-glacier relationships and the stress instability of ice.   Nat. Geogr. Soc. Res. Rpts., 1966 Projects, pp. 157-196, illus.

MILLER, MAYNARD M.; EGAN, CHRISTOPHER P.; and BESCHEL, ROLAND E.

1968. Neoglacial climatic chronology from recent radiocarbon and dendrochronological dates in the Alaskan Panhandle.   19th Alaska Sci. Conf., AAAS, Whitehorse, Yukon Territory, August 1968. (Abstract.)

PINCHAK, A. C.

[1972]. Observations of glacier meltwater streams on the Gilkey and Vaughan Lewis Glaciers, Alaska.   Proc. Arctic and Mountain Environments Symposium, Michigan State University, April 1972. (In press.)

PINCHAK, A. C., and LOKEY, W. M.

[1972]. Seasonal and meteorological factors affecting serac avalanching in the Vaughan Lewis Icefall, Alaska.   Proc. Arctic and Mountain Environments Symposium, Michigan State University, April 1972. (In press.)

SHAPLEY, HARLOW

1953. Climatic change. 318 pp. illus.   Harvard University Press.

TALLMAN, A. M.

[1972]. Frost mound investigations in the Atlin region, northern British Columbia, using electrical resistivity.   Proc. Arctic and Mountain Environments Symposium, Michigan State University, April 1972. (In press.)

TARR, RALPH S., and MARTIN, LAWRENCE

1914. Alaskan glacier studies, 498 pp., illus.   National Geographic Society.

ZENONE, C.; MILLER, M.; and HELMERS, A. E.

[1972]. Glacio-hydrology and the Jökulhlaup phenomena in Juneau Icefield glaciers, Alaska.   Proc. Arctic and Mountain Environments Symposium, Michigan State University, April 1972. (In press.)

MAYNARD M. MILLER
JAMES H. ANDERSON

Ethnological Survey of Khorasan Kurds

Principal Investigator: Robert E. Peck, Polytechnic of Central London, London, England.

Grant No. 652:   For a study of the Khorasan Kurds, Iran.

[Editor's Note: The account that follows is abstracted from a preliminary report transmitted to the National Geographic Society on January 1, 1969, by Dr. Peck, who was then associated with the Free University of Berlin. Subsequent efforts have failed to elicit replies to correspondence with him in an effort to obtain a later report on the work done under this grant that would cover the concluding stages of the research, and he has not reviewed the final draft of what follows.]

"Kurdistan" is the ethnographic designation for that region in which Kurds constitute the majority of the population. It corresponds approximately to the area of the Zagros Mountains along the western border of Iran. The Kurdish population in this region is estimated at between 5 and 6 million and is distributed between Iran, Iraq, Turkey, Syria, and the USSR. The Kurds may be generally described as a mountain people. They speak an Iranian (Indo-Germanic) language, are for the most part Sunni Moslems, and can be distinguished somatically from the surrounding peoples (Turks, Arabs, and Persians). In spite of their central position in the relatively well-investigated Middle East, there are but few historical or ethnological studies dealing with the Kurds.

Topography. My main activity in the present study necessarily was geographic and demographic rather than ethnographic, primarily because of the considerable transportation difficulties encountered and the unreliability of existing maps of the area. The Volkswagen I took with me was inadequate for all but the main roads. Because travel by horse, which I had originally intended, was found far too slow and uncertain, I was forced to buy a jeep. Even by jeep, however, my range of operation was limited, since I was restricted to main and secondary roads, which are few in number and in very poor condition. The few times I was forced to strike out across roadless tracts were nerve-wracking as well as time-consuming, not to mention punishment to the vehicle. Many villages, however, are not located directly on the roads but are hidden off in the hills, accessible only by animal or on foot and with the help of a guide.

In addition to these problems, the lack of adequate maps made it virtually impossible to plan trips in advance. I found that even the routes of the main highways were in error on the most recent U. S. and British maps I had of this region. Only a fraction of the existing villages are represented, usually spelled in a manner that leaves the user to guess what could be meant. Main truck and gendarmery routes are seldom included, while the roads that are indicated may turn out to be donkey trails leading up the face of a cliff. Not even the topographical data can be trusted; for instance, most maps show a defile cutting through the Allahu-Akbar Mountains between Kapkan and Deregaz. Actually, however, it is one of the highest and steepest mountain passes in the vicinity. Consequently, I seldom had any choice but to embark in the desired direction and hope that the road would not dead-end into a mountainside or a river gorge.

Schematically, the research area (i.e., that region in which Kurdish settlements occur) may be thought of as quartered by the main east-west and north-south routes, and bordered on the north and south by the Soviet frontier and the Tehran-Sabzewar-Meshed railway line, respectively. Hence it is considerably larger than I had originally anticipated.

The east-west road is at present the main international artery between Iran and Afghanistan. Coming from Meshed, it goes through the center of a wide and well-developed valley, the eastern part draining to the Kashaf-Rud or Meshed River, the western part to the Attrak. It passes through Quchan, Shirvan, and Bujnurd, each of which is a "shahr" or county seat. Between the two last-mentioned towns the valley narrows to a defile and the river turns off to the northwest, running into the Gorgan Plain and emptying into the Caspian. The road continues in an easterly direction, passing through the Semulghan Valley and leaving the research area at Dasht, the head of the Gorgan defile.

Parallel to this road in the north and extending along the Turkmenian border is the Kopet-Dagh range, consisting of a series of ridges running approximately southeast to northwest. The highest elevation in the west is around 9,800 feet and in the east around 10,000 (according to U. S. Air Force maps). The valley towns lie at between 3,000 and 4,000 feet.

To the south of the road another parallel range separates the Attrak Valley from those of Nishapur, Isfarain, and Juvain. The eastward extension of the Elburz range, it consists of the Alla-Dagh, Shah Jehan, and Binalud Mountains, with peak elevations of over 10,000 feet. Between the latter two runs the only major north-south road, coming from Sultanabad in the south to Quehan and continuing across the northern mountains to Bajgiran on the Soviet frontier, and thence to Ashkhabad. The distance between Meshed and Dasht is about 400 kilometers; between Sultanabad and Bajgiran about 200.

Ethnic Overview. The ethnic situation is, as expected, extremely heterogeneous, the Kurds constituting only one of several different language groups. The earliest inhabitants appear to have been the Persians, and I found no evidence of a later Persian migration to the area. Probably at about the time of the Mongol invasions the region was occupied by the Turks, primarily of the Geraili tribe. When Persians and Turks proved unable to resist the incursions of the Uzbeks from the north, Kurdish tribes (according to tradition the Shadillu, Zafaranlu, Kaiwanlu, and Amarlu) were brought from the Turkish border by Shah Abbas the Great. Later, Turkoman tribes from central Asia, succeeding the Uzbeks, moved into the desert north of Khorassan, where they became the adversaries of the Kurds in a state of permanent border warfare. Some Turkoman groups also moved into Iranian territory, seeking the protection of and becoming allied with the Kurds. Later Turkoman migrations took place after the Russian conquest of Transcaspia and after the Russian Revolution.

In addition to those four major groups, northern Khorassan is populated also by a scattering of Arabs, Mongol Barbaris, Sistanis, and, farther south, Baluchis and Timuris.

The remarkable thing about this is not the multiplicity of origin, the natural result of turbulent history, but the fact that the area has not turned into a "melting pot." On the contrary, each group has retained its own ethnic identity. People are able to designate themselves without hesitation as Kurd, Turk, Persian, etc. Even though bi- and polylinguality are the rule, at least among men, there are no signs of linguistic synthesis. Just as surprising is the lack of ethnic sub- or superordination; neither in a tangible nor intangible sense does any group appear to enjoy greater or lesser prestige than the others. This is the case in spite of the fact that villages of different origin have coexisted for centuries in closest proximity, that there are no religious or social barriers to intermarriage, and that mixed villages are not unusual. It is a moot question how long this situation will continue, but it seems significant that it has existed this long.

In terms of general culture, on the other hand, there is a prevailing similarity, apparently the result of uniform economic and ecological influences. I have not yet been able to establish any basic differences in the customs, thought, or way of life between the majority of Kurds, Turks, and Persians.

Music. Of the various groups here represented the Kurds appear to be by far the most musically inclined. Radio Meshed brings a 30-minute program of Kurdish folk music each evening, the melodies and style of which bear little resemblance to those of Kurdistan or other parts of Iran, and are apparently peculiar to this area. Kurdish villages without at least one musician are extremely rare, and radios and record players are present in respectable numbers. This is not the case, for instance, among the majority of Turks, who are likely to rely on their Kurdish neighbors for their musical needs, e.g., at weddings and celebrations.

There are, moreover, some 10 or more Kurdish villages specializing in music. These have well-known "orchestras" of folk-dance groups, and provide much of the entertainment in their respective vicinities.

The standard dance, performed principally at weddings and circumcision ceremonies, is round, with no specified number of dancers. There are no singing, physical contact, or use of props (e.g., handkerchiefs) on the part of the dancers. The same dances are performed by men and women, although not mixed, and there is considerable hand-clapping and finger-snapping.

The standard musical instruments are the dohtar (a two-stringed, long-necked lute), the qushma (a whistlelike instrument, made of wing-bone), the frame drum, and the flute. In larger and/or more urban groups the oboe, violin, and bass drum may also be found.

The songs apparently do not display the variety of type and repertoire to be found in Kurdistan proper. Choral music is unknown, and virtually all songs are either religious or romantic in theme. They are usually sung by a single male vocalist, and although female singing occurs among the nomads, it is rare in the villages. It is possible for two women to sing together, but it would be considered effeminate for men to do so.

Until more information on the music of the other ethnic groups is collected, however, it will not be possible to say to what extent music actually constitutes a distinguishing characteristic of the Kurdish population. The melodies of all groups appear to be quite similar, and it is conceivable that the only basic difference involved is the language of the respective lyrics.

Language. With respect to the linguistic phase I have been extremely fortunate, inasmuch as the research done nearly 50 years ago by W. Ivanow has proved as valid as if it had been done today. All my studies so far have served only to verify Ivanow's findings and analysis. It is still necessary, however, to supplement the rather short vocabulary presented by him. Comparison of local words with the two recently published Kurdish dictionaries seems to confirm Ivanow's statement that this dialect belongs to the northwestern group.

There is still no universally accepted orthography for the transcription of Kurdish dialects, neither with Latin nor with Arabic symbols. Most systems so far, including that of Bedr Khan, widely used in Turkish Kurdistan, are generally too complicated or peculiar to be easily read without preliminary instruction. At the risk of contributing to this anarchy, therefore, I decided to employ my own system, which I hope will faithfully represent the phonetics and also be generally intelligible.

Social Organization. This has proved so far to be the most difficult area of study, since the traditional group, the taife, has, except among the nomads, ceased to exist as a functional unit. It is still possible to collect a large number of taife names, but it seems unlikely that these could be of use either as ethnogeographic categories or for historical reconstructions. Since evidently there are no great regional differences within the Kurdish community, it may best be regarded as a single unit. The same names have cropped up in widely dispersed areas, and in former times the taife was probably always the basic unit, and the so-called tribe, or il, was likely not a closed supra-organization but an open and flexible confederation of taifes under the leadership of the strongest. But I still have much checking to do before this is conclusive.

Of the four traditional tribes, only the Shadillu have retained their prominence to the present day. This is the family name of some greater and lesser aristocrats in the Bujnurd area, all tracing descent from the last great Kurdish chief, Yar Mohammad Khan, who ruled all of western Korassan and large parts of Mazanderan province during the latter part of the last century. He had upward of 30 wives and was extremely prolific. His most prominent sons were given a mass execution by Shah Reza the Great in the 1920's, and his most prominent grandsons (especially Khonlar Khan, Hushang Khan, Khosro Khan, and Firuz Khan) were my hosts and best informants.

Khonlar Khan, Bujnurd representative to the Iranian parliament, placed his summer house at my disposal, references to which I later discovered in the literature. I quote two extracts, the first from Fraser (1838, pp. 234-235), the second from Baker (1876, p. 284):

> Jaffer Koolee asked me to ride with him out to a garden about three miles distant, to spend the day in greater comfort than the heat of the dusty town would permit. It was a rambling wilderness of apricot, peach, and apple trees, and vines half smothered in grass and weeds; but was pleasant from its freshness and shade. There was a summer-house in the centre, in which played a fountain and cascade . . . (July 11, 1833.)

> * * * * *

> We were still about four miles distant (from Boojnoord), when we were met by an escort of two hundred men, headed by a chief; and it was notified that a house had been prepared for us in the town, and also one outside, and that we could occupy whichever we liked. Choosing the latter, we were taken to a summer palace which had been occupied by the Shah on his visit here. It was a handsome building standing in a large garden, but we soon discovered that it would be very cold for this season of the year. (November 6, 1873.)

In the fall of 1968 it was just as cold, and later I moved quarters into town.

The garden and residence mentioned are directly adjacent to a Kurdish village named Aliabad, which is, incidentally, one of the music villages referred to above. It is also one of the most picturesque and tradition-conscious villages I anywhere encountered. The house is built as a duplex, no doubt originally intended for the separation of the sexes. One half was occupied by me, the other by the village headman and his family, affording me a chance to observe domestic life at fairly close range. I also had the opportunity to be present at several weddings, and on one occasion my services were enlisted to chauffeur the bride from a distant mountain village.

With Aliabad as a base, I was able to make a number of trips in the Bujnurd and Shirvan regions during the fall months.

Further Plans for the Study. My main plan was to complete a comprehensive map of the ethnic distribution of northern Khorassan. It is possible that such a study has already been made—by the Soviets during their occupation of the area in World War II—but I know of no reliable and detailed publications by them to date. In any case such a study is a necessary preliminary to any deeper research into the anthropology of the region. Especially in view of the cartographic situation, this is a tedious job, involving the cataloging and plotting of several thousand individual villages.

Second, I wished to concentrate as much as possible on the nomadic groups. Nomads are characterized by their archconservatism, and they doubtless represent the original Kurdish culture at its purest. During the summer they are in the mountains (mainly the Alla-Dagh and Binalud ranges) and are extremely inaccessible. I was able, however, to make contact with a number of them during the fall migrations. Their winter areas are in the northern part of the Gorgan plain (Turkoman desert), the low country south of Sabzewar (Dasht-i-Iaqi), and the Deregaz plain—all but the last of which being outside the research area proper—and it was my intention to work among them in these places.

REFERENCES

BAKER, VALENTINE
    1876. Clouds in the East: Travels and adventures in the Perso-Turkoman frontier, 376 pp., illus. London.
FRASER, JAMES BAILLIE
    1838. A winter's journey, (TÂtar) from Constantinople to Tehran, vol. 2, 511 pp. London.

ROBERT E. PECK

Exploration of a 16th-century Bahaman Shipwreck

Principal Investigator: Mendel L. Peterson, National Museum of History and Technology, Smithsonian Institution, Washington, D. C.

Grant No. 605:   For exploration and analysis of a 16th-century shipwreck in the Central Bahamas.

Even though the Bahama Islands lie alongside the two major routes by which shipping left the Caribbean Basin, the Spanish failed to settle and fortify them. After first touching here, Columbus sailed to the south and never returned to explore them further. This remained the task of later Spanish explorers and the slave raiders who largely depopulated the archipelago in the first years of Spanish mining and farming activity in Santo Domingo. The islands became a geographical backwater and were deserted. Pirates and privateers moved into the void bent on attacking the ships carrying the growing riches that the Spanish were exporting from America through the Old Bahama Channel along the northern coast of Santo Domingo and later the route up the Florida Straits. The hundreds of small inlets, ideally suited to the swift shallow-draft vessels of sea marauders, offered hiding places for ships and men secure from the deep-draft Spanish vessels of war. As the pirating problem increased, the Spanish sporadically sent smaller armed ships and galleys into the islands to clean out the enemy, but these attempts were like trying to remove a widespread infection with a scalpel. When the French Huguenots established a fort on the Florida coast alongside the Florida Channel, the Spanish moved swiftly to destroy this threat to their life line of treasure as the enemy here was concentrated and could be dealt with. This was not true of the Bahamas, and the islands continued for two centuries as a haven for sea robbers.

Discovery of the Wreck Site

In the fall of 1965 three Americans, Robert Wilkie, Jack Robinson, and Clint Hinchman, were skin diving and spear fishing several hundred yards off the northwestern coast of Highborn Cay, one of the northern keys of the Exuma chain. After being over the site for some time, they noticed strange shapes on the bottom about 20 feet below them. An examination proved

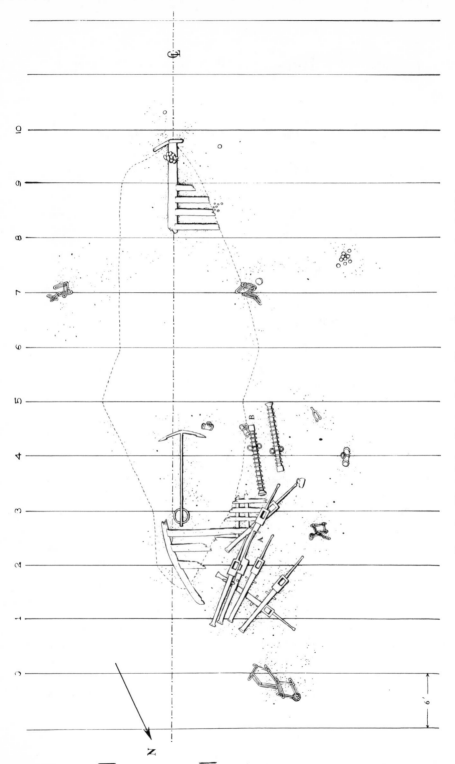

FIG. 1. Plan of the shipwreck site. Lines represent intervals of 6 feet.

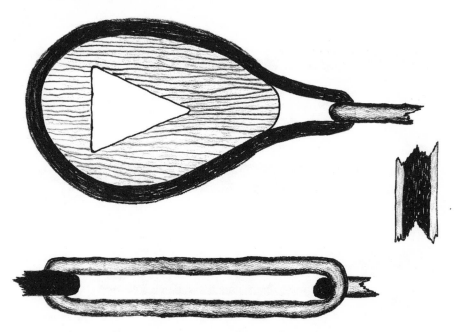

FIG. 2. *Top,* deadeye, soft wood in wrought-iron bracket; length of bracket 12 inches, width 6½ inches. *Bottom,* chain plate link, wrought-iron, length 11¼ inches.

these shapes to be coral- and sand-encrusted cannon. Scattered about the site were two comparatively large guns, several smaller guns of two sizes, and several smaller objects shaped like beer mugs. A well-camouflaged pile of ballast stone formed a small rounded reef down the center of the area, and an encrusted anchor lay on the pile at one end (fig. 1). Other slender shapes, like iron bolts and chain links, were seen (figs. 2, 3). To attempt to identify the find the discoverers communicated with me and furnished pictures of the site. Meanwhile, a license to explore the site was requested of the Government of the Bahamas by the owner of Highborn Cay, William Wickoff Smith, who has an aloe plantation and extraction plant on the island. This license was granted in March 1966.

Preliminary Investigation of the Site

Two months later I went to the site to work with the discoverers on a preliminary exploration in an attempt to estimate the age of the wreck and evaluate the historical significance of the discovery.

The location of the site indicated that the ship had been blown or had

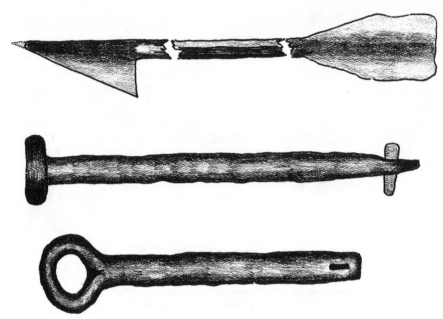

FIG. 3. *Top,* wrought-iron harpoon, length 6 feet, width 3¾ inches. *Middle,* wrought-iron keyed bolt (lengths varied from 10 to 18 inches). *Bottom,* wrought-iron eye bolt to secure chain plate to hull, length 11¾ inches.

FIG. 4. Wrought-iron anchor recovered from area of ballast pile; length 9 feet 10 inches.

sailed up Exuma Sound probably after having come through the Old Bahama Channel and Crooked Island Passage. Evidence indicated that the ship had been in trouble. The ordnance appeared to have been stowed on the ballast before the sinking to lower the center of gravity of the ship. Two anchors, found by the discoverers about 150 yards off one end of the ballast pile toward the northwest, were in the position they would have had if dropped in anchoring. This fact is very good evidence that the ship dropped her anchors, rode back on the cables, and then sank sometime later while at anchor. One of the anchors weighed about 400 pounds, the other 600-700 pounds. The anchor on the ballast pile weighed about 400 and appeared to be the matching bower anchor found ahead of the site (figs. 4, 5). The fact that the heavier anchor had been rigged and one of the bowers stowed would indicate the ship had been in trouble and that the crew had rigged one of the heavier sheet anchors before the vessel sank.

It is possible that the wreck was the result of a hurricane. The position, if we assume that the ship came up the Exuma Passage blown by a storm, would indicate the wind had shifted 180°, sinking the ship as it rode at anchor. This wind pattern is, of course, a common feature of hurricanes.

A detailed examination of the surface of the site, without any disturbing of the objects observed, revealed the guns and anchor as shown in preliminary photographs; chain plates were in a position that indicated they had fallen from the hull of the vessel as it disintegrated under water. A rudder pintle alongside the main axis of the deposit of ballast suggested that the rudder had broken away and floated toward the bow of the ship before disintegrating. A careful probing around the periphery of the site and at random in the sand bottom surrounding the ballast pile produced a number of lead cannonballs with iron cores (fig. 6). These represented an early form of projectile, which was generally replaced with a cheaper and better cast-iron ball in the 1560's and 1570's. Nails and hull pins of iron were also turned up, and two breech chambers for the swivel guns were brought up for examination and proved to be of a pattern used as late as the 1590's. A single musket ball and an instrument that may have been a scraper for cleaning the bores of the guns were also found.

The encrusted guns were clearly wrought-iron breechloaders. The reinforcing bands of the tubes and the lifting rings on the tubes and chambers of the larger pieces, the lombards (fig. 7), were clearly visible. The smaller pieces had the shape of swivels used throughout the 16th century and referred to in the literature as versos (fig. 8). Swivels of identical type were found on the Tucker Treasure Site, Bermuda, ca. 1594 (Peterson, 1971).

The nature of the wrought-iron lombards and swivels, and, more im-

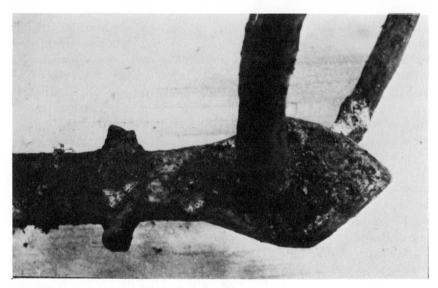

FIG. 5.   Detail of "Gothic" finial of shank of anchor found on the ballast pile.

FIG. 6.   Lead shot with wrought-iron cores for lombards and swivel guns (diameters varied from 1⅜ to 2½ inches).

FIG. 7. Wrought-iron lombards. *Top,* bore 2⅛ inches, length 89 inches. *Bottom,* bore 2 inches, length 94 inches.

portantly, the iron-cored lead balls for them, all indicated a period no later than the 1560's or 1570's. The location of the wreck indicated a sinking at anchor from causes unknown. The size of the ballast pile suggested a ship of some 200 tons, average for small warships in the Western Hemisphere at that period. This evidence fully justified a complete exploration effort, and on return to Washington I applied to the National Geographic Society for a grant to make possible full exploration of the site and collection of the artifacts, which promised to be historically important.

Exploration of the Site, January-May 1967

On receipt of the grant I began immediate preparations for the work. Winter being good diving months in the central Bahamas, work could begin without delay. The discoverers had been making preparations since the fall of 1966, and their foresight in selecting the proper boat and other equipment was a large element in the success of the subsequent exploration. A Chesapeake Bay lugger, purchased the year before, was converted to a div-

FIG. 8. Wrought-iron breech-loading swivel gun carried on the rails of the ship. Over-all length 72¼ inches, bore 2 inches.

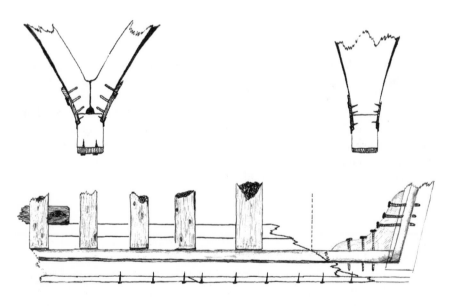

FIG. 9. Reconstruction of ship timbers at sternpost. Length of section shown 11 feet.

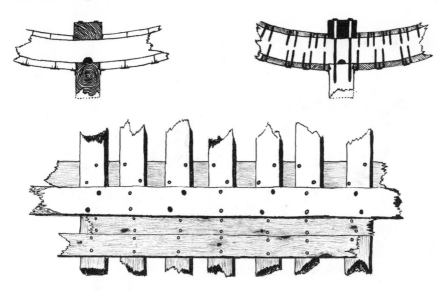

FIG. 10. Reconstruction of timber remains of ship timbers at keel amidships. Length of section shown 10 feet.

ing vessel. Compressors to support the hose, diving gear, and air lifts had been installed and a large lifting boom on the bow refurbished. A diving platform on the starboard side of the boat provided a "grand staircase" from which to enter the water, as opposed to the normal narrow diving ladder that sometimes gets crowded when a shark appears. The diving gear was of the hose type with DESCO and Visonaire masks. In shallow depths this has proved to be the most useful type. With the hose there is no necessity to come to the surface frequently for new bottles of air, and so one can remain down half a working day. In addition, the hose provided a means of pulling oneself to the boat. When the tide conditions were very severe, grapnel anchors were set uptide and the divers were literally anchored on the wreck to perform the work. Overburden was moved with a 4-inch air lift that could be throttled down for fine pumping in the artifact area. These air lifts performed well and were completely satisfactory. Specimens were collected and tagged in nylon net bags as recovered. On-shore pits, lined with concrete, were prepared, and the iron objects were immediately placed in fresh water as they were brought ashore. On the vessel, while we were waiting transport to the base, objects were kept in tubs of fresh water or covered with wet canvas.

Most of the recovery and record work was performed by the discover-

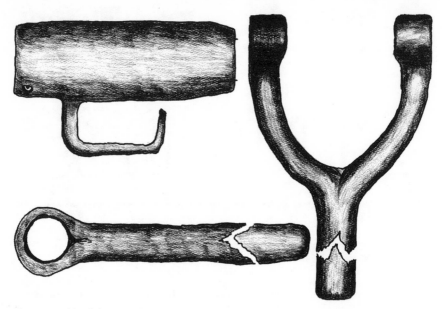

FIG. 11. *Top left*, wrought-iron breech block for swivel gun, length 8½ inches. *Bottom left*, side view of wrought-iron yoke for swivel gun, length 13½ inches. *Right*, front view of wrought-iron yoke for swivel gun, inside width at top 7 inches. Drawings by Edward Tucker.

ers and by Edward Tucker and Robert Canton of Bermuda, veteran underwater explorers who joined the expedition at my request. Mr. Canton, an experienced marine engineer, provided critical service with the equipment, while Mr. Tucker performed vital services in recovery of objects and the preparation of detailed drawings of objects and timber remains illustrated in this report. Messrs. Wilkie, Robinson, and Hinchman all worked very diligently at the task of recovering specimens from the site and preserving them ashore. Mr. Wilkie prepared the sketch of the site from which the accompanying over-all drawing of the site was prepared by Peter Copeland of the Smithsonian exhibits staff. Although the site was comparatively small and the timber remains fragmentary, Mr. Tucker was able to get sufficiently precise vertical and horizontal measurements (figs. 9, 10).

The actual exploratory work was carried on in February, March, and April 1967. The collections recovered are now in the hands of discoverers awaiting final preservation and disposition. Photographic coverage of the operations was made by Otis Imboden, of the National Geographic Society staff, and the participants in the actual exploration.

Nature and Significance of Some Objects Recovered

2 wrought-iron lombards (fig. 7)
11 wrought-iron swivel guns (fig. 8)
4 Lombard breech blocks (fig. 7)
15 swivel-gun breech blocks (fig. 11)
3 anchors (figs. 4, 5)
2 chain plates (fig. 2)
Wrought-iron fittings for swivel guns (fig. 11)
Lead cannon shot with iron core (fig. 6)

The battery of the ship, two long-range lombards and 11 short-range swivels, could indicate a vessel built for pursuit designed to damage the quarry at medium-long range and then to close on the victim and finish it off with a shower of shot from the many swivels on the rails.

The timber remains indicated a lightly built ship with sharp bow and stern built for speed and probably lateen rigged to permit it to sail close to the wind, again evidence indicating a pursuer. The estimated weight of ballast — some 50 tons — indicated a ship of some 200 tons burden, for the period a medium-size vessel with room for a crew of 35-50 men.

The position of the two bower anchors indicates that the ship sank at anchor possibly from a sudden storm or from previously sustained damage from storm or battle. It suggests also the possibility that the ship was scuttled by her crew. The absence of any personal belongings on the ship lends credence to this theory. In short, the evidence indicates the ship to have been a pirate or privateer that sank at anchor from an undetermined cause.

Another theory must be mentioned here. The suggestion has been made that the ship could have been one of two lost by Vicente Yáñez Pinzón in 1500 while returning from an exploration of the northern coast of South America. He is believed to have lost two vessels in the Bahamas, probably in the Exumas, through a violent storm that struck them while at anchor. There is nothing in the collection from the site that would definitely contradict this theory.

The ordnance aboard was as appropriate to 1500 as to 1550. The other materials could date from the earlier period, and the size of the site is compatible with a caravel of the type Pinzón might have used, and a vessel on exploration would probably have been armed and manned much like a pirate ship. A further search of the site and surrounding area, if turning up another similar site, would be a strong case for the identification with Pinzón. A thorough search of the primary records in Seville will also be necessary.

REFERENCE

PETERSON, MENDEL L.
    1971. Bermuda underwater exploration, 1965.   Nat. Geogr. Soc. Res. Rpts.,
        1965 Projects, pp. 203-211, illus.

MENDEL L. PETERSON

Marine Biological Research in Southeastern Polynesia

Principal Investigator: Harald A. Rehder, National Museum of Natural History, Smithsonian Institution, Washington, D. C.

Grant No. 624:   In support of the National Geographic Society–Smithsonian–Bishop Museum Expedition to the Marquesas to investigate the marine biology of the Marquesas and Pitcairn Islands.

For a number of years I have been studying the marine mollusks of Polynesia, that group of islands in the tropical Pacific lying east of Tonga and the Samoan Islands. In an account of an expedition in 1965 to some of these Polynesian islands published in these *Reports* (Rehder, 1971), I outlined briefly the nature of my research program. Basically it is an analytical study of the marine mollusks found living on the reefs and shores and in the lagoons and the deeper offshore waters of the islands and atolls of Polynesia. I use this geographical term to denote the roughly triangular area whose apices are formed by the following islands: at the north, Palmyra Island and Kingman Reef, some 750 miles south of the island of Hawaii; at the east, Easter Island; and at the southwestern apex, the Cook Islands. Within this area lie, besides the last-named group, the Society Islands, the Tuamotus, the Tubuai group, Rapa, the Pitcairn Islands, Easter Island, the Marquesas, and the Line Islands. (Fig. 1.)

The composition of the marine fauna of Polynesia, particularly as represented by the mollusks and crustaceans and possibly other invertebrate groups, is considered by many biologists as having many distinctive characteristics that differentiate it from the faunas of other adjoining and nearby island groups. It has for this reason been considered to represent a distinct biogeographical province within the vast Indo-Pacific region. It is also of particular interest to the marine biologist because of its marginal location, bordered on the east by the deep water between it and South America, and on the south by the deep and cold water stretching down to the Antarctic Continent. Naturally, the fauna of those islands that lie on these borders, such as Easter, Pitcairn, and Rapa, has a special importance to the biogeographer. The goal of my study has been quite simply to test the validity of this distinct biogeographical Polynesian Province, to analyze the

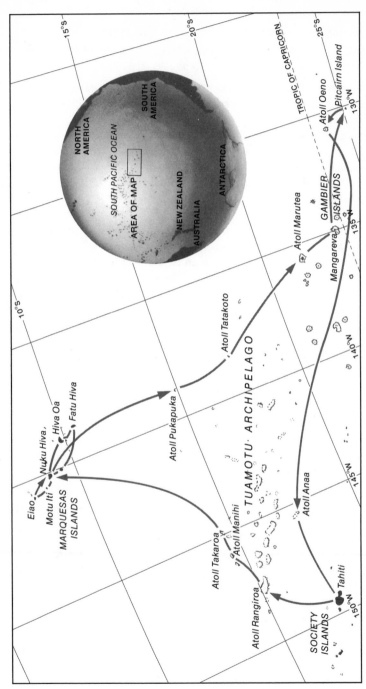

FIG. 1. Map of the area of the Polynesian Province, showing route of the cruise of the *Pele*, 1967.

faunas of the various island groups within this province, and to attempt to determine the factors that underlie any fundamental faunistic differences that my study may reveal.

The objectives outlined above necessitated extensive field work, and in the years between 1957 and 1967 considerable progress was made in gathering specimens and ecological data from the islands within Polynesia and in certain areas adjacent to the Polynesian triangle. Some of this work I carried out personally, and some was done by collectors under my direction and with my encouragement. In addition, of course, use has been made of material present in museums that was gathered by earlier collectors in the areas under study.

In spite of all this exploration there were — and still are — some notable areas of which nothing or very little was known of the marine life. One of these was the Marquesas Islands, lying about 800 miles northeast of Tahiti; another was the islands making up the Pitcairn Group.

Early in 1966 I wrote to the late Mrs. Mary Eleanor King of Honolulu, owner of the motor research vessel *Pele,* and asked if she might be interested in taking the *Pele* to the South Pacific on a scientific collecting expedition. I had been acquainted for some years with Mrs. King, an enthusiastic amateur malacologist and patron of the Bernice P. Bishop Museum of Honolulu. After sponsoring marine biological expeditions to the southern Philippines in 1957 and Western Australia in 1960 she had in 1961 purchased a wooden-hulled 83-foot Coast Guard cutter and had her overhauled and fitted out for deep-water dredging and related biological work. In her Mrs. King did extensive dredging in Hawaiian waters, and in January and February 1964 the *Pele* was in the Sulu Sea in the Philippines on a collecting-dredging expedition.

After considerable correspondence and planning, the time of the expedition was set for the late summer and early fall of 1967. Support was obtained from the National Geographic Society, which thus became co-sponsor with Mrs. King of the expedition. Additional support was given in the form of personnel and equipment by the Smithsonian Institution and the Bernice P. Bishop Museum.

On August 29, 1967, the *Pele* with its crew reached Papeete, Tahiti, from Honolulu. I had arrived in Tahiti some days earlier, and on the 31st I met the rest of our team at the airport. From Honolulu came Mrs. King, Dr. Dennis M. Devaney, marine biologist from Bishop Museum, and Dr. Thomas Richert, practicing physician and amateur malacologist; from Perth, Western Australia, came Dr. Barry Wilson, curator of mollusks at the Western Australian Museum. On September 2 Otis Imboden of the National

Geographic Society staff arrived from Washington, assigned as photographer to the expedition. After a busy five days taking in supplies and making all necessary arrangements we left Papeete on September 5. It was a beautiful afternoon as we went through the pass and headed for the Tuamotus and the Marquesas.

We visited three islands in the Tuamotus—Rangiroa, Manihi, and Takaroa—spending a day or two at each. We did some dredging in the lagoon of Rangiroa but otherwise confined our operations to reef collecting, diving for specimens, and underwater photography.

Two and a half days of rather rough voyaging brought us from Takaroa to Nuku Hiva, which was almost hidden in rain clouds as we first sighted it under overcast skies early in the morning of September 14. As we came closer the clouds partially lifted and we could see the steep cliffs along the coast line and the sharply pinnacled mountains densely covered with vegetation. A little after noon we entered Taiohae Bay; soon the anchor was let down, and we were at last in calm waters. We spent six days dredging and exploring the bays of the eastern half of Nuku Hiva, making 34 dredge hauls in and off four bays in 18 to 82 meters. Ours was the first extensive dredging ever to have been carried out in the Marquesas.

On September 20 we left Nuku Hiva for the northernmost islands of the group, all small and uninhabited. Later that day we reached Motu Iti, three steep-sided rocky islets, the home of many sea birds. Our dredging attempts here were not very successful because of the rough nature of the bottom, and after three hauls we left for Eiao, 53 miles northwest of Nuku Hiva. We reached the island about midnight, and the next day we sailed along the lee side and in our rubber raft investigated one of its several bays but found that the surf made landing too dangerous. We therefore contented ourselves with making dredge hauls, one in the channel between Eiao and the nearby island of Hatutu and another off the northern end of Hatutu.

About 10 miles northeast of Hatutu lie some low islands variously known on the charts and in sailing directions as Îles de Sable, Îles de Corail, or Cotar. As their two French names indicate, very little is known about them, and so from Hatutu we headed for these islands to attempt to determine their true nature. From a distance we saw what looked like a low white sand bar, and on coming closer we found that there is only one low island, about 200 feet long, composed apparently of coral rubble and fragments. Contrary to previous accounts there is, at least now, no vegetation on the island, which we estimated to be no more than 15 feet high. To the east and south stretched shoal water covering a bank that is apparently the easternmost part of the submarine ridge from which Eiao and

FIG. 2. The *Pele* at anchor in Hatiheu Bay, Nuku Hiva, Marquesas.

Hatutu arise and that undoubtedly is the source of the coral debris of which the island is formed. Without question the island's contour must change as a result of storms and high seas in this area. We wanted to explore the island, but the rough sea and shallow water between us and the Îles de Corail made us give up the attempt.

We therefore left for Nuku Hiva, which we reached very early the following morning. Here we made five dredge hauls off two bays on the northwest coast and also did some shore collecting. Early in the afternoon we left for Ua Pou, reaching there 3½ hours later. We spent 2½ days on the western side of the island, making nine dredge hauls in 40 to 128 meters and carrying out shore collecting, underwater photography, and collecting with scuba gear.

Later in the evening of September 24 we left Ua Pou, and in the morning we sighted Fatu Hiva. Approaching this island we could see that it presented a striking difference from the other islands we had already visited. Its mountains and cliffs were more luxuriantly clothed with vegetation, and even where the cliffs fell steeply to the sea their green mantle reached almost to the water's edge. Fatu Hiva is the southernmost and wettest of the Marquesas, and Hanavave and Omoa Valleys, which terminate in their respective bays on the western or lee side, are the most richly tropical valleys in the archipelago; the finest oranges are grown here, and grapefruit are plentiful.

We spent only three days in and around the bays of Hanavave and Omoa, two beautiful and strikingly different bays: Hanavave with its weather-sculptured pinnacles and cliffs forming a portal to the valley beyond and forming a backdrop to the village only partly visible under the palm trees that front on the small cobble beach at the head of the bay; Omoa with its wide black sand beach fronting the village and the broad valley behind from both sides of which slope upward the coconut-planted hills. During these three days we made five dredge hauls and established four diving stations in the rich submarine coral-reef area in the bays. In addition we collected from three stations on the shore.

On September 28, before dawn, the *Pele* raised anchor and we left for Tahuata to the northwest. In 5 hours we were off the southernmost point of Tahuata and immediately began dredging in about 45 fathoms. We made eight dredge hauls in coarse yellow sand and rubble and broken shells on a wide submarine flat shelf that extends for a mile and a half west of the southwestern coast of Tahuata. In the afternoon a diving party worked in 15 to 50 feet off the point to the south of Vaitahu Bay where the *Pele* was anchored. On the following day shore parties went north in the Boston Whaler

FIG. 3.   Shore party attempting to land on reef at Takaroa Atoll, Tuamotus, from rubber raft.

to Hana Moe Noe Bay on the north coast of the island and made several collections in the littoral zone.

Next day we sailed to Hiva Oa across Ha'ava Straits, also called Bordelais Channel, which separates this island from Tahuata, and entered Traitors Bay, anchoring in nearby Toahuku Bay. After a day on Hiva Oa we returned to Tahuata, and a shore party consisting of Rehder, Wilson, and Imboden was set ashore at Hana Hevane Bay where we did both shore collecting and diving.

Sunday, October 1, we spent in dredging, first in shallow water within Hana Moe Noe bay, where we had anchored for the night, and then in deeper water off the bay's entrance and in Ha'ava Straits, where we made 13 dredge hauls in 30 to 40 fathoms. These were very productive, many unusual and rare mollusks, brittlestars, sea fans, and Crustacea coming up. On the next day we made three more dredging stations in Ha'ava Straits. That night, October 2, we left once more for Nuku Hiva, which we reached the following morning, anchoring in Taiohae Bay. In Tahuata we had learned that the trading schooner *Taporo* from Papeete, with the fuel oil on which we had counted to replenish our dwindling supply, would arrive in Taiohae Bay two weeks later than expected. However, through the cooperation of local authorities, M. François Ollier, the administrator for the Marquesas

FIG. 4.   Sorting out specimens brought up in the dredge, Ha'ava Channel, between
Tahuata and Hiva Oa. From left to right, Harald A. Rehder, Dennis M. Devaney;
Mrs. Mary E. King.

M. Marc Perret, and his assistant M. Tixier, we were able to borrow 20
drums of diesel fuel, enough to enable us to continue our voyage as scheduled. Similarly we received two drums of fuel from M. Maurice McKittrick,
local merchant. By dusk of the 4th we were on our way again, and we
steamed out of Taiohae Bay headed for the Tuamotus, Mangareva, and
Pitcairn.

Early in the afternoon of the second day after our departure we reached
the atoll of Pukapuka, where we spent the afternoon of one day and the following morning working from three collecting stations on the reef and in
the lagoon, and one diving station off the edge of the reef. In midafternoon
of October 7 we left for Tatakoto atoll, reaching there early next morning.
We stayed on Tatakoto all day making three collecting stations on the reef
flat and in the lagoon. Transportation between ship and the shore was carried
out solely by native outrigger canoes as these were deemed safer than our
rubber raft in landing on the reef through the breakers. On leaving I was
given the accumulated mail to be taken to Papeete, which we expected to
reach in three weeks; schooners visit this island very infrequently.

A day and a half later we were at the atoll of Marutea, which we found to be uninhabited. Barry Wilson, Dennis Devaney, Tom Richert, and Bill Hartford of our crew headed for the island in the rubber raft after we had cruised along the lee shore of the atoll looking for the best landing place. The surf made it impossible to land on the reef, and so three of the party swam the last few yards to the reef and spent two hours exploring the reef and lagoon. In the lagoon they found that fine large pearl oysters abound in relatively shallow water. On the following morning, October 11, we were at Mangareva in the Gambier Islands, once more moored to a dock in a sheltered lagoon. We were able to be here for only three days as we were unable to obtain any additional fuel here, and we had only enough to get to Pitcairn and back to Papeete; we hoped to be able to pick up more fuel at Pitcairn Island.

From the time we left Mangareva on the evening of the 13th to the morning of the 16th when we reached Pitcairn rough weather cut down our cruising speed considerably and made our arrival a day later than expected. As two of us — Bill Kelly, the engineer, and I — had been on Pitcairn before, we saw numerous friends both in the launch that came out to take some of us in and on the dock when four of us landed from the launch in Bounty Bay; we left the *Pele* in the lee of the island off Tedside in a more sheltered anchorage. Most of the men of the island had been taken to Henderson Island on a U. S. Army ship to gather miro wood (*Thespesia populnea*) for carving and were expected back in a day or so. For three days various memers of our group were ashore visiting these friendly hospitable people and making shore collections at various points on this rocky island. One afternoon our doctor, Tom Richert, spent all day at the dispensary seeing persons who sought medical attention, since a doctor visits the island only very infrequently.

On the second day of our visit the Army vessel returned from Henderson Island, and the load of wood they had collected was unloaded and brought to the landing in Bounty Bay. When all of it was on the dock and the island launch had been hauled up into one of the boat sheds, Pervis Young, the chief magistrate, called a council meeting and explained our need for fuel. As a result, we received nine drums of diesel fuel, used on the island to run the generators, five from the local government supply and the other four from individuals; we agreed to send the replacement drums by the next Army vessel due at Pitcairn in the middle of November.

On the following day, as soon as the fuel was loaded into the launch, and the fruit and vegetables that the people gave us were taken on board, as well as the bread the women had baked for us with the flour we brought ashore, our party jumped aboard, followed by many of the islanders who wanted to go with the launch to the *Pele* at her anchorage. There the islanders scrambled up over the side of the *Pele* and were shown over the ship while the fuel was pumped aboard. Late in the afternoon of the 18th the islanders began leaving the ship, and soon, after warm farewells, the launch returned to Bounty Bay. We remained at our anchorage that night.

During the next two days we dredged off the northeast and northwest points of Pitcairn and off the south coast, where we found an unsuspected wide submarine shelf with a rich coral growth. This made dredging difficult in 20 to 25 fathoms so that only four dredge hauls were made here. Off the northern side, however, 28 hauls were made in varying depths of from 20 to 70 fathoms. These 32 dredgings were the first ever made in this Pitcairn area, yielding examples of many species whose presence was unsuspected in this part of the tropical Pacific and including numerous mollusks and other invertebrates new to science.

On the evening of the 20th we left for Oeno, a small coral atoll belonging to the Pitcairn Group, reaching it early the next morning. In four trips the shore party of six was deposited on the reef, from where we waded through the shallow lagoon to the tree-covered islet, a not too difficult task at low water. After spending all day collecting in the lagoon and along the shore of the islet, a combination of sandy beaches and areas of sharp coral rock, four of us made camp and spent the night on the island. The next morning, after further shore and lagoon collecting, we left in two trips in the rubber raft through the pass indicated on the chart, a relatively simple procedure.

During the next five days we steamed westward toward Anaa in the Tuamotus. Here we spent two and a half days collecting on the shore and reef and diving off the reef edge. On Sunday, our last day here, we were dinner guests of the local chief of public works and his wife (both from Papeete) and the chief of the village and his wife. That afternoon, October 29, we left Anaa for Papeete. Approaching Tahiti we came up on the small high island of Mehetia on the morning of the 30th and decided to try some dredging in its vicinity. We encircled this steep-sided uninhabited island, with sea birds and goats as its only visible occupants, but as we found no suitable place for dredging we continued on. It was dusk when we reached the eastern end of Tahiti, and we saw only glimpses of it through its shroud of rain clouds. A little after 9:30 the light at Pointe Venus was sighted, the engine was slowed, and when the motor was finally shut down the *Pele* drifted during the rest of the night off the north coast of Tahiti.

Early the next morning the *Pele* entered the pass into Papeete harbor

FIG. 5. The catch from one dredging station in 26-32 fathoms, Hatuatua Bay, Nuku Hiva, Marquesas.

and docked at the commercial wharf, back after a cruise of almost two months through French Polynesia and the Pitcairn Islands. After a few days of collecting and dredging along the north and west coasts of Tahiti, the members of our scientific party gradually left to return home. I was the last to leave, on November 7, and a day later the *Pele* left with her crew to return to Honolulu.

Inasmuch as the material gathered on this trip has not all been processed and itemized, no quantitative report on the collections made can at this time be given. Certain very real benefits arising from this voyage of the *Pele* can be mentioned, however.

The opportunity to do extensive dredging in moderately deep waters in the southeastern tropical Pacific was the principal reason for this expedition. My hopes for success were fully rewarded. This was the first extensive dredging ever carried out in this area. The only prior dredging of which I am aware was done in Taiohae Bay, Nuku Hiva, by R. B. Hinds during the voyage of circumnavigation of H.M.S. *Sulphur.* This was in 1838, and in depths of only 7 to 10 fathoms. The *Pele* made a total of 131 dredge hauls, 83 of them in the Marquesas and 33 off Pitcairn Island. The rest were made in

Rangiroa lagoon (9) and off the coast of Tahiti (6).

In the Marquesas we collected many specimens not only of species that are endemic to these islands but also of numerous species that are undoubtedly new to science. At Pitcairn, whose marine fauna was relatively unknown, the dredge brought up examples of many species, well represented in the more tropical parts of the central Pacific, whose presence at Pitcairn with its cooler waters and reduced coral representation and consequent impoverished littoral fauna, was unsuspected. Here again, at Pitcairn, new species were found. When the material is finally completely sorted and identified, we will have a very much clearer picture of the marine invertebrate faunas of the biogeographically marginal areas of the Marquesas and Pitcairn and of their relationships with the faunas of the adjoining faunistically richer island groups.

The vast amount of material gathered on this trip by dredging, reef-collecting, and diving has at the present been sorted into the main animal groups and is being studied by specialists all over the world. Most of the species that were recognized as possibly new have proved to be new in the process of examining the contents of the dredge as they were emptied onto the sorting table—always an exciting and usually a rewarding task. At the present time at least five or six new species of mollusks from the Marquesas and Pitcairn have been noted. Four new species have been found among the starfishes and brittlestars, and at least one new crab was collected. Several papers describing these collections and new species are now in preparation.

REFERENCES

DEVANEY, DENNIS M.
    1970. Studies on ophiocomid brittlestars: I, A new genus *(Clarkcoma)* of Ophiocominae with a reevaluation of the genus *Ophiocoma.* Smithsonian Contr. Zool., no. 51, 41 pp., illus.
REHDER, HARALD A.
    1968. The marine molluscan fauna of the Marquesas Islands. Amer. Malac. Union Ann. Rpt. for 1968, pp. 29-32.
    1971. Malacological expedition to the tropical South Pacific. Nat. Geogr. Soc. Res. Rpts., 1965 Projects, pp. 213-218.

HARALD A. REHDER

Field Studies of Primates in Río Muni, West Africa, 1967-1968

Principal Investigator   Arthur J. Riopelle, Delta Regional Primate Research
and Director: Center of Tulane University, Covington, Louisiana.

Scientific Investigator: Clyde Jones, Delta Regional Primate Research Center of
Tulane University, Covington, Louisiana.

Grant Nos. 630, 642,   In support of the second and third years of intensive
732:   studies of wild primates in Río Muni.

The purpose of this research program, initiated in 1966, was to conduct studies on several aspects of the biology of primates in Río Muni, West Africa, with emphasis on the ecological relationships of lowland gorillas and chimpanzees. Several major and extensive field studies of gorillas and chimpanzees in separate geographic areas (fig. 1) were previously made by Kortlandt (1962), Goodall (1965, 1968), Reynolds and Reynolds (1965), Schaller (1963), and Bournonville (1967); however, no detailed studies have been made of either lowland gorillas or gorillas and chimpanzees in sympatry.

The data summarized herein were gathered mostly by Clyde Jones, who was in Río Muni from February 1967 until July 1968. Jorge Sabater Pi, who was made available for this project by the Zoological Park of Barcelona, participated in various ways throughout the investigation. Arthur Riopelle made a trip to Río Muni in June 1968 to gather information on primates. Frances L. Miller spent about 8 months in Río Muni and gathered information for a dissertation on the ecology of the gray-cheeked mangabey, *Cercocebus albigena*. Although not financed by the aforementioned program, Frances Miller's research and dissertation were supervised by the junior author.

The specific objectives of the second and third years of this research program were (1) to conduct intensive studies of gorillas and chimpanzees and the interrelations between them, as well as the interrelations between the apes and other species of primates, and (2) to collect as much information as possible about the primates other than gorillas and chimpanzees that occurred in Río Muni.

Areas for intensive studies of gorillas, chimpanzees, and other primates were selected previously (Riopelle and Jones, 1973). However, it was

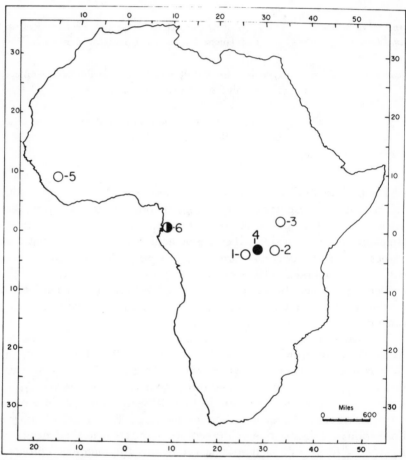

FIG. 1. Areas where extensive field studies of *Gorilla gorilla* and *Pan troglodytes* have been conducted since 1960. Localities where gorillas were studied are indicated by dots; sites of studies of chimpanzees are marked by circles. 1, Eastern Congo (Kortlandt, 1962); 2, Gombe Stream Reserve, Tanzania (Goodall, 1965, 1968); 3, Budongo Forest, Uganda (Reynolds and Reynolds, 1965); 4, Albert National Park, Congo (Schaller, 1963); 5, Republic of Guinea (Bournonville, 1967); 6, Río Muni.

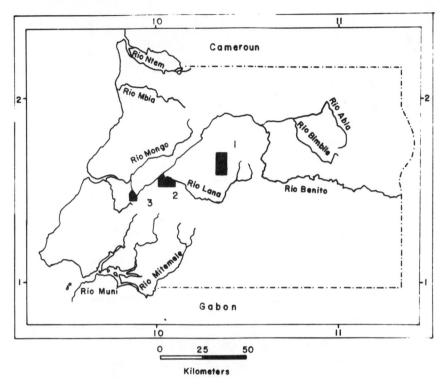

FIG. 2.   Areas in Río Muni where *Gorilla gorilla* and *Pan troglodytes* were studied intensively. 1, Study area for gorillas and chimpanzees; 2, study area for gorillas; 3, study area for chimpanzees.

necessary to locate several new places because some of the areas selected previously for intensive studies of primates were no longer suitable for long-term investigations. This resulted from the increased pressures on the animals by hunting and by deforestation of large areas either for agricultural purposes or for exploitation of timber by lumber companies that had extensive holdings and operations in Río Muni. The problem of destruction of habitats was intensified by the efforts to extract as much lumber as possible before the country became independent in 1968.

Intensive studies of gorillas and chimpanzees were conducted mostly in three localities (fig. 2). In one area gorillas were present, in one area chimpanzees were present, and in one area both gorillas and chimpanzees were found. At least four additional species of primates occurred in each of the study areas.

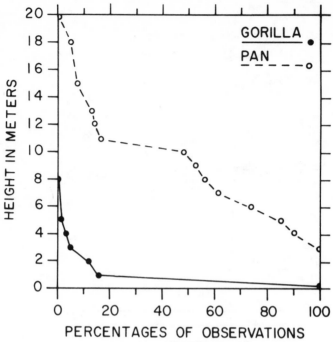

FIG. 3.   Vertical stratification of apes in Río Muni.

Some data have already been published with regard to several aspects of the ecology of the primates in Río Muni (see References). Some of the ecological relationships between gorillas and chimpanzees, as well as the ecological relationships between apes and other species of primates, in Río Muni, are summarized briefly in the following paragraphs.

Utilizations of habitats by the apes are summarized in table 1. Gorillas are forest-edge animals found mostly in dense thickets and enter well-developed forests rather infrequently. Chimpanzees live in well-developed forests, but they occasionally enter thickets and regenerating vegetation.

The terrestrial and arboreal habits of gorillas and chimpanzees are depicted in figures 3 and 4. Gorillas are almost completely terrestrial, but chimpanzees are arboreal and terrestrial. In addition, the former sleep in beds located mostly on the ground; the latter in beds built above the ground in trees.

Because of temporal utilization of habitats and terrestrial and arboreal habits, gorillas and chimpanzees seemingly frequent portions of their

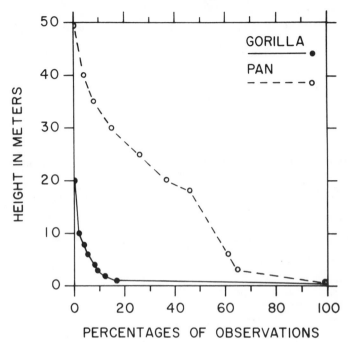

FIG. 4. Height above the ground of gorilla and chimpanzee beds in Río Muni.

habitats at appropriate times either to accumulate or lose body heat in relation to the ambient temperature. The responses to temperature exhibited by these apes are perhaps of considerable importance as related to thermoregulatory functions.

With regard to habits of diet, gorillas were observed to eat only plant materials, but chimpanzees ingest plant materials as well as some animal materials. Gorillas are mostly herbivorous but somewhat frugivorous. Chimpanzees are mostly frugivorous but somewhat herbivorous. In addition, chimpanzees in some areas feed frequently on termites (Jones and Sabater Pi, 1969).

An interesting example of mutualism was apparent between gorillas and plants of the genus *Aframomum*. Gorillas made great use of these plants for the construction of beds; in addition, gorillas consumed pith and mature fruits of these plants. *Aframomum* was dispersed by gorillas in that viable seeds were passed through the gastrointestinal tracts and deposited in their feces.

TABLE 1.—UTILIZATION OF HABITATS BY GORILLAS AND CHIMPANZEES IN RÍO MUNI.

	Mature forest			Regenerating forest			Montane forest		
	Feed	Rest	Sleep	Feed	Rest	Sleep	Feed	Rest	Sleep
Gorilla......X		X		X	X	X	X	X	
Pan X		X	X	X	X		X	X	X

TABLE 2.—TIMES THAT OTHER PRIMATES WERE EITHER SEEN OR HEARD DURING 46 DIRECT OBSERVATIONS OF GORILLAS IN RÍO MUNI.

Species	Number	Percent
Cercopithecus nictitans	21	34.4
Cercopithecus cephus	9	14.8
Cercopithecus pogonias	5	8.2
Colobus polykomos	4	6.6
Pan troglodytes	3	4.9
None	19	31.1
Totals	61	100.0

TABLE 3.—TIMES THAT OTHER PRIMATES WERE EITHER SEEN OR HEARD DURING 36 DIRECT OBSERVATIONS OF CHIMPANZEES IN RÍO MUNI.

Species	Number	Percent
Cercopithecus nictitans	19	38.6
Cercopithecus pogonias	7	14.4
Cercopithecus cephus	5	10.2
Colobus polykomos	3	6.1
Gorilla gorilla	3	6.1
Papio sphinx	2	4.1
Cercocebus torquatus	2	4.1
None	8	16.4
Totals	49	100.0

Several species of nonhuman primates were associated frequently with gorillas and chimpanzees (tables 2, 3). Gorillas were not associated closely with other species of primates; ecological associations between chimpanzees and other primates occurred because chimpanzees frequented most of the strata available to primates (Riopelle and Jones, 1973). Although overlaps of habitats between apes and other primates were noted, complete ecological overlaps did not occur because of apparent niche specializations of the species studied. Among the apes and other primates studied, interspecific differences such as temporal utilizations of habitats, arboreal and terrestrial habits, and natural diets, probably enhanced ecological separation and reduced competition for such things as food and space.

REFERENCES

Literature Cited

BOURNONVILLE, D. DE
  1967. Contribution à l'étude du chimpanze en République de Guinée. Bull. Inst. Franç. Afrique Noire, vol. 29, pp. 1189-1269.
GOODALL, JANE
  1965. Chimpanzees of the Gombe Stream Reserve. Chap. 12 (pp. 425-473) *in* "Primate Behavior," Irven DeVore, ed., 654 pp., illus. Holt, Rinehart & Winston, New York.
  1968. The behavior of free-living chimpanzees in the Gombe Stream Reserve. Animal Behavior Monogr., vol. 1, pt. 3, pp. 161-311, illus.
KORTLANDT, ADRIAAN
  1962. Chimpanzees in the wild. Sci. Amer., vol. 206, pp. 128-138, illus.
REYNOLDS, VERNON, and REYNOLDS, FRANCES
  1965. Chimpanzees of the Budongo Forest. Chap. 11 (pp. 368-424) *in* "Primate Behavior," Irven DeVore, ed., 654 pp., illus. Holt, Rinehart & Winston, New York.
RIOPELLE, ARTHUR J., and JONES, CLYDE
  1973. Field studies of primates in Río Muni, West Africa. Nat. Geogr. Soc. Res. Rpts., 1966 Projects, pp. 219-223, illus.
SCHALLER, GEORGE B.
  1963. The mountain gorilla, 431 pp., illus. University of Chicago Press.

Publications Resulting from the Project

JONES, CLYDE
  1969. Notes on ecological relationships of four species of lorisids in Río Muni, West Africa. Folia Primatol., vol. 11, pp. 255-267.
  1970. Stomach contents and gastro-intestinal relationships of monkeys collected in Río Muni, West Africa. Mammalia, vol. 34, pp. 107-117.
  1971a. The bats of Río Muni, West Africa. Journ. Mamm., vol. 52, no. 1, pp. 121-140, illus.

1971b. Notes on hairy frogs *(Trichobatrachus robustus* Boulenger) collected in Río Muni, West Africa. Herpetologica, vol. 27, no. 1, pp. 51-54.

1971c. Notes on the anomalurids of Río Muni and adjacent areas. Journ. Mamm., vol. 52, no. 3, pp. 568-572.

1972a. Natural diets of wild primates. Pp. 57-77 *in* "Pathology of Simian Primates," pt. 1, R. Fiennes, editor. S. Karger, Basel, Switzerland.

1972b. Observations on dental deposits and deficiencies of wild talapoin monkeys *(Cercopithecus talapoin)* collected in Río Muni, West Africa. Laboratory Primate Newsletter, vol. 11, pp. 28-34.

1972c. Comparative ecology of three pteropid bats in Río Muni, West Africa. Journ. Zool., London, vol. 167, pp. 353-370.

1973. Body temperatures of *Manis gigantea* and *Manis tricuspis.* Journ. Mamm., vol. 54, no. 1, pp. 263-266.

JONES, CLYDE, and SABATER PI, JORGE

1968. Comparative ecology of *Cercocebus albigena* (Gray) and *Cercocebus torquatus* (Kerr) in Río Muni, West Africa. Folia Primatol., vol. 9, pp. 99-113, illus.

1969. Sticks used by chimpanzees in Río Muni, West Africa. Nature, vol. 223, pp. 100-113, illus.

1971. Comparative ecology of *Gorilla gorilla* (Savage and Wyman) and *Pan troglodytes* (Blumenbach) in Río Muni, West Africa. Bibliotheca Primatológica, no. 13, 96 pp., illus. S. Karger, Basel, München, etc.

JONES, CLYDE, and SETZER, HENRY W.

1970. Comments on *Myosciurus pumilio.* Journ. Mamm., vol. 51, no. 4, pp. 813-814.

RIOPELLE, ARTHUR J., and JONES, CLYDE

1973. Field studies of primates in Río Muni, West Africa. Nat. Geogr. Soc. Res. Rpts., 1966 Projects, pp. 219-223, illus.

SABATER PI, JORGE, and JONES, CLYDE

1967. Notes on the distribution and ecology of the higher primates of Río Muni, West Africa. Tulane Stud. Zool., vol. 14, pp. 101-109, illus.

Papers Delivered at Scientific Meetings

JONES, CLYDE

Comparative ecology of lowland gorillas and chimpanzees in Río Muni, West Africa. 49th annual meeting of American Society of Mammalogists, New York. June 15-21, 1969.

MILLER, FRANCES L.

The ecology of the gray-cheeked mangabey, *Cercocebus albigena,* and its relationships to the white-collared mangabey, *C. torquatus,* in Río Muni, West Africa. 49th annual meeting of American Society of Mammalogists, New York. June 15-21, 1969.

ARTHUR J. RIOPELLE
CLYDE JONES

Preliminary Results of Investigations of the Lepidoptera of Aldabra Atoll

Principal Investigator: Jay C. Shaffer, George Mason University, Fairfax, Virginia.

Grant No. 667: In aid of biological studies of the Lepidoptera of Aldabra Atoll, Indian Ocean.

Aldabra Atoll is located in the western Indian Ocean 9°24′ south of the Equator and approximately 400 miles east of Africa and 260 miles northwest of Madagascar. It is 21 miles long and between 5 and 9 miles wide and has a land area of 60 square miles apportioned among four main islands of very unequal size. A large shallow lagoon occupies the center of the atoll. The land is flat and for the most part the surface is extremely rugged. Aldabra and its nearby neighbors (Assumption, Astove, and Cosmoledo) comprising the Aldabra Group of islands are unusual in that they have been uplifted by about 30 feet. The habitat diversification resulting from this slight uplift has permitted the establishment of a relatively large number of plant and animal species.

Aldabra is further unusual because, being very unattractive to man, it has been little affected by his activities. The atoll is nearly devoid of soil and fresh water and, unlike its neighbors, lacks commercially exploitable phosphate deposits. As a result of its elevation, its relative nearness to Africa and Madagascar, and its inhospitableness it survives today with a richness of native fauna and flora unequaled on any other isolated coral atoll. There are many endemics. About 18 percent of the higher land plants are endemic to the Aldabra Group, most being found only on Aldabra. About half of the land birds are endemic species or subspecies, and about 23 percent of the insects are endemic to Aldabra and another 16 percent endemic to the Aldabra Group. The Old World giant land tortoise, once widespread on the islands of the western Indian Ocean, now survives only on Aldabra.

Thus Aldabra is a priceless asset to science as a unique natural laboratory for the study of evolution and ecology. The integrity of that ecosystem was threatened in 1964 when the United Kingdom Ministry of Defence announced plans (since rescinded) for construction of an airbase intended to convert Aldabra to a refueling stop between England and the Far East.

While the scientific community sought to save Aldabra from development the Royal Society initiated an extensive scientific expedition to Alda-

263

bra to collect data on the ecology of the atoll. I was a member of Phase III (wet season) of the expedition and traveled as a collaborator of the Smithsonian Institution to study the Lepidoptera of the Atoll.

Previous studies of the Lepidoptera of Indian Ocean islands that included Aldabra were published by Fletcher, Fryer, Hampson, Holland, and Meyrick around the turn of the century, and more recently Legrand (1965) published a monograph of the Lepidoptera of the Seychelles and Aldabra. From these works it was apparent that little was known of the biology of the approximately 130 species of Lepidoptera then known to occur on Aldabra.

My objective was twofold: (1) To provide an inventory of the Lepidoptera of Aldabra through intensive collection and (2) to contribute to knowledge of the ecology of these insects through field observations, rearing of larvae, and studying insect-hostplant relationships and insect-parasite relationships.

I arrived on Aldabra on January 8, 1968, and began working at the expedition's main base on Île Picard (West Island), also the site of a small semi-permanent settlement of perhaps 40 Seychellois. Nighttime collecting by blacklight was carried out at a site approximately 100 yards east of the settlement and at the boundary between *Casuarina* and mixed shrub communities.

From January 31 to February 19 I collected in a variety of localities near the Takamaka Camp and then on the 24th moved on to Cinq Cases Camp. The wet season, which was of unusually short duration, began at this time. About 10 days later the rain had stimulated abundant new foliage, which made profitable intensive collecting and rearing of larvae. On March 11 I continued my collecting and rearing work at Middle Island Camp at the eastern tip of Middle Island; then on the 28th I returned to the settlement to complete work and prepare for the April 7 departure from Aldabra.

My activities were similar at each of the above-mentioned camps. From twilight until about midnight, I collected Lepidoptera and other insects at a light consisting of two 15-watt fluorescent lamps, one ultraviolet (blacklight) and one daylight, powered by a 300-watt portable Honda AC-DC generator. Each light was positioned about 5 feet high and in front of a white sheet suspended vertically between the ground and a clothesline rope. Specimens were hand collected from the sheet and from nearby soil and vegetation as the insects flew toward the lamps and alighted on nearby objects. Lepidoptera were taken in standard entomological cyanide jars. Other insects generally were collected in ethyl alcohol to which a small quantity of glycerine had been added.

During the daylight hours my time was devoted to pinning material collected the previous night, caring for and making photographs and observations of larvae being reared, general photography, occasional housekeeping duties, and conducting field explorations, usually in the vicinity of camp.

Some specific purposes of the field explorations were to discover potential areas for night collecting, collect flying insects, search for immature stages of Lepidoptera, search for nonflying adult insects and other animals in a variety of situations, and document photographically the island's fauna, flora, and topography. When deemed profitable much time was devoted to hunting lepidopterous larvae.

In all, approximately 10,000 specimens of Lepidoptera and 2,370 of other insect orders were taken. The Lepidoptera are representative of about 29 families and about 227 species. Although the majority of the species have not yet been identified beyond the family level, approximately 30 percent appear to be previously unrecorded from Aldabra. Clearly, when his material has been fully studied our knowledge of the Aldabra Lepidoptera will have been significantly increased.

About 80 percent of the species of Lepidoptera belong to but 5 of the 29 families on the atoll. The approximate number of species in each of these five families is: Pyralidae 70, Noctuidae 58, Gelechiidae 26, Geometridae 18, and Olethreutidae 11.

I reared about 10 percent of the species of Aldabra Lepidoptera. Some of the established insect-hostplant relationships are newly discovered; just how many will not be known until all reared species have been properly identified. In summary, six species of Gelechiidae were reared; two on *Sideroxylon inerme*, one on *Phyllanthus cheloniphorbe*, one on *Phyllanthus casticum*, one on *Gossypium* (cotton); one gelechiid was taken among persistent dead leaves on *Pandanus tectorius?*, and another species was taken in clumps of the grass *Sclerodactylon macrosthyium*. Five species of pyralids were reared, one each on *Sideroxylon inerme* and *Apodytes dimidiata*, one feeding in the fruits of *Xylocarpus granatum*, one as a stem borer of *Scaevola taccada*, and one as a stem borer of *Ficus nautarum*.

One species of Gracilariidae was reared on leaves of *Phyllanthus cheloniphorbe*, and a species of Glyphipterygidae on leaves of *Ficus thonningii*.

Two species of Opostegidae were reared; one on leaves of *Plumbago aphylla* and another as a leaf-miner of *Ochna ciliata*.

One geometrid and one noctuid were each reared from leaves of *Gagnebina pterocarpa*.

I also reared three species whose hostplants were reported by Legrand. *Acraea terpsicore legrandi* was reared on *Turnera ulmifolia*. Both larvae and adults of this species were very abundant at Settlement. Larvae of *Utetheisa lactea aldabrensis* were taken on *Tournefortia argentea* at Settlement and Dune Jean Louis. One larva of *Phalanta phalanta aethiopica* was taken on *Flacourtia ramontchii?* near Cinq Cases, but rearing attempts were unsuccessful.

My present work is proceeding along two lines, the identification of reared species and the preparation of a paper on the Aldabra Pyralidae.

REFERENCES

COGAN, B. H.; HUTSON, A. M.; and SHAFFER, JAY C.
  1971. Preliminary observations on the affinities and composition of the insect fauna of Aldabra. Phil. Trans. Roy. Soc. London, ser. B (Biol. Sci.), vol. 260, pp. 315-25, chart.
LEGRAND, HENRY
  1965. Lépidoptères des Îles Seychelles et d'Aldabra. Mém. Mus. Nat. Hist. Nat., Paris, ser. A (Zool.), vol. 37, pp. 1-210, illus.
STODDART, DAVID R., ed.
  1967. Ecology of Aldabra Atoll, Indian Ocean. Atoll Res. Bull., no. 118, 141 pp., illus. Smithsonian Institution, Washington, D. C.

JAY C. SHAFFER

A Search for Pleistocene Archeological Evidence in the Calico Mountains of Eastern California [1]

Principal Investigators: Louis S. B. Leakey, Centre for Prehistory and Palaeontology, Nairobi, Kenya; Thomas Clements, University of Southern California, Los Angeles, California; Ruth D. Simpson, San Bernardino County Museum, San Bernardino, California.

Grant Nos. 627, 633, 656, 669. In support of fourth season's excavations at a possible Early Man site in the Calico Mountains, Mojave Desert, California.

Excavations planned for the fourth season at the Calico Mountains archeological site were predicated upon work done and specimens recovered during the first three seasons' operations, November 1964-May 1967 (see Simpson, 1969, 1971, 1973). It is necessary here to repeat only the following basic facts:

"Excavations were conducted in section 22, R.2E., T.10 N., under permit from the United States Department of the Interior. The site is recorded as San Bernardino County Museum Site 1500 (SBCM 1500). The purpose of the project was primarily to determine whether or not man-made artifacts are contained in the Pleistocene alluvial fan deposits known as the Yermo formation. This fan spread out of the eastern Calico Mountains, over the ancient eroded Miocene Barstow formation, and into Lake Manix Basin.

"While excavation began in numerous scattered pits and trenches during the first season, the crucial work was done in the Master Pit, a 25-foot-square area selected in 1963 by Dr. Louis Leakey. Extreme care and controls were observed throughout the excavation, which, in some of the 5-by-5 sections of the Master Pit, had reached a depth of 96-108 inches by May

---

[1] In previous reports in this series dealing with work at the Calico Mountains archeological site, certain terms such as "tools," "artifacts," and "implements" were placed in quotation marks by the editor. This was done to suggest that there was no unanimity among archeologists concerning the claimed evidence of the presence of Early Man at the site. In the present report the omission of quotation marks does not mean that the author's and Dr. Leakey's interpretations are not still challenged in many quarters. — EDITOR

1965. Virtually all work had been concentrated in the western and northern sectors of the Master Pit. Few specimens were recovered above the 48-inch level, and the quantity increased with the increase in depth." (Simpson, 1971, p. 231.)

On the advice of visiting scientists who held a symposium at the site at the invitation of the National Geographic Society in the spring of 1966, it was decided that a control pit should be excavated a short distance from the main site. The third season of the project was concentrated upon the excavation of two such pits. No artifacts were found in either. Such work as was done in Master Pit I indicated that the yield of archeological evidence decreased sharply as contact with the underlying Barstow formation of Miocene age was approached.

Dr. Leakey decided that a second Master Pit should be excavated 40 feet northwest of Master Pit I. He selected the location and applied to the National Geographic Society for funds to carry on the work. Half of the requested funds were granted, and the project administrator, Dr. Gerald A. Smith, director of the San Bernardino County Museum, was notified that no further funds for the project would be forthcoming from the Society. Plans for the fourth field season were therefore curtailed sharply; all work by the paid crew in outlying pits was halted; half of the crew was dismissed; and the geological program was reduced.

Work was started on October 15, 1967. Just as the season was beginning, Dr. François Bordes visited the site and examined the collection at length. As a technician he found the flakes of great interest and in his opinion to be certain evidence of man's workmanship. He segregated several classes of flakes not previously distinguished in the assemblage.

During the early weeks of the season, work progressed rapidly in Master Pit II. It was 15 by 15 feet in size and was divided into 5-foot squares. It was possible to incorporate Master Pit II into the same numbering system as Master Pit I. Hence the squares were designated H-11 to 13, I-11 and 13, and J-11 to 13. I-12 was retained intact as a central witness column. A worker was continuously employed in each of the excavated squares.

The major trench extending westward from Master Pit I indicated that 8 to 10 feet of stratified sands and gravels might be expected in the upper levels of Master Pit II. These were found resting on a spectacular boulder level, in which some of the boulders weighed 500-600 pounds. This was only weakly represented on the old fan surface in Master Pit I. This representation of the old fan surface occurred at the same elevation as in Master I. Beneath it, excavation exposed the same artifact-bearing deposits the crew had found in Master Pit I.

Removal of the boulder level was a long operation. While it was proceeding, excavation of an entrance trench was assuming major proportions. It was part of the on-going student-training program. Here it was possible to view in profile the extensive erosion of the fan and the weakening of the boulder level to the east.

A concentration of specimens was recorded in the stratified material above the boulder level. Preliminary analysis indicated this to have been a weak concentration, but it is significant because these stratified upper beds had been removed by erosion in the area of Master Pit I. Large cobbles were rare in the upper strata, and most of the rock material displayed a greater degree of rounding than the rocks below the boulder level. Decomposing volcanic tuff, so characteristic of the lower strata, was seldom recorded above the boulder level. Preliminary analysis of Master Pit II specimens suggests that complete tools are not as numerous here as in Master Pit I. However, technically significant flakes are markedly more numerous. These are flakes showing characteristics that in our opinion, and in the opinion of Dr. Bordes, John Witthoft, and others, reflect human workmanship rather than natural fracture.

In the spring of 1968 the site was visited by Drs. F. Clark Howell of the University of California (Berkeley) and Karl W. Butzer of the University of Chicago. Dr. Butzer agreed that the deposits are old and suggested geological projects that might assist in determining more specifically the age of the alluvial fan. Dr. Howell agreed with us that many of the specimens selected for examination by Dr. Leakey and the writer are man-made, and he discussed fully the reasons for this opinion. Among those also present at the meeting were Dr. Matthew W. Stirling, Dr. T. Dale Stewart, Dr. Emil Haury, Dr. Leakey, Dr. Clements, Dr. Smith, and the writer.

In March, shortly after the visit of Drs. Howell and Butzer, plans leading to the preservation of the Calico Mountains archeological site were activated by the Bureau of Land Management and the Nature Conservancy. These plans were blocked by a local miner's efforts to evict the Calico project in lieu of payment of $25,000,000 to him. A year later, the Solicitor General ruled in favor of the project and its continuation in section 22.

Supplemental funds from other organizations, primarily the Wilkie Brothers and the Isotope Foundations, supported continuation of the work until the first of June and enabled us to roof the two main pits, thus protecting them from major erosional damage. Although funding by the National Geographic Society ended with the fourth season, work on the Calico Mountains site and related geological problems continued with funds from various sources. In 1969-70, emphasis was switched from archeology to related geology, since limited funds made extensive work on both facets of the project impractical. In 1970 an international conference was held at the Calico site, at the San Bernardino County Museum, and at San Bernardino Valley College. Papers presented have been assembled and published by the San Bernardino County Museum (Leakey et al., 1972). This is one of several significant publications on the results of the work at the site that have appeared.

As this report is prepared (1972) a great deal of work remains to be done — archeological excavation, geological field work, laboratory analysis of the specimens — before the main technical publications can be prepared. Also preservation of the site through action at institutional, county, state, or federal level is urgently needed.

REFERENCES

LEAKEY, LOUIS S. B., et al.
> 1972. Pleistocene man at Calico: A report on the international conference on the Calico Mountains excavations, San Bernardino County, California, 1970, Walter C. Schuiling, ed., 82 pp., illus. San Bernardino Museum.

LEE, THOMAS E.
> 1971. Calico Mountains Conference. Anthrop. Journ. Canada, vol. 9, no. 4, pp. 11, 12.

SIMPSON, RUTH D.
> 1969. A search for Pleistocene archeological evidence in the Calico Mountains of eastern California. Nat. Geogr. Soc. Res. Rpts., 1964 Projects, pp. 219-225
> 1971. A search for Pleistocene archeological evidence in the Calico Mountains of eastern California. Nat. Geogr. Soc. Res. Rpts., 1965 Projects, pp. 231-237.
> 1973. A search for Pleistocene archeological evidence in the Calico Mountains of eastern California. Nat. Geogr. Soc. Res. Rpts., 1966 Projects, pp. 225-233.

STEPHENSON, ROBERT L.
> 1971. Thoughts on the Calico Mountains site. Univ. South Carolina Inst. Archaeol. and Anthrop. Notebook, vol. 3, no. 1, pp. 3-9.

RUTH D. SIMPSON

Suspended Sediment Transport at the Shelf-break and on the Slope, Wilmington Canyon Area, off Delaware Bay [1]

Principal Investigator: Daniel J. Stanley, National Museum of Natural History, Smithsonian Institution, Washington, D. C.

Grant No. 606:   For a study of sedimentation patterns in submarine canyon heads.

Clay and silt are the predominant textural sediment types on the continental slope and rise on the Atlantic margin off North America and also form the surficial cover of the outer margin in the vicinity of Wilmington Canyon, 140 kilometers southeast of Delaware Bay. Previous surveys revealed high concentrations of material in suspension on outer-shelf and upper-slope sectors in the vicinity of Wilmington Canyon. The present study was initiated, therefore, to evaluate the concentration, composition, distribution, and origin of suspended particulate matter in the mid- and near-bottom water masses on the outer continental shelf and upper- and mid-slope region near this canyon. The composition of the suspended particulate matter in mid- and near-bottom water masses near the shelf-break was determined. An attempt was made to relate suspended particulate matter with topography of the sea floor and with water-mass movement near the shelf-break

---

[1] In preparing the final report on this research (to be published elsewhere) I have had the generous collaboration of Dr. Anil K. Lyall, of the Smithsonian Institution's Division of Sedimentology, and Harry N. Giles and Alvan Fisher, Jr., of the U. S. Navy Oceanographic Office. Grateful acknowledgment is made also to the U. S. Coast Guard for providing shiptime for the collection of water samples and hydrographic data used in this study and to the captain, officers, and men of the U.S.C.G.C. *Rockaway* for their support in the work at sea on cruises RoS5 (March 1969), RoS6 (September 1969), and RoS7 (December 1969). Shipboard assistance in collecting water samples was given by Dr. G. Kelling, Dr. F. C. Wezel, and students of the University of Illinois, Urbana. Thanks are due also to G. A. Gotthardt and J. L. Kerling and the officers and crew of Oceanographic Development Squadron Eight (VXN-8) for providing the airborne measurements. In addition to the grant from the National Geographic Society, the study was supported by a research grant from the Smithsonian Institution.

environment, as well as the dispersal of fines in the outer shelf and slope environments, an aspect of primary importance. These data and interpretations shed light on the role of suspended sediment transport in deposition on the lower slope and rise of this part of the continental margin. Movements of water masses are evidently important because they control the transport and distribution of fine particulate matter. Thus, in addition to the suspended material examined in water samples, STD (salinity-temperature-depth), XBT (expendable bathythermograph), and ART (airborne radiation thermometer) measurements from various flights and cruises over this area were considered.

Continuous echograms were made in the Wilmington Canyon region on U.S.C.G.C. *Rockaway* cruise RoS7 (December 1-7, 1969). These records and those obtained in the same region on six previous cruises were used in constructing a bathymetric chart. The depth of the shelf-break, the narrow zone where there is the greatest change in gradient between the outer shelf and upper slope, is 70 to 75 fathoms (128 to 137 meters). Wilmington Canyon is cut about 18 kilometers within the outer continental shelf; the head of the canyon lies at a depth of 45 fathoms (82 meters).

Results and Conclusions

High concentrations of particulate matter of clay to sand size were observed in water samples (140-liter) collected on the outer shelf, shelf-break, and slope near the canyon. Values ranged from 0.134 to 1.107 mg/l. The organic fraction ranged from 9.9 to 68 percent of the total suspended matter; near-bottom samples north of the canyon head on the shelf generally yielded the highest organic fractions. Midwater samples in the canyon also comprised high organic values (>31 percent). The relatively consistent concentration and composition of suspended sediment in near-bottom water samples between outer shelf and slope are a reflection of sediment transport and nondeposition at and near the shelf-break. Distribution of suspended sediment is related with sea-floor topography and with water-mass movement at the shelf-edge, as determined from STD, XBT, and ART measurements. Cold- and warm-water masses move back and forth across the outer shelf.

The triggering mechanism for suspension is not turbidity current activity but resuspension by turbulence induced by large-scale short-term displacement of water masses at the shelf-break. Turbid layers on the bottom and in the water column within the canyon and on the midslope probably extend onto the rise, where they have been recognized by other workers as nepheloid layers. The long-term lateral introduction (by resuspension) and dispersal of fine-grained material along the shelf-break would explain some of the clay and silt of shallow water origin in the lower slope and rise wedge off the Mid-Atlantic States.

In studies conducted in California it has been suggested that periodic slumping of material on relatively steep slopes associated with upper-slope and submarine environment is possibly responsible for bringing sediment into suspension (Gunnerson and Emery, 1962). Benthic organisms are also responsible for ejecting fines into the water column. An even more probable means of bringing large amounts of fine sediment into suspension are low-density low-velocity turbidity currents (Moore, 1966; Gorsline et al., 1968; and others). The presence of the near-bottom layer of sediment-laden water on the continental rise off the U. S. east coast led to the hypothesis that nepheloid layers on the rise are fines injected onto the outer continental margin by turbidity currents. However, the nepheloid layer on the rise on the western margin of the North Atlantic is believed to be a continuous and permanent feature (Eittreim et al., 1969). We believe that another triggering mechanism would better fulfill the conditions observed: resuspension by turbulence induced by large-scale, short-term displacement of water masses along much of the shelf-break.

If, as here suggested, relatively high turbulence on the outermost shelf and in the shelf-break environment results in a nearly continuous resuspension of sediments from the bottom, one would expect the amount of sediment in suspension in water masses overlying these environments to be high during most of the year. This conclusion conforms with seismic evidence (Kelling and Stanley, 1970) showing that the shelf-break in the vicinity of Wilmington Canyon is a zone of erosion and nondeposition. Furthermore, petrologic data, such as the distribution of micas in surficial deposits (Doyle et al., 1968), also indicate that the outer shelf and upper slope along much of the Atlantic margin is an area of erosion and nondeposition.

It is tempting to suggest that displacement of water masses, modified by storms and tidal effects, is a likely trigger for the formation of layers of suspended particulate matter of the type noted by other workers on the continental rise off the eastern margin of the United States. Turbid layers at or near the bottom and within the water column noted on the midslope in the study area probably extend seaward toward the continental rise. Particularly noteworthy in this respect is the very high quantity of suspended matter, most of it inorganic, in the middle of the water column in the canyon proper. The limited number of water samples processed from the Wilmington Canyon area, however, does not permit a definition of the three-dimensional configuration of the suspension-rich layers, nor at this time can we relate these outer shelf-slope layers with the nepheloid layer noted on the rise north and east of this area by Ewing and Thorndike (1965) and Eittreim et al. (1969). As suggested elsewhere (Stanley, 1970, fig. 12), resuspended fines from the shelf edge that move downslope and onto the rise are eventually deflected in a southwesterly direction. On the rise, such clay and silt in suspension would be transported in a direction roughly parallel to bathymetric contours by the Western Boundary Undercurrent (Swallow and Worthington, 1961; Barrett, 1965; Heezen et al., 1966; Schneider et al., 1967).

In conclusion, this study provides evidence that in the Wilmington Canyon area fines move by suspension from the outer shelf into deeper-water environments. The high amounts of particulate matter observed in outer shelf and slope waters may well be a key to understanding sedimentary patterns in deeper environments. The long-term lateral introduction and movement of fine-grained material along the shelf-break is a reasonable working hypothesis, and one that would certainly account for some of the clay and silt of shallow-water origin comprising the lower continental slope and rise off the mid-Atlantic States.

REFERENCES

BARRETT, J. R., JR.
    1965. Subsurface currents off Cape Hatteras. Deep-Sea Res., vol. 12, pp. 173-184.
DOYLE, L. J.; CLEARY, W. J.; and PILKEY, ORRIN H.
    1968. Mica: its use in determining shelf-depositional regimes. Marine Geol, vol. 6, pp. 381-389.
EITTREIM, S.; EWING, MAURICE; and THORNDIKE, EDWARD M.
    1969. Suspended matter along the continental margin of the North American Basin. Deep-Sea Res., vol. 16, pp. 613-624.
EWING, MAURICE, and THORNDIKE, EDWARD M.
    1965. Suspended matter in deep ocean water. Science, vol. 147, pp. 1291-1294, illus.
GORSLINE, DONN S.; DRAKE, D. E.; and BARNES, P. W.
    1968. Holocene sedimentation in Tanner Basin, California continental borderland. Bull. Geol. Soc. Amer., vol. 79, pp. 659-674.
GUNNERSON, C. G., and EMERY, KENNETH O.
    1962. Suspended sediment and plankton over San Pedro Basin, California. Limnol. Oceanogr., vol. 7, pp. 14-20.
HEEZEN, BRUCE C.; HOLLISTER, CHARLES, D.; and RUDDIMAN, WILLIAM F.
    1966. Shaping of the continental rise by deep geostrophic contour currents. Science, vol. 152, pp. 502-508, illus.

KELLING, G., and STANLEY, DANIEL J.
  1970. Morphology and structure of Wilmington and Baltimore Canyons, Eastern U.S.A. Journ. Geol., vol. 78, pp. 637-660.
MOORE, D. G.
  1966. Structure, litho-orogenic units and post-orogenic basin fill by reflection profiling: California continental borderland, 151 pp. U. S. Navy Electronics Laboratory.
SCHNEIDER, E. D.; FOX, P. J.; HOLLISTER, C. D.; NEEDHAM, H. D.; and HEEZEN, B. C.
  1967. Further evidence of contour currents in the Western North Atlantic. Earth and Planetary Sci. Letters, vol. 2, pp. 351-359.
STANLEY, DANIEL J.
  1970. Flyschoid sedimentation on the outer continental margin off northeast North America. *In* "Flysch Sedimentation in North America," J. Lajoie, ed. Geol. Assoc. Canada Spec. Paper 7, pp. 179-210.
SWALLOW, J. C., and WORTHINGTON, LAWRENCE V.
  1961. An observation of deep counter current in the western North Atlantic. Deep-Sea Res., vol. 8, pp. 1-19.

DANIEL J. STANLEY

A Research Vessel for
Marine Biological Investigations

Principal Investigator: Walter A. Starck, 2d, Marine Research Foundation, Chino, California.

Grant No. 625:   For planning the construction of a research vessel as a mobile base for coral-reef biological studies.

Coral reefs comprise and harbor what is probably the richest animal community on earth. Their faunas are rich not only in numbers of species but also in phylogenetic composition, adaptive specializations, and even total biomass. In spite of their tremendous interest to biologists these communities are relatively poorly studied owing to their inaccessibility, being both under water and in remote geographical locations.

To carry out significant scientific work on reefs requires a considerable mass of equipment, including tanks, compressors, a decompression chamber, and other diving equipment, collecting and preserving materials in bulk, a good fast small boat, instruments, and, ideally, sufficient tools and spare parts to keep everything functioning. Not only is the operation of shipping everything needed to a remote location impractical but also the job of setting up a land base and getting from there to the study site leads to considerable inefficiency in itself.

Ideally the answer is a fully equipped self-propelled floating base of operations that can function independently for several months at a time. The purpose of the present study was to develop a design for a vessel to serve such a function in a long-term program of coral-reef research that I had planned.

Multihulls, planing hulls, sail boats, and conventional displacement hulls had been considered and rejected. Multihulls perform poorly when heavily loaded, have reduced usable space within the hull, and are relatively expensive to construct. Planing hulls also yield poor performance when heavily loaded and are inefficient in fuel mileage. Sailing vessels are expensive, have a greater draft than desirable for use around reefs, and require increased crew and maintenance. Displacement hulls were closest

277

Fig. 1. *El Torito*

to the desired parameters, but conventional designs offer less deck and hull space and more draft than desired.

Maximum deck space, hull space, and stability with minimal draft and low maintenance are combined in a barge. A barge, however, is difficult to propel through the water. A preliminary design was developed involving a barge type of hull with lines modified so as to ease passage through the water. The American Marine Corporation of New Orleans, an experienced builder of barges, tow boats, and offshore supply vessels, was then consulted. No objections to the concept were raised by the company's marine architects and a complete design was requested of them.

Subsequently a steel vessel, named *El Torito*,[1] was constructed to this design for me by this corporation and has been in active service since. It has met or exceeded all expectations, and the basic design affords several advantages over more conventional vessels for a variety of applications.

The specifications of *El Torito:*

Length: 64 feet.

Beam: 28 feet.

Draft: 4 feet 6 inches light, 5 feet 6 inches loaded.

Propulsion: Twin GM 6-71 N diesels w/3:1 reduction.

Electrical power: 30 KW 208/117 V 3 phase.

Fuel[2]: 8,000 gallons.

Water[2]: 1,500 gallons.

Range: 5,000 miles.

Duration: 5 persons for 3 months.

Equipment: Wood Freeman Automatic pilot, Pierce-Simpson 55-watt marine radio-telephone, APN 9 Loran, Bendix 555 RFD, Raytheon 100 fathom recording fathometer, Ray Jefferson 240-foot indicating fathometer, 17-cubic-foot refrigerator, 17-cubic-foot freezer, electric stove, 25-ton air-conditioner, metal lathe, drill press, radial arm saw, bench grinder, belt sander, 7½-ton capacity hydraulic crane, double lock 400-foot deck decompression chamber, 400-foot submersible decompression chamber, 22-foot Aqua Sport fiberglas skiff with 100-horsepower outboard, 12-foot aluminum skiff with 10-horsepower outboard, Make K 13 and K 14 SCUBA compressors, closed circuit mixed gas and open circuit SCUBA.

Research equipment includes a binocular microscope, desk calculator, tape recorders, closed-circuit underwater television, portable hydrophones, a small library, and a complete range of 35-millimeter still and 16-millimeter motion-picture equipment for above and under water. Radar, single sideband radio, a fresh-water distillation unit, and microfilm research library are planned for the near future.

---

[1] *El Torito,* the little bull, is also the common name of the cowfish *Lactophrys quadricornis* in the Spanish-speaking Caribbean. The cowfish is a reef fish with a rigid external boxlike armor. Only the fins are movable to permit propulsion.

[2] An additional 2,500 gallons of either fuel or fresh water may be carried in the forward ballast tanks.

The vessel has proved itself exceptionally well suited to its purpose. The unusually beamy hull design provides great stability, the deck and hull space desired, and a relatively shallow draft, in a vessel small enough to be operated and maintained with minimal crew.

The low center of gravity and great beam provide stability so great that objects such as bookcases, filing cabinets, and the like do not have to be fastened down, and there has never been an instance when dinnerware on the table or pots on the stove have not stayed in place even in 40-mile-per-hour winds. The stability is also greatly appreciated at anchor while one is working with a microscope or photographing small specimens.

The conventional ship's bow eliminates pounding, and the flare makes for very dry operation as well as affording maximum deck space forward. The large deck area enclosed by bulwarks provides ample space for the skiffs, decompression chambers, hydraulic crane, and containers for larger specimens, with a large area left over for processing specimens or other work.

The wheelhouse serves for writing up field data and setting up breathing apparatus and underwater cameras while at anchor. A large storage space beneath the wheelhouse accommodates the air-conditioner, compressors, a variety of hand power tools, and miscellaneous parts and supplies.

All other accommodations are below decks. The lazarette contains a bank of gas cylinders for mixed gas diving, collecting and preserving materials, paint, and other bulk supplies. The engineroom is large enough to facilitate access to all the machinery and to accommodate a small machine shop for building and repairing equipment.

The galley and salon are incorporated in a large room running the full width of the vessel and constituting the main living area.

Forward are two double staterooms with private baths, and in the bow are two smaller rooms. One of the latter serves as an office-laboratory; the other, originally intended as a wet lab, has been converted to an additional stateroom. It has proved far preferable to work with specimens on deck rather than in a lab; hence the elimination of the wet lab. A 20-by-30-foot awning and wooden benches make a comfortable, spacious, and convenient work area on deck. Banks of floodlights provide light for night work.

Watertight bulkheads separate the lazarette, engineroom, galley-salon, staterooms, and laboratories.

The cruising speed of *El Torito* is 8 knots, only about 1 knot less than conventional displacement hulls of the same length and power but with only half the gross tonnage. Nine knots is possible at the full rated engine speed of 2,100 rpm. Eight knots is attained at 1,850 rpm.

The wide spacing of the twin screws and the tugboat style rudders with longitudinal strokes to direct the water flow contribute to excellent handling characteristics.

Hull maintenance is simplified by the uncomplicated exterior protected by epoxy over inorganic zinc primer. The sealed air-conditioned interior eliminates dampness and mildew problems with books, instruments, and other interior appointments. Stove, refrigerator, freezer, and air-conditioner are standard household types rather than specialized marine ones. None has given any problem after continual use. It has been my experience that marine appliances tend to be well constructed but poorly engineered compared to mass-market household items. As a consequence the marine appliances cost much more and break down more often, and it is more difficult to obtain parts or service for them. Changing engine oil is normally the only maintenance that has been required of the vessel while on expeditions, which have normally run for two months. Full time has been available for the scientific work. Maintenance of the scientific and diving equipment is, of course, another matter, as something is almost always in need of work with such equipment. With the machine shop aboard, however, and the stock of parts and raw materials carried, maintenance of this equipment is much simpler than it would be at a temporary base of a land-based expedition. Also, we can and do construct entirely new equipment in the field when a specialized need arises.

The characteristics of this design would make it advantageous over vessels now in use for a variety of purposes other than coral-reef investigations. Its outstanding stability would make it ideal as a mother ship for small submersibles. The large deck and hull space would also make it well suited for inter-island freight, and a whole range of oceanographic research needs could be served more comfortably and economically than they are by present vessels.

Finally, the economics of *El Torito* are quite favorable. Operation, maintenance, insurance, and amortization total approximately $200 per day based on 180 days per year operation. Vessels with equivalent capabilities at major oceanographic institutions cost a project $700 to $1,000 or more per day without amortization.

Hopefully this type of hull design will be further exploited in the future.

WALTER A. STARCK, 2D

An Occurrence of Great Stone Spheres in Jalisco, Mexico

Principal Investigator: Matthew W. Stirling, Archeologist Emeritus, Smithsonian Institution, Washington, D. C.

Grant Nos. 660, 683:   For a study of the large stone spheres discovered near Ahualulco de Mercado, Jalisco, Mexico.

During the summer of 1967, Ernest R. Gordon, a mining engineer, reported to me that he had seen several large stone spheres on a mountaintop near the town of Ahualulco de Mercado, about 40 miles west of Guadalajara in the state of Jalisco, Mexico. At my request he later sent me photographs of five of these. They averaged about 6 feet in diameter, were quite perfect in form, and reminded me of the large artificially made stone spheres first reported by Dr. Doris Stone from the Diquis delta in southwestern Costa Rica, the larger of which are about the same size.

In the course of my archeological investigations in Mexico I had previously found a few man-made stone spheres shaped from basalt. These seemed to belong to the late Olmec period and constituted an archeological puzzle. As a result I was eager to visit the Jalisco site and determine whether or not these examples were artificially made.

In December 1967, after receiving a permit from the Mexican Government, my wife and I flew to Guadalajara where we met Mr. Gordon, who drove us to the ruins of the old "Piedra Bola" mine headquarters. Dr. Stone accompanied us, and we climbed up the mountain to an elevation of about 6,000 feet, where we saw the five stone balls lying on top of a mountain spur. From this elevation, which the natives called "Mano de León," there was a magnificent view of the valley below. On the flat area of the spur was a small rectangular foundation of stones. All in all it seemed like an ideal location for a ceremonial site.

We returned to Ahualulco and hired a small crew to excavate the half-buried stones. After three days of work we not only exposed the buried spheres but also found an additional 17 in the immediate vicinity. All these ranged from 4 to 7 feet in diameter. During all the digging we did not find a single fragment of pottery or any other artifact indicating human occupation. The spheres although almost perfect in form did not exhibit the fine

283

FIG. 1.   Excavating stone sphere at Mano de León site, Sierra de Ameca, Jalisco.

surface finish that distinguished the Costa Rican specimens, and I was beginning to doubt their man-made origin.

Finally one of our workmen suggested that we would save ourselves a lot of labor if we went a few miles farther up the mountain, for at a place called Agua Blanca he said there were many more spheres, the majority fully exposed. Naturally we lost little time in getting horses, and after a two-hour ride we reached the crest of the Sierra de Ameca. First we began to see spheres singly or in pairs, and as we progressed many more lay in clusters along shallow depressions. We estimated that there were hundreds, and all doubt as to their natural origin vanished. However, we still had a problem, geological this time rather than archeological. It was obvious that the spheres were of volcanic origin. They varied in diameter from a minimum of 2 feet to a maximum of 11 feet. I had never heard of such a spectacular occurrence and decided that a geological specialist should study the site. At the Mano de León site the balls had relatively smooth surfaces, both because the location is protected and most of the balls were buried. At Agua Blanca, where they were exposed to the elements, the surfaces were rougher.

Back in Washington I consulted with Dr. Robert L. Smith of the U. S.

FIG. 2. Stone spheres averaging about six feet in diameter at Agua Blanca site, Sierra de Ameca, Jalisco.

Geological Survey, one of the few geologists qualified for this sort of study. In March 1968, Dr. Smith, guided by Ernest Gordon, visited the site. His examination in the field and his subsequent petrological analysis decided beyond reasonable doubt the origin of the phenomenon. He determined that the deposit was of Tertiary age. An avalanche of superheated ash descended from the volcano had covered the area.

Crystallization at high temperatures in the fiery tuff resulted in the formation of the spheres. The matrix consisted of about four-fifths hot volcanic glass particles by weight, with pore space composing slightly more than half of its bulk. At the presumed temperatures of between 1,000° and 1,400° F., with slow cooling the glassy volcanic ash could crystallize. This began in nuclei of single glass particles. Gases released from the glass moved outward in all directions, promoting crystallization of adjacent glass particles and thus formed the spheres. This process continued until stopped by cooling.

Dr. Smith reported: "I found one sphere still inclosed in an undisturbed ash matrix, which, although consolidated, was softer than the stone ball. But from the great majority of the spheres the matrix had eroded away, leaving only the exposed balls. I know but one other area of occurrence of similar spheres in ash deposits. This is near Los Alamos, New Mexico, where my colleague R. A. Bailey and I have found about six sites within an area of 500 square miles. The largest sphere there measured only 2 feet in diameter. The Jalisco examples, which range in diameter from 2 to more than 11 feet, may be unique in the world."

REFERENCE

STIRLING, MATTHEW W.
    1969. Solving the mystery of Mexico's great stone spheres.   Nat. Geogr. Mag., vol. 136, no. 2, pp. 294-300, illus.

MATTHEW W. STIRLING

Mineralogy of the Skarns in the Copper Mountain Mining District, Alaska

Principal Investigator: George S. Switzer, National Museum of Natural History, Smithsonian Institution, Washington, D. C.

Grant No. 637: In aid of a mineralogical study of the skarns in the Copper Mountain Mining District, Alaska.

The Copper Mountain mining district, Prince of Wales Island, Alaska, was active from 1902 to 1923 (Wright, 1915; Kennedy, 1953). The major mine in the district, the Jumbo, produced 5,000 tons of copper during that period — about one week's output of the great open-pit copper mine at Bingham, Utah. Since then it has been abandoned. Recently there has been some interest there in large-scale operations for low-grade copper ore, but only preliminary prospecting and drilling have taken place.

In addition to copper the locality is world famous for the large, brilliant, greenish-black crystals of epidote found in pockets in the rock (Palache, 1902). Specimens of this epidote can be seen in all the major mineralogical museums of the world. The last group to collect there went in 1935 (Montgomery, 1937), and the occurrence of the epidote and other unusual minerals found there has never been adequately studied.

In 1967 the National Geographic Society supported an expedition to the locality to study its mineralogy. Dr. George S. Switzer, the principal investigator, coordinated the over-all effort, supervised preparations, and visited the site late in July. The leader of the field party was Dr. Peter B. Leavens, at that time a postdoctoral research associate at the Smithsonian Institution. The other members were Richard W. Thomssen, an experienced field geologist from Tucson, Arizona, and Douglas Toland, an undergraduate at the University of Delaware. The field party spent two months on Prince of Wales Island, from June 18 to August 17.

We extend our thanks to Eskil Anderson, owner of the Copper Mountain and Green Monster area claims, for his cooperation in permitting exploration and sampling of the locality. John N. Patterson and Frank Ramboseh, of the U. S. Forest Service, South Tongass National Forest, gave valuable advice and assistance in the field. Members of the Pamp Meiers Lumber Co. were friendly and helpful at all times. Tamgass Airways provided reliable transportation under difficult field conditions. Dr. Edward P. Henderson and Dr. Arthur Montgomery, members of the 1935 expedition to the Copper Mountain district, gave much helpful advice on field conditions.

It is important to note that the epidote localities are on private property and that unauthorized collecting is illegal. Apparently there have been trespassing and blasting on the property since our expedition. This is unfortunate.

Setting

Prince of Wales Island, located in the southeastern panhandle of Alaska near the Canadian border, is part of Tongass National Forest. The Copper Mountain district is in the southern part of the island, at the head of Hetta Inlet. Ketchikan, the sixth largest city in Alaska, with a population of about 7,000 (1970 census), is 40 miles to the east by air, and the Indian village of Hydaburg is 15 miles distant by water. The small towns of Sulzer and Coppermount and extensive mine buildings, including an aerial tram and an ore-loading dock, were built in the district during mining days, but now these are abandoned and collapsed. The area may be reached most easily by pontoon-equipped airplane.

The topography is extremely steep and rugged, for the region was glaciated in the recent geologic past. The Jumbo Mine itself is perched on the wall of a glacial valley, and slopes in the vicinity of the mine average about 40°.

The climate is mild and wet. Our log shows that it rained every day between June 30 and July 20, and on most days it rained lightly but constantly. The mountains catch low clouds, and much more rain falls in the area of the mine than in the valley below.

The vegetation is very lush; on the valley floors is a forest of hemlock, spruce, and cedar. Some of the spruce trees are more than 5 feet in diameter. On the valley slopes the trees thin out, and timberline is at about 1,500 feet, near the level of the Jumbo Mine. Above timberline there is a thick scrub of alder and other brush. This gives way at about 1,800 feet to alpine meadow with mosses, small growth, and a few stunted trees. Above 3,000 feet extensive snowfields persist throughout the summer on the flanks of Copper Mountain (3,946 feet) and Mount Jumbo (3,464 feet).

General Geology

The rocks of the Copper Mountain district include marble, calcareous schist, quartz-mica schist, and greenstones. These were tightly folded, metamorphosed, and intruded by granitic magma during the Mesozoic era (Buddington and Chapin, 1923). The granitic rocks form a stock, about 10 square miles in area, in the center of the district; a small satellite stock is exposed on the flank of Green Monster Mountain. The rock of both stocks is predominantly granodiorite and shows signs of late hydrothermal alteration (Kennedy, 1953).

At the contacts between the granodiorites and the surrounding rocks extensive reaction took place, forming mixed rocks, or skarns, of calcium garnet, diopside, and epidote. The copper-ore deposits and many of the mineral-bearing pockets are found in a mass of limestone and calcareous schist, which was surrounded by the intruding magma. This inclusion is about 2½ miles long and comprises much of the summit area of Copper Mountain.

Jumbo Mine Area

Epidote is locally an abundant mineral in the skarn at the Jumbo Mine, which is situated in a nose of the inclusion. Kennedy (1953) distinguished three modes of occurrence for the epidote: irregular grains and clots replacing garnet, clusters of radiating crystals with quartz and calcite, and large crystals filling pockets, with quartz, actinolite, stilbite, and other minerals. The first two are normal occurrences for epidote in a skarn, but the third appears unique although similar in many respects to the fissure or vein deposits of the Tyrolean and Swiss Alps (Parker, 1960).

The epidote pockets have formed by hydrothermal alteration of the garnet skarn, for the pockets have envelopes of punky, altered garnet. Epidote is similar to calcium garnet in composition but contains water. The formula of epidote is Ca_2 (Al, Fe)$_3$ $(SiO_4)_3$ (OH); that of garnet Ca_3 (Al, Fe)$_2$ $(SiO_4)_3$.

Several small basaltic dikes occur in the Jumbo Mine area. None of the epidote pockets that we found was more than a few feet from identifiable dike rocks, and we feel that these dikes are the source of the altering solutions. A detailed discussion of this hypothesis and evidence in its support will be presented in another paper.

In the schists on the slopes of Copper Mountain above the Jumbo Mine, pockets are quite common; some are large enough for a person to crawl into or even sit in. The size of these cavities indicates that considerable material was removed during pocket mineralization. The minerals found in the pockets include adularia, andradite garnet (Ca and Fe rich), quartz, and pyrite. Actinolite and epidote are minor accessories. Some of the adularia crystals are more than an inch across and approach those from the Swiss alpine veins in their form and beauty. These pockets are not restricted to the vicinity of dikes and presumably have a different origin from that of the epidote pockets. The fact that garnet crystals are found in these pockets shows that they formed at a fairly high temperature, whereas the epidote pockets formed by the alteration of the garnet skarn at lower temperatures.

Green Monster Mountain Area

Three miles east of the Jumbo Mine, on the southwest slope of Green Monster Mountain, there is another garnet skarn, formed at the contact of the stock and the limestone country rock. Epidote pockets associated with late dikes are found here also.

Crystals within the pockets are generally large; single epidote crystals over 5 inches long and weighing several pounds were found in three of the pockets. Unfortunately, from the collector's point of view, many of the crystals are somewhat dull.

Minerals associated with the epidote in these pockets are quartz, actinolite variety amianthus, and hematite. In some pockets epidote crystals are altered to actinolite.

Most of the epidote crystals are detached from the pocket walls and occur embedded in a rubble of rock fragments and dark-brown mud rich in plant roots and other organic debris. Some of the crystals were broken during mineralization of the pockets, for they are cemented by quartz druzes and show signs of regrowth on the broken surfaces. However, much of the breaking is apparently the result of weathering, including frost wedging, and the action of roots, which extend deeply into every pocket and crevice on the steep slopes.

Contact Aureole of the Green Monster Stock

An unusual skarn is found at the crest of Green Monster Mountain, at the contact between limestones and the small stock mentioned above. This skarn attains a maximum thickness in outcrop of over 100 feet. We spent two days mapping this skarn and collected a suite of 40 samples. Field and laboratory studies show that it may be divided into several zones: altered igneous rock, diopside skarn, a zone characterized by the minerals diopside, fosterite, calcite, spinel, and talc, an outer zone characterized by monticellite and xanthophyllite, and a zone of slightly altered predazzite marble with minor spinel and fosterite.

Monticellite, a rare calcium-bearing member of the olivine family, is found only in a few high-temperature contact deposits. Talc, on the other hand, is characteristic of low temperature deposits, and the assemblage diopside-fosterite-talc-calcite has not been observed before or synthesized.

We hope that detailed chemical and textural studies will help explain this occurrence, and we plan to publish further information as our studies continue.

REFERENCES

BUDDINGTON, ARTHUR F., and CHAPIN, THEODORE S.
    1929. Geology and mineral deposits of southeastern Alaska. U. S. Geol. Surv. Bull. 800, 398 pp., illus.

KENNEDY, GEORGE C.
    1953. Geology and mineral deposits of Jumbo Basin, southeastern Alaska. U. S. Geol. Surv. Prof. Paper 251, 46 pp., illus.

MONTGOMERY, ARTHUR
    1937. The epidote localities of Prince of Wales Island, Alaska. Rocks and minerals, vol. 12, no. 7, pp. 195-208, illus.

PALACHE, CHARLES
    1902. A description of epidote crystals from Alaska. Proc. Amer. Acad. Arts and Sci., vol. 37, pp. 531-5, illus.

PARKER, R. L.
    1966. The fissure deposits of the Swiss Alps, their distribution and character. Cursillos y Conferencias del Institute "Lucas Mallada," fasc. 7, pp. 91-95.

WRIGHT, CHARLES WILL
    1915. Geology and ore deposits of Copper Mountain and Kasaan Peninsula, Alaska. U. S. Geol. Surv. Prof. Paper 87, 110 pp., illus.

PETER B. LEAVENS

The Olfactory Sense of the Kiwi *(Apteryx)*

Principal Investigator:　　Bernice M. Wenzel, School of Medicine, University of California, Los Angeles, California.

Grant No. 631:　　To study the specialized olfactory mechanism of the kiwi in New Zealand.

The olfactory habits and prowess of the kiwi have long been subjects of speculation for both anatomical and behavioral reasons. The feeding behavior of this flightless and nocturnal bird, for example, consists of probing the soil with its beak to obtain such items as earthworms, grubs, and small insects. Early observers noted that the bird's visual capacity seemed to be very limited in spite of its nocturnal existence, an observation that immediately suggested the importance of an alternative sense. Olfaction was implicated by two anatomical features. First, the kiwi is unique among extant birds in having its external nares located at the tip of the beak rather than at the base; second, the size of the olfactory bulbs relative to the rest of the forebrain is greater than that of almost any other bird for which such measurements have been made. In spite of much curiosity, virtually no experimentation of any kind has been done and no systematic work has ever been attempted. Nevertheless, some investigators have made the undocumented decision that olfaction is the critical sense in kiwis' food-getting behavior.

The expedition described here was undertaken to answer two questions: (1) Can kiwis locate food by means of olfactory cues alone and (2) how does their olfactory acuity compare with that of other birds that have much smaller olfactory bulbs? Though the grant was made in 1967, this research was done the following year.

Methods

These questions were attacked in separate experiments conducted in two different places and will be described consecutively. Both were made possible through the continuous and never-failing cooperation of the Wildlife Service of the Department of Internal Affairs of New Zealand.

Field Observations. This research was carried out at the Mount Bruce Native Bird Reserve, 17 miles north of Masterton, North Island, New Zealand. The general procedure was to establish three adjacent feeding stations in each of two enclosed aviaries containing two kiwis apiece. The fact that the birds ate there regularly made it possible to manipulate certain features of the food supply in order to evaluate the birds' ability to detect and respond to changes in the olfactory character of the food supply.

Each feeding station consisted of two parts, (1) a slightly tapered aluminum tube, which held the food and was sunk into the ground, and (2) an aluminum outer ring, which surrounded the opening of the tube and rested on the surface of the ground. The ring served as a detection device, for it contained an infrared light source and a photocell. The beam of infrared light extended across the top of the food dish and was broken whenever a kiwi approached the food even with only the tip of the beak. Each of the detection rings was connected by buried wires to an amplifier and recorder. The entire circuitry was powered through a time switch so that everything was turned on automatically at nightfall and was turned off at dawn. A separate channel on the recorder was used for each feeding station; every time the beam was broken at that station a mark was recorded on the appropriate channel. The stations were arranged about 2 feet apart in a gentle arc. In aviary 1 they were placed about a yard away from a shallow concrete drinking pool and close to the trunks of some tree ferns but otherwise in an open area. In aviary 2 they were about a foot away from the edge of a similar pool in open grass with a thicket about a yard to the right.

Five kiwis were available for participation in the experiments at Mount Bruce. The two in aviary 2 were entirely wild and were rarely seen. The inhabitant in aviary 1 at the beginning of the experiments was a single bird that had a history of illness and varied medication. This bird frequently emerged from the burrow in bright daylight during the afternoon and often approached human beings who might be in the aviary at the time. Midway through the experimental work this bird was removed to another section and was replaced by two other kiwis that had been in a third aviary and had been used for exhibition to the public. One of these birds had lost a foot and the lower part of one leg in a trap in the wild but was in good health at the time of the experiments and had no difficulty in maintaining itself in captivity. The other bird was a young adult that had been in captivity from a fairly early age so that it was less resistant to being handled than kiwis naturally are. Neither of these birds spontaneously emerged before nightfall.

There was no difficulty in establishing normal feeding behavior at the new feeding stations. By the second night all birds were eating their normal amount of food from the deep tubes. The regular diet for kiwis at Mount Bruce consisted of a redolent mixture of strips of raw steak, large water-soaked raisins, starter mash, and vitamin powder.

Two types of experiments were conducted. In the first, a foreign odorant was introduced on a small piece of cotton wrapped in screening at the bottom of one of the three tubes of food in each aviary. Unscented cotton was added to the tubes. The number of visits to the specially scented tube was then compared with those to the other tubes. The four odorants used were amyl acetate, trimethylpentane, pyridine, and synthetic musk. The last-named was used for a special test of olfactory attraction. It was added to a pot of dirt in one station, while the other two stations contained unscented dirt. Food was provided nearby in an open tray. If the musk proved to be an attractant, it was expected that the birds would make more visits to the scented station.

The second experiment consisted of covering the containers very tightly with semirigid nylon screening after food was put in one and dirt in the others. I had already determined that the birds would puncture such screening with their beaks and withdraw food placed underneath. Therefore, by screening the food and the dirt and leaving at least an inch of space between the top of the contents and the screen so that the contents could not be identified by licking the top of the screen, the ability of the kiwis to choose the food-baited container by odor cues alone could be tested. In a slight alteration of the latter procedure, huge earthworms were placed in pots of dirt that were completely enclosed with screen at one station while the other pots contained dirt alone.

Control nights, i.e., nights on which no experimental treatment was applied, were interspersed in the beginning with experimental nights so that the normal pattern of visits to each of the three stations could be determined. It was important to know whether the birds ate consistently more heavily from one point than from another, as well as whether there was any systematic shifting of preference among the three stations.

Laboratory Observations. To obtain some idea of the kiwis' sensitivity to odors, laboratory measurements were made in the Department of Physiology at the University of Otago Medical School in Dunedin. The procedure followed was essentially the same as that used in my laboratories at the University of California at Los Angeles and at the Institute for Comparative Biology at the San Diego Zoo with several other avian species. It consisted of continuous recording of heart and respiratory rates while the bird rested in a gentle stream of pure air, which can be odorized at known intensities from time to time. Changes in physiological index coincident with presentation of an odorous stimulus can be interpreted as a sign of perception of that stimulus. A dilution olfactometer was constructed as well as a fiberboard enclosure in which the bird was restrained lightly and maintained in a resting condition. It contained a DC light and high-fidelity loudspeaker in addition to the inlet of the olfactometer. Recording was done on either an Ediswan recorder or a Grass polygraph.

Two kiwis were available for this phase of the experimentation. One was the young bird on which feeding data had already been collected at Mount Bruce, and the other was a much older kiwi that had been living for a number of years in virtual seclusion at the Botanic Garden in Dunedin. The bird from Mount Bruce was housed at the Botanic Garden under reasonably natural conditions and was driven to the laboratory shortly before each experimental session and returned to the Garden immediately after. Because of the kiwis' nocturnal habit, experimental sessions were usually scheduled in the late afternoon and early evening so that the birds would be rested and partly awake but not yet in their most active food-gathering phase. The old Dunedin bird proved to be so restless and resistant to handling that no complete sessions were accomplished with it; therefore, virtually all the data to be reported on this part of the project were collected from one kiwi. Enough data were obtained from the old bird, however, to validate the general procedure and some of the impressions gained from the younger one.

Recording of heart rate was done by means of needle electrodes inserted into the skin over the left pectoral muscle and on the left thigh. A third electrode, as ground, was inserted into the right thigh. Respiration was recorded through a crystal transducer placed lightly in contact with the chest wall. EEG recordings were made with two Grass needle electrodes that penetrated the scalp slightly to the left and right of the midline and about 1½ inches posterior to the margin of the orbit. There was a lateral separation of about a quarter of an inch between electrode tips.

The odorous stimuli were amyl acetate, pyridine, trimethylpentane, whole and cut-up earthworms, and the birds' regular food. As control stimuli the light bulb inside the box was turned on or a pure tone was presented at 1,000 cycles and 80 decibels. The duration of each of these stimuli was 10 seconds. Two other auditory stimuli were presented for their own sake, viz., a recording of kiwi calls made in the bush and pure tones at frequencies of 20,000 and 25,000 cycles.

Results

Field Observations. The first important observation was the fact that the birds showed neither any consistent preferences for one feeding station over the others nor any tendency to avoid one station consistently.

The effect of adding the foreign odor underneath the regular food in one of the three feeding tubes interacted with a number of factors. The most significant of these was the particular odorant used, but other influences included the location of the scented station, the amount of moisture in the soil of the aviary (the softer the soil, the more the birds could dig up their own food), and the amount the birds had eaten on the previous night.

In one aviary amyl acetate was used on six nights alternating with six nights of normal feeding. The location of the amyl acetate was varied systematically so that each station was scented twice but not in a regular progression. On three of the six nights the birds ate less food from the scented dish than from the two unscented ones; on the other three nights the same amount of food was eaten from each tube. If any tube was visited less often than the others, it was always the scented one, but the scent alone was not enough to keep the birds away consistently. Essentially the same results were obtained on three out of four nights in the other aviary. The exception was one night during which more eating was done from the scented station than from the others. Combining the results for all the tests with amyl acetate, we can generalize that if any station is visited less often than the others, it is the scented station.

Trimethylpentane was used on three nights and had no effect. On each of these nights there was more activity at the scented station than at one or both of the others.

Pyridine was used sparingly because of its possible toxic effects. Two tests were made in one aviary about two weeks apart. In the first test pyridine was added to one station; the food there was barely touched, while the other two were almost completely emptied. In the second test pyridine was added to two of the stations with the result that 75-85 percent of the food was taken from these two while the third station was completely emptied. Pyridine was also used three times in the other aviary, but it seemed to have no effect.

In two tests all three of the above odorants were used, with one in each tube. The rationale of these tests was to obtain some indication of the relative effectiveness of each compound, but the results were inconclusive. On one night the station with amyl acetate added was visited most frequently, while on the second night the amyl acetate tube was visited least often. On both of these nights the center station was visited most frequently, and it contained a different odorant on each night. This type of experiment would probably be fruitful if it could be conducted over a longer period of time with many interspersed control nights.

The expectation was not supported that musk might attract activity to the feeding station where it was used. When visits to one station containing musk-scented dirt were compared with visits to stations of normal dirt, the results were ambiguous. Sometimes the former was visited most often and sometimes least often. In the latter instance, interpretation was complicated by the fact that the total number of visits to all stations was extremely low. This type of experiment would also be a profitable one to continue on a longer-range basis.

The other general experiment, testing ability to locate food, provided completely conclusive results. Except for two tests with the single kiwi, which failed to puncture the covers over the tubes of food, all the food dishes were broken into in every test and none of the dishes of dirt was opened except for one very small hole in one cover on one night.

The birds' ability to identify the location of the food extended to the situation in which the feeding tubes were only partly filled with food so that the top of the food could then be covered with a small, plastic, dirt-filled, tightly screened pot that had a hole punched in the bottom of it. In order to obtain the food from the tube it was necessary for a bird to break through the fly screen over the small pot, penetrate the dirt in the pot with its beak, pass the beak through the hole in the bottom of the pot, and then withdraw the food from the aluminum tube. This test was completely passed. In each aviary the tube that contained nothing but dirt beneath the pot was untouched, as was the dirt-filled screened pot on top of it, but the two tubes that contained food covered by the small screened pot of dirt had been broken into and at least a portion of the food consumed. Holes had been made in the screens over the small pots covering these tubes, and the pots had actually been removed from the tubes.

On one night one station was three-quarters full of dirt with one-quarter of a tube of food on the top, the second station contained entirely food, and the third station was filled with dirt. Each of the stations was tightly screened, and about a quarter-inch of dirt was spread over the top of each screen. The first kiwi visited the stations very shortly after they were set up. The bird went first to the dish that was filled with food and probed very briefly, and then moved on to the dish that was one-quarter food and three-quarters dirt. It worked hard at the screen for a while and then visited each dish again. It moved away from the stations at this point. Inspection of the dishes showed that the bird had made several holes in the screen over the tube that was part food and part dirt and one hole in the tube filled with food. The dirt film was undisturbed over the screen covering the tube that contained nothing but dirt. Somewhat later the other kiwi approached the stations, went directly to the tube filled with food, moved to the other station with some food in it, and finally left. In the morning the dirt film remained completely undisturbed over the screen covering the tube of dirt, while the covers on both of the other two tubes were thoroughly punctured.

The only tests that approximated the kiwi's natural feeding behavior in the bush were those in which one or more earthworms were put into a screened pot of dirt in one feeding station in each aviary, while the other stations contained either dirt or the birds' prepared food. Giant-size earthworms were available only briefly and were used in two tests involving three kiwis. As with the food tests, the single bird proved unenterprising and failed to break into any of the pots. The birds in the other aviary, however, made many holes in the screen over the pot containing the worm in one test, and the worm was gone in the morning. No holes were made in the covers over the pots that contained dirt alone and almost no visits were made to these stations (one and three visits, respectively). In this test not only were the pots tightly screened all around, so that the birds had to break in to get the worm and the worm could not crawl out by itself, but also a one-inch cover of dirt was placed on top of the screens. The implication of the results is that one or both birds detected the worm through the dirt cover and also ruled out the presence of a worm in the other two stations, which were left untouched. In the first of the two tests with these worms the birds did not break into the baited pot, but in that case the bait consisted of living pieces of giant worms whereas in the second test one whole worm was used. In two other tests involving the use of worms, only small worms were available and the pots containing them were not broken into. In these tests one of the other stations contained prepared food and was broken into. It may be that the competition of the full tube of the meat mixture completely overcame any appeal for small earthworms in a pot of dirt.

Laboratory Observations. Surprisingly, the kiwi's heart rate proved to be almost totally unresponsive to a variety of environmental stimuli, so that it could not be used as an indicator of perception. The rate in any given session was remarkably constant regardless of the presentation of olfactory, auditory, and visual stimuli. Both the respiration and EEG gave reliable evidence of perception, however, so that estimates of absolute sensitivity to olfactory stimuli could be made. The changes in respiration occurred in pattern rather than in rate. They varied somewhat for different odors as well as for stimuli in other modalities. The general effect was irregularity accompanied by a considerable flattening of the record, which indicated a reduction in amplitude. With amyl acetate, respiration became shallow and irregular, whereas with pyridine the main characteristic was the extreme shallowness of otherwise regular breathing. In the case of odorous stimuli, the changes typically began immediately after the first inhalation following the onset of stimulus presentation and continued until a few seconds after the stimulus had been turned off. A feature of the DC lighting circuit used was a gradual buildup of current, so that the intensity of the light reached its maximum a few seconds after it was turned on. The slow onset of the respiratory change tends to confirm the claim of poor visual sensitivity for the kiwi, because it indicates that the light had to be very bright before it was perceived.

The change in the EEG was an alteration from high-amplitude, low-frequency activity to low-amplitude and high-frequency waves, which is the familiar accompaniment of a behavioral alteration from drowsiness or inattention to alertness. Although it was possible to record these changes in only two sessions of stimulus presentations, these records provided valuable evidence for a correlation between the EEG change and the respiratory change, making it safe to conclude that whenever the respiratory change occurred it was an indication of behavioral alerting due to perception of the stimulus. It can be said that the respiratory changes described here were never observed in any session at a time other than during stimulus presentation. The resting record contained no instances of such changes although other types of irregularities were seen from time to time which, in turn, were not seen during a stimulus. By the same token, the changes that tended to accompany the presentations of perceptible stimuli were not seen during the presentation of the control stimuli in which the stimulus valve was turned as if to deliver a stimulus but the olfactometer contained no odorant.

From analysis of the respiratory records, supplemented by the EEG data, it can be said that the kiwi's absolute thresholds for the olfactory substances used in these experiments were lower than those of other birds that have been studied in this way. In the time available it was possible only to establish this relationship. Accurate determination of the threshold value for many different compounds would require much more testing.

The over-all conclusions of the entire expedition were, in terms of the questions posed at the beginning: (1) Kiwis are capable of locating food, both natural and prepared, by means of olfactory cues alone; (2) their olfactory acuity, in terms of absolute thresholds for test chemicals, is lower than that of other birds with smaller olfactory bulbs.

BERNICE M. WENZEL

The Systematics, Ecology, Evolution, and Zoogeography of African Turtles

Principal Investigator: Roger Conant Wood, Stockton State College, Pomona, New Jersey.

Grant Nos. 632, 668: In aid of research, both field and laboratory, on the living and fossil turtles of Africa.

In the course of my studies on the fossil turtles of Africa I found it necessary to know something about the ecology of and variation within and among species of living African turtles. When confronted with this necessity, however, I discovered that existing museum collections and publications based on them were inadequate for these purposes. Within the genus *Pelusios,* for example, one of the most widespread of the endemic African turtles, there has been no general agreement as to either the number of species or the diagnostic traits that characterize them. As few as four (Loveridge, 1941) and as many as ten (Laurent, 1965) species of *Pelusios* have been recognized at various times. In order to analyze meaningfully the usually fragmentary and often sparse remains of African fossil turtles it was necessary to understand the kinds of parameters useful in delimiting species of their living relatives. Therefore, with support from the National Geographic Society I spent six months in East Africa from October 1967 to March 1968 acquiring population samples of living turtles from selected localities. By observing their distribution and habitats in the field, and then combining the resulting information with museum studies of their morphology, I have been able to resolve a number of problems concerning the ecology and taxonomy of living African turtles, particularly those endemic forms belonging to the family Pelomedusidae. These studies have in turn afforded a solid foundation for my work on their fossil precursors.

My original intention had been to make collections at a number of localities reflecting a wide range of habitats in Kenya, Uganda, and Tanzania. Unfortunately, for a variety of reasons—the onset of the rainy season, dwindling funds, and the repeated breakdown of my battered field vehicle—I was unable to carry out any significant field work in Tanzania, nor did I encounter success at every one of the localities I was able to visit in Kenya and Uganda. Nevertheless, I collected several hundred specimens, using a wide variety of techniques. (These specimens are now part of the herpetological collections of the Museum of Comparative Zoology at Harvard.) Primary reliance was placed on trapping techniques recommended by Prof. J. M. Legler of the University of Utah (Legler, 1960), and I am particularly grateful to him for lending me some of his own traps to use on my expedition. In the larger lakes where the traps proved to be relatively ineffective, I was able to supplement my own collections with specimens obtained from local fishermen. In several places young schoolchildren were a useful source of specimens. On occasion, the use of dip nets over the side of a boat or while wading in very small ponds or pools proved to be an effective means of capturing aquatic turtles. Sometimes it was simplest merely to chase a turtle and grab it by hand.

Much of my success, wherever I collected, was made possible only by the friendly cooperation of local people, too numerous to mention individually. I am particularly grateful to my two field assistants, Daniel Ngumi and Simeon Rueben, for their unremitting enthusiasm and effort. They cheerfully endured conditions that were often trying and at times either hazardous or unpleasant or even occasionally both.

Scientific Results

After returning from East Africa I concentrated largely on studying the endemic side-necked turtles belonging to the family Pelomedusidae. I did so for three reasons: (1) Considerably less is known about the living African pelomedusids than about the other living African turtles, which have been the subject of a comprehensive and relatively recent revision (Loveridge and Williams, 1957); (2) most of the specimens I was able to collect on my expedition were pelomedusids; and (3) work on this family has been an essential prerequisite for my study of the fossil turtles of Africa, since the preponderance of these are pelomedusids.

Systematics. Taxonomic changes on the subfamilial, specific, and subspecific levels have resulted from my studies of the living African pelomedusids.

Zangerl (1948) subdivided the Pelomedusidae into two subfamilies, the Pelomedusinae and the Pelusiinae. Only a single genus, *Pelusios,* was assigned to the Pelusiinae, while the remaining genera recognized by Zangerl were all included in the Pelomedusinae. These conclusions were based primarily on a single feature of shell morphology, the size and position of the mesoplastra. *Pelusios* is the only pelomedusid having large, quadrangular meso-plastra meeting at the midline, whereas all the others are characterized by small, laterally placed hexagonal or subrounded mesoplastra. But if Wil-liams's contention (1954) that the large mesoplastra of *Pelusios* have been secondarily derived from the small ones typical of all other pelomedusids is correct, then this character is probably not of taxonomic significance above the generic level. Quite a different picture of pelomedusid relationships is obtained, however, by an analysis of skull structure. On the basis of an ex-amination of a suite of skulls that I prepared, I have confirmed the remark-able similarity, first commented on by Williams (1954), between the skulls of *Pelomedusa* and *Pelusios*. Without associated shell material, it is often vir-tually impossible to determine whether a skull belongs to a representative of one genus or another. Furthermore, the skulls of these two genera can easily be distinguished from those of any other pelomedusids. Consequent-ly, I suspect that *Pelusios* and *Pelomedusa* are much more closely related to each other than either is to any of the other pelomedusid genera. To for-malize this opinion I am including these two genera within the same sub-family, the Pelomedusinae, thus eliminating the subfamily Pelusiinae. But, except for *Pelomedusa* and *Pelusios,* none of the other genera that Zangerl included within the Pelomedusinae (or that have subsequently been de-scribed) properly belongs there. For these taxa I am proposing a new sub-familial name (Wood, 1971). Of Zangerl's two pelomedusid subfamilies, therefore, I have eliminated one (the Pelusiinae) and retained the other (the Pelomedusinae) but drastically altered its contents.

Laurent (1965) recognized six more species of *Pelusios* than did Love-ridge (1941), but of these I suspect that only two *(P. nanus* and *P. niger)* are valid. On the basis of studies still in progress, I believe that the others *(P. bechuanicus, P. carinatus, P. castaneus,* and *P. williamsi)* are all probably geographic variants of *P. subniger,* a species in which there is evidently a great degree of intraspecific variation. To cite one striking example of poly-morphism, even within a local population of this species, at Lake George in western Uganda there are marked differences in carapace coloration among adults, some being entirely black while others are uniformly light brown.

Osteological analysis of the shells of living representatives of the genus *Pelusios* has convinced me that two species groups can be recognized. One of these, in which I would include the species *P. adansonii, P. gabonensis, P. niger,* and *P. nanus,* is characterized by generally smaller shell size, medially tapering mesoplastra, and relatively restricted distributions just below the southern margin of the Sahara Desert and in parts of western Africa. The other group, containing *P. sinuatus* and *P. subniger,* is in contrast characterized by large shells, rectangular mesoplastra that do not taper medially, and widespread distributions that cover large portions of sub-Saharan Africa. Similar partitioning of the genus has previously been suggested by Siebenrock (1909) and Williams (1954).

Loveridge (1941) recognized two subspecies of the monotypic genus *Pelomedusa, P. subrufa subrufa* and *P. subrufa olivacea*. The latter was distinguished from the former solely in having pectoral scutes which did not meet in the midline (Loveridge, 1941). But population samples of *Pelomedusa subrufa* from central Uganda revealed that this is a variable character. Specimens from a single locality exhibit the pectoral scute arrangements characteristic of both of these supposed subspecies, and in some individuals an intermediate condition may be seen in which one of the pair of pectoral scutes reaches the midline of the plastron whereas the other does not. Thus, continued recognition of the subspecies proposed by Loveridge is clearly no longer merited.

Ecology. Pelomedusa subrufa is found throughout most of sub-Saharan Africa. Yet this species seems to have rather narrowly defined and highly specialized habitat preferences. Wherever I collected samples of *P. subrufa* in East Africa, it invariably occurred as small populations localized in streams and pools subject to seasonal drying up. For this reason I would agree with Buxton (1937) and Loveridge (1941), who both have suggested that this species must burrow into the ground and estivate during periods of drought. Such an unusual niche probably accounts for the extreme rarity of *Pelomedusa* in the African fossil record. Fossiliferous terrestrial sediments are normally deposited in lake beds, river channels, or across flood plains. Strata representing other kinds of environments, such as the temporary rock pools or ephemerally flowing streams in which *Pelomedusa* commonly occurs, are rarely encountered in the sedimentary record. If we assume that the present habitat preferences of this genus have been typical of it during most or all of its evolutionary existence, then its rarity as a fossil follows as a natural consequence of its ecology (Wood, in press).

Cases of sympatry in *Pelusios* sometimes involve members of the two different species groups. *P. subniger,* for example, has overlapping distributions with both *P. gabonensis* and *P. nanus*. However, sympatry occurs also within species groups; there are partial coincidences in the distributions of *P. gabonensis* with both *P. adansonii* and *P. niger,* as well as of *P. sinuatus* with that of *P. subniger*. Unfortunately, no instances of sympatry occurred in that part of East Africa where I was collecting. All my specimens of *Pelusios* belong to the species *P. subniger*. But an analysis of these specimens, now in progress, is providing basic information on intraspecific variation in terms of morphology and feeding habits. Using this knowledge of *P. subniger* as a key to interpreting other species less well represented in museum collections, I may eventually be able to explain sympatric situations within this genus in terms of character displacement and differential food preferences.

Evolution and Zoogeography. Only the fossil record provides direct evidence concerning the evolutionary history and past distribution of any group of organisms. My research on the fossil pelomedusids of Africa has revealed that the evolution of this group has been quite extraordinary (Wood, 1971), but since I am preparing an extensive monograph on this subject for publication elsewhere I will not discuss this particular aspect of my pelomedusid studies here. One important outgrowth of these paleontological studies, however, has been the publication of several papers on non-African fossil pelomedusids (Wood, 1970; Wood and Gamero, 1971), as well as another on a specimen originally lent to me in the belief that it represented some sort of pelomedusid but which actually proved referable to the Toxochelyidae, an extinct family of marine turtles previously known only from North America and Europe (Wood, 1973).

Nevertheless, indirect inferences regarding the evolution of any particular group can sometimes be derived from studying its living representatives. With this idea in mind, I attempted to collect pelomedusids in Lake Logipi, a saline lake located in the remote and barren Suguta Valley of northwestern Kenya. Paleontological evidence indicates that most of the earliest pelomedusids were apparently marine forms that subsequently developed their present ability to live in fresh water. If this were the case, I thought it possible that living forms might still have retained some degree of tolerance for salty water, and I was hoping to find specimens at Lake Logipi that might provide neontological evidence tending to corroborate a hypothesis originally suggested solely on the basis of paleontological evidence. In this endeavor, however, I was unsuccessful.

In many groups of organisms it is possible to assess the degree of relationship among the contained taxa on the basis of cytogenetic studies. Relationships determined by this method presumably reflect the amount of evolution that has occurred since various lineages diverged from one another. Because the present techniques involved in karyotypic analysis require fresh blood samples, I sent a shipment of live African turtles via air freight from Nairobi to Harvard in March 1968. Owing to negligence on the part of airport employees, these unfortunate creatures were frozen solid (and hence were useless for their intended purpose) when a representative from the museum picked them up. Consequently this potentially informative line of investigation could not be pursued systematically, but I still hope eventually to obtain the specimens necessary for completing this project. Several African pelomedusid species subsequently secured have already been karyotyped, but much remains to be done, and no conclusions based on this approach are yet possible.

REFERENCES

BUXTON, D. R.
  1937. A natural history of the Turkana fauna. Journ. East Africa and Uganda Nat. Hist. Soc., vol. 13, pp. 85-104, illus.
LAURENT, R. F.
  1965. A contribution to the knowledge of the genus *Pelusios* (Wagler). Ann. Mus. Roy. Afr. Centrale, Tervuren, ser. 8 (Sci. Zool.), no. 135, pp. 1-33, illus.
LEGLER, JOHN M.
  1960. A simple and inexpensive device for trapping aquatic turtles. Proc. Utah Acad. Sci., Arts, and Letters, vol. 37, pp. 63-66.
LOVERIDGE, ARTHUR
  1941. Revision of the African terrapin of the family Pelomedusidae. Bull. Mus. Comp. Zool., vol. 88, no. 6, pp. 467-524.
LOVERIDGE, ARTHUR, and WILLIAMS, ERNEST E.
  1957. Revision of the African tortoises and turtles of the suborder Cryptodira. Bull. Mus. Comp. Zool., vol. 115, no. 6, pp. 163-557, illus.
SIEBENROCK, F.
  1909. Synopsis der rezenten Schildkröten, mit Berücksichtigung der in historischer Zeit ausgestorbenen Arten. Zool. Jahrb., Suppl. 10, pp. 427-618.
WILLIAM, ERNEST E.
  1954. A new Miocene species of *Pelusios* and the evolution of that genus. Breviora, no. 25, 7 pp., illus.
WOOD, ROGER C.
  1970. A review of the fossil Pelomedusidae (Testudines, Pleurodira) of Asia. Breviora, no. 357, 24 pp., illus.
  1971. The fossil Pelomedusidae (Testudines, Pleurodira) of Africa. Ph.D. thesis, Biology Department, Harvard University.
  1973a. Fossil marine turtle remains from the Paleocene of the Congo. Ann. Mus. Roy. Afr. Centrale, Tervuren, ser. 8 (Sci. Géol.), no. 75, pp. 1-35, illus.
  1973b. A possible correlation between the ecology of living African pelomedusid turtles and their relative abundance in the fossil record. Copeia, 1973, pp. 627-629.
WOOD, ROGER C., and GAMERO, M.
  1971. *Podocnemis venezuelensis,* a new fossil pelomedusid (Testudines, Pleurodira) from the Pliocene of Venezuela and a review of the history of *Podocnemis* in South America. Breviora, no. 376, 23 pp., illus.
ZANGERL, RAINIER
  1948. The vertebrate fauna of the Selma formation of Alabama, pt. 2: The pleurodiran turtles. Fieldiana: Geol. Mem., vol. 3, no. 2, pp. 19-56, illus.

ROGER CONANT WOOD

The Icefield Ranges Research Project, 1967

Principal Investigator: Walter A. Wood, Arctic Institute of North America, Washington, D. C.

Grant No. 647: For continued support of the glaciological, geological, and climatological investigations in the St. Elias Mountains of Alaska and Yukon Territory, Canada, under the auspices of the Arctic Institute of North America.

Among the dramatic events that occur in nature the sudden acceleration of the flow rate of a valley glacier deserves a high ranking. Known as "catastrophic surges," literally billions of tons of glacier ice flow downstream at velocities known to exceed 100 times the "normal" rate of advance and create a chaos as disruptive to the glacier's mass as it is to topographic features in its path.

It has long been known that some glaciers may advance suddenly, but, largely through the work of Meier and Post (1969), we have come to understand that most of these sporadic advances belong to a new class of glacierflow phenomena and that they are not as uncommon as they were once thought to be. Into this class falls the Steele Glacier, which drains a portion of the northeastern flank of the St. Elias Mountains in Yukon Territory.

Most surge-type glaciers occur in remote mountain systems. Consequently recognition of a surge commonly occurs long after the chaotic event. Steele Glacier, on the contrary, was first explored in 1935, and photogrammetric surveys by Wood in that year and in 1936, 1939, 1941, and 1947 provide the basis of a chronology useful in comparing the pre- and postsurge geometry of the glacier. Finally, the onset of the catastrophic surge of Steele Glacier was observed by Post in August 1965, and its progress was documented by elements of the Icefield Ranges Research Project in 1966 and 1967; thus, Steele Glacier provides a rare opportunity to observe and study a glacier while in the act of surging.

A glacier surge results from the sudden decoupling of the glacier from its bed. The mechanism whereby this takes place has become the subject of wide scientific discussion, and the explanation involves the most important problem awaiting solution in the dynamics of glacier flow — the slip of a glacier along its bed. This factor alone, while critical, is insufficient to explain

FIG. 1. The lower trunk and terminus (August 1967) of the Steele Glacier surge. Photographs reproduced as figures 2 and 3 were taken from a survey station indicated by the triangle, and their axes were oriented approximately at right angles to the axis of glacier flow. Photograph by Walter A. Wood.

these events. Other contributing elements involve a knowledge of the gross geometry of the glacier before, during, and after surge; the subglacier topography, surface profile, thermal regime, and velocities; and the life history of the surge.

By June 1967 the surge of Steele Glacier had been in progress for 22 months, and from observation of five well-defined features on the glacier surface that had survived downstream transport it became apparent that surface movement of the middle third of the glacier's length (some 11 kilometers) had been approximately 5,000 meters. Moreover, surface velocity in midstream was measured in August 1966 to be of an order of 15 meters per day, a rate consistent with the average monthly advance since August 1965.

In May, and again in August 1967, surface velocity measurements were made in the same area of flow as in 1966, and these show an average daily rate of about 7 meters. Thus, downstream surface motion had slowed rough-

FIG. 2. Looking north across lower Steele Glacier in July 1941. The stagnant ice of the glacier is almost completely covered by a mantle of debris (light-colored material in middle distance). The trimline on the north side of the glacier is 2 kilometers from the camera station. Photograph by Walter A. Wood.

ly 50 percent since the month of August 1966. (These velocities are consistent with the results obtained photogrammetrically by Stanley, 1969). This decrease in surface velocities throughout the middle third of Steele Glacier in 1967 was even more dramatically noted in the terminus of the surging ice. Whereas during the first year of chaotic advance the tongue of active ice had moved at velocities only slightly less than those observed in the higher reaches of the glacier, by August 1967 it was obvious that terminal motion had slowed almost to a halt and it was apparent that, unless newly generated dynamics were to come into play, the surge of Steele Glacier would end before the 1968 field season.

Twice in 1966 and again in 1967 Steele Glacier and its tributaries were photographed for purposes of large-scale mapping by the Department of Energy, Mines, and Resources, Canada. Similar aerial coverage is planned for the early post-surge period. Thus provision has been made for detailed analysis of a number of important elements of the surge that can be derived

FIG. 3.   Photograph taken in July 1967 from the same location as figure 2. Compare the ice horizon of the surging glacier with easily identifiable fixed reference points on the valley walls in background. Photograph by Walter A. Wood.

from examination of surface features. As an interim aid to these surveys, the chronology of the surge was recorded in three aerial flights in May, July, and August 1967 using high and low oblique photography, under National Geographic Society grant no. 647. Moreover, 14 ground stations established in the pre-surge years of 1935, 1939, 1941, and 1947 were reoccupied and photopanoramas exposed to illustrate portions of Steele Glacier throughout its length. These stations were tied in by conventional ground-surveying techniques to a major ground-control network established in 1967 by the Canadian Army Map Service.

It had been hoped that geophysical stations might be established on the surface of the surging glacier and that these would result in determination of the volume of ice involved in the surge and in an assessment of the longitudinal profile of the glacier bed. So chaotic was the surface, however, that only with difficulty was it possible to land a helicopter at appropriate sites; and where landings were made it was found impossible to maintain the stability of instruments! Gravity and seismic surveys were therefore abandoned.

It has been stipulated by Meier and others that if we are to understand why and how a glacier surges we must work from knowledge of the glacier's total environment prior to surge and bracket the period of chaotic advance, when many facets of behavior are difficult if not impossible to observe, with reassessment of internal and external environments as the glacier subsides to a quiescent state. The Society grant permitted the initiation of such assessments.

Upon the recommendation of Austin Post, "Fox" Glacier, a small valley glacier within the confines of Steele Valley, but independent of Steele Glacier, was selected for study. This glacier has surged in the past, probably in this century; and since surges of individual glaciers are known to be recurring events it can be expected that Fox Glacier will again surge in the foreseeable future. Studies begun in 1967 aim at an understanding of the glacier's mass balance and included accumulation, ablation, surface motion, and water discharge. Three-dimensional studies encompassed seismic and gravity profiles, and a thermal drilling program provided opportunities to assess internal motion and to accommodate thermistors for the determination of englacial temperatures. Thus, Fox Glacier came under intensive study, a physical examination as thorough in scope as that accorded most human beings. It is hoped that these studies will be continued periodically, and indeed expanded, so that when Fox Glacier next surges we may have a firm springboard from which to launch a new chapter in the study of glacier-flow phenomena.

REFERENCES

COLLINS, SAM G.
  1971. Exploration on a surging glacier. Explorers Journ., vol. 49, no. 2, pp. 124-9, illus.
MEIER, MARK F., and POST, AUSTIN S.
  1969. What are glacier surges? Can. Journ. Earth Sci., vol. 6, no. 4, pt. 2, pp. 807-817.
STANLEY, A. D.
  1969. Observations of the surge of Steele Glacier, Y. T. Can. Journ. Earth Sci., vol. 6, no. 4, pt. 2, pp. 819-30.
WOOD, WALTER A.
  1936. The Wood Yukon Expedition of 1935: An experiment in photographic mapping. Geogr. Rev., vol. 26, pp. 228-46, illus.
  1942. The parachuting of expedition supplies: An experiment by the Wood Yukon Expedition of 1941. Geogr. Rev., vol. 32, pp. 36-55, illus.
  1967a. Steele Glacier surge. Amer. Alpine Journ., vol. 15, no. 2, pp. 279-81.
  1967b. Chaos in nature. Explorers Journ., vol. 15, no. 2, pp. 79-87, illus.
  1969. The Alaska-Yukon Icefield Ranges Research Project, 1964, 1965, and 1966. Nat. Geogr. Soc. Res. Rpts., 1964 Projects, pp. 257-261.

WALTER A. WOOD

APPENDIX

List of Grants for Research and Exploration Made by the National Geographic Society, 1972

Nos. 1037, 1038, 1139: To Dr. Kenan T. Erim, New York University, New York City, to continue his exploration and excavation of the Greek and Roman archeological site of prehistoric Aphrodisias in Turkey.

No. 1039: To Dr. J. Alan Holman, Michigan State University, East Lansing, Michigan, for a study of amphibians and reptiles of a Lower Pliocene site in Kansas.

No. 1040: To Dr. Raymond B. Manning, Smithsonian Institution, Washington, D. C., in aid of a study of brachyuran crabs from the Gulf of Guinea.

No. 1041: To Prentiss M. Thomas, University of Tennessee, Knoxville, Tennessee, for a settlement-pattern survey of the Becan area, Campeche, Mexico.

No. 1042: To Dr. John K. Adams, Temple University, Philadelphia, Pennsylvania, for a sedimentological study of the Volta Delta, West Africa.

No. 1043: To Dr. Christy G. Turner, 2d, Arizona State University, Tempe, Arizona, to study Russian influence on Aleut ecology, culture, and physical anthropology.

No. 1044: To Peter G. Mickelson, University of Michigan, Ann Arbor, Michigan, to continue studies of the breeding biology of cackling geese on the Yukon-Kuskokwim Delta, Alaska.

Nos. 1045, 1101: To Dr. William W. Fitzhugh, Smithsonian Institution, Washington, D. C., to continue his study of environmental archeology and cultural systems in Hamilton Inlet, Labrador.

No. 1046: To Dr. Keith Stewart Thomson, Yale University, New Haven, Connecticut, for research on the coelacanth (*Latimeria chalumnae* Smith).

No. 1047: To Dr. Jared M. Diamond, University of California Medical Center, Los Angeles, California, for a study of the recolonization of exploded volcanic islands by New Guinea birds.

No. 1048: To Dr. Vincent J. Maglio, Princeton University, Princeton, New Jersey, for exploration of Pliocene fossil localities in the Rift Valley, Kenya.

Nos. 1049, 1128: To Dian Fossey, Ruhengeri, Rwanda, for continued observations of behavioral patterns of the mountain gorilla and study of its population distribution within the Virunga Mountains.

No. 1050: To Dr. Michael E. Moseley, Harvard University, Cambridge, Massachusetts, and Dr. Carol Joy Mackey, San Fernando Valley State College, Los Angeles, California, to continue studies of prehistoric urban-rural relationships on the north Peruvian coast.

No. 1051: To Dr. Donald R. Nelson, California State College, Long Beach, California, for continued support of his study of the social behavior and aggression in the gray reef shark.

No. 1052: To Dr. Gordon L. Kirkland, Jr., Shippensburg State College, Shippensburg, Pennsylvania, for a study of the micro-distribution of small mammals at the coniferous-deciduous ecotone.

No. 1053: To Dr. Gilbert P. Waldbauer, University of Illinois, Urbana, Illinois, to study the phenology of stinging Hymenoptera, their mimics, and insectivorous birds.

No. 1054: To Dr. Fred Barker, U. S. Geological Survey, Denver, Colorado, to study trondhjemites, their development and the earth's early sialic crust.

No. 1056: To Patricia D. Moehlman, University of Wisconsin, Madison, Wisconsin, to continue her study of the social organization and communication behavior of feral burros.

No. 1057: To Hamo Sassoon, Kampala, Uganda, for an archeological survey and excavation in Karamoja District, northeast Uganda.

No. 1058: To Dr. Bernard Nietschmann, University of Michigan, Ann Arbor, Michigan, to study the exploitation and ecology of hawksbill sea turtles.

No. 1059: To Dr. B. Lennart Johnson, University of California, Riverside, California, to study the origin and ancestry of the cultivated wheats.

No. 1060: To Dr. George A. Bartholomew, University of California, Los Angeles, California, to study the ecological role of the nest of the sociable weaver.

No. 1061: To Dr. H. Dean Fisher, University of British Columbia, Vancouver, British Columbia, to study the biology of Steller's sea-lion.

No. 1062: To Dr. James B. Pritchard, University Museum, University of

Pennsylvania, Philadelphia, Pennsylvania, to continue his excavation of the Phoenician and Biblical city of Sarepta (Zarephath) in Lebanon.

No. 1063: To Dr. Mary D. Leakey, Centre for Prehistory and Palaeontology, Nairobi, Kenya, to continue the study of prehistoric archeology at Olduvai Gorge, Tanzania.

No. 1064: To William H. Whyte, American Conservation Association, New York City, for a sociological study of the life of city streets.

No. 1065: To Dr. Cynthia Irwin-Williams, Eastern New Mexico University, Portales, New Mexico, to continue her study of the structure of Pueblo society on the Middle Puerco River.

No. 1066: To Dr. David Sanger, University of Maine, Orono, Maine, for an archeological study at the Hirundo site, Maine.

No. 1067: To Dr. Charles M. Kirkpatrick, Purdue University, Lafayette, Indiana, for a botanical study of the Kokechik Bay area, Alaska.

No. 1068: To Dr. Robert J. Sharer, Pitzer College, Claremont, California, for archeological investigations in the northern Maya Highlands.

No. 1069: To Dr. Robert M. Hunt, Jr., Columbia University, New York City, to study the stratigraphy and faunas of early Miocene rocks of northwestern Nebraska.

No. 1070: To Dr. Richard S. MacNeish, Robert S. Peabody Foundation for Archaeology, Andover, Massachusetts, to continue his archeological investigation of the city state of Coxcatlan, Puebla, Mexico.

No. 1071: To Dr. Emiliano Aguirre, University of Madrid, Madrid, Spain, for research on accumulated bones in a Villafranchian cave with scavengers.

No. 1072: To Dr. Allen W. Stokes, Utah State University, Logan, Utah, to study the social behavior of Alaska brown bears.

No. 1073: To Dr. Richard H. Chesher, Marine Research Foundation, Key West, Florida, for a 70-year evaluation of pollution at the Dry Tortugas, Florida.

No. 1074: To Albert E. Sanders, Charleston Museum, Charleston, South Carolina, for the excavation and preparation of Oligocene cetacean remains from South Carolina.

No. 1075: To Dr. Richard L. Hay, University of California, Berkeley, California, to study the stratigraphy and paleogeography of Beds III and IV, Olduvai Gorge, Tanzania.

No. 1076: To Dr. Louis S. B. Leakey, Centre for Prehistory and Palaeontology, Nairobi, Kenya, in furtherance of Dr. Leakey's archeological and paleontological researches in Tanzania and Kenya.

No. 1077: To Dr. A. William Laughlin, Kent State University, Kent, Ohio, to study the origin of ultramafic inclusions and their relationship to basalt genesis.

No. 1078: To Dr. Edward S. Belt, Amherst College, Amherst, Massachusetts, for a statistical analysis of Carboniferous delta deposits, Fife, Scotland.

No. 1080: To Dr. Colin P. Groves, University of Cambridge, Cambridge, England, for a survey of the Tana River red colobus and agile mangabey.

No. 1081: To Dr. Albert S. Rouffa, University of Illinois at Chicago Circle, Chicago, Illinois, for a study of the primitive vascular plant *Psilotum* in Japan, its classical culture, mutants, and wild occurrences.

No. 1082: To Dr. Stephen Williams, Peabody Museum, Harvard University, Cambridge, Massachusetts, in support of his continuing archeological survey in southwestern Mississippi.

No. 1083: To Dr. Geoffrey Moriaso Ole Maloiy, University of Nairobi, Nairobi, Kenya, for a study of the physiology and behavior of the topi antelope in the Mara Game Preserve, Tanzania.

No. 1084: To Dr. William J. L. Sladen, Johns Hopkins University, Baltimore, Maryland, to study the migrations of the whistling swan between Alaska and its wintering grounds.

No. 1085: To Dr. Asen Balikci, Massachusetts Institute of Technology, Cambridge, Massachusetts, for a cultural-ecological study of Pashtoon pastoral nomadism in Afghanistan.

No. 1086: To Dr. William S. Laughlin, University of Connecticut, Storrs, Connecticut, for a study of Aleutian survivors of the Bering Land Bridge.

No. 1087: To Dr. James R. Koplin, Humboldt State College, Arcata, California, in support of his continuing studies of the distribution, abundance, and breeding success of ospreys in northwestern California.

No. 1088: To Robert A. Bye, Jr., Harvard University, Cambridge, Massachusetts, for a study of the ethnoecology of the Tarahumara people, Mexico.

No. 1089: To Dr. Ward B. Watt, Stanford University, Stanford, California, to study comparative population ecology of pierid butterflies.

No. 1090: To Susan E. Riechert, University of Wisconsin, Madison, Wisconsin, for a niche analysis of the funnel-web building spider in the Carrizozo Malpais, New Mexico.

No. 1091: To Dr. Carl Widmer, University of the Pacific, Stockton, California, for ecological studies of Lake Titicaca, Peru-Bolivia.

No. 1092: To Dr. C. Vance Haynes, Southern Methodist University, Dallas, Texas, in support of his continuing studies of the paleoecology at the Murray Springs archeological site in Arizona.

No. 1093: To Dr. Donald H. Menzel, Harvard University and Smithsonian Astrophysical Observatory, Cambridge, Massachusetts, for photography of the spectrum, polarization, and form of the solar corona.

Nos. 1094, 1138: To Dr. Bradford Washburn, Museum of Science, Boston, Massachusetts: Supplemental grants in aid of a project to map the Grand Canyon of the Colorado.

No. 1095: To Dr. Paul B. Kannowski, University of North Dakota, Grand Forks, North Dakota, for a feasibility study of expansion of Theodore Roosevelt National Memorial Park in western North Dakota.

No. 1096: To Dr. Warren P. Stoutamire, University of Akron, Akron, Ohio, for pollination studies of terrestrial Australian orchids.

No. 1097: To Robert L. Brownell, Jr., Smithsonian Institution, Washington, D. C., to study the life history, behavior, and acoustics of the Franciscana dolphin.

No. 1098: To Michael L. Katzev, Oberlin College, Oberlin, Ohio, in further support of his project for the reconstruction of an ancient Greek merchant ship wrecked near Kyrenia, Cyprus.

No. 1099: To Dr. William L. Peters, Florida Agricultural and Mechanical University, Tallahassee, Florida, to study zoogeographical connections of selected aquatic insects in New Caledonia.

No. 1100: To Dr. Roger S. Payne, Rockefeller University, New York City, in support of his studies of the behavior of the southern right whale *(Eubalaena glacialis)*.

No. 1103: To Jeremy Lorn Anderson, Natal Parks Game and Fish Preservation Board, Pietermaritzburg, Natal, South Africa, to study the ecology and conservation management of the nyala.

No. 1104: To Dr. Thomas B. Croat, Missouri Botanical Garden, St. Louis, Missouri, for phytogeographic studies of the Burica Peninsula of Panama and Costa Rica.

No. 1105: To Dr. Storrs L. Olson, Smithsonian Institution, Washington, D. C., to study the past avifauna of Fernando de Noronha Island, South Atlantic.

No. 1106: To Jack Chardon Turner, University of California, Riverside, California, in support of a study of the environmental and physiological biology of the desert bighorn sheep.

No. 1107: To Dr. Tyson R. Roberts, Museum of Comparative Zoology, Harvard University, Cambridge, Massachusetts, for an ichthyological survey of the Congo River's lower rapids.

No. 1108: To Dr. M. Philip Kahl, International Council for Bird Preservation, Naples, Florida, to study the ecology and reproductive biology of flamingos.

No. 1109: To Dr. Stanley L. Welsh, Brigham Young University, Provo, Utah, to study the hanging gardens of the Colorado Plateau.

No. 1110: To Dr. R. Gordon Gastil, San Diego State College, San Diego, California, to study basement rock and Tertiary volcanic correlations across the Gulf of California.

No. 1111: To Joan Dorothy Fuller, University of St. Andrews, Fife, Scotland, for an investigation of the reproductive biology of osteoglossid fishes in South America.

No. 1112: To Dr. Richard D. Estes, Museum of Comparative Zoology, Harvard University, Cambridge, Massachusetts, to study the biological significance of the reproductive system of the wildebeest.

No. 1113: To Dr. Robert J. Rodin, State Polytechnic University, San Luis Obispo, California, to study the ethnobotany of the Kwanyama linguistic group, Ovamboland, South-West Africa.

No. 1114: To Donald R. Whitehead, Indiana University, Bloomington, Indiana, for a study of the postglacial environmental history of the Argolid Peninsula, Greece.

No. 1115: To Edwin Martin Shook, Museum of Science, Miami, Florida, for an archeological study of Monte Alto, Guatemala, and preclassic cultures on the Pacific Coast.

No. 1116: To Dr. Arthur G. Miller, Yale University, New Haven, Connecticut, for an archeological study of the mural painting of Tulum and Tancah, Quintana Roo, Mexico.

No. 1117: To Dr. Eldon E. Ball, Australian National University, Canberra City, Australia, to study biological colonization of a recently formed volcanic island.

No. 1118: To Dr. Terry A. Vaughan, Northern Arizona University, Flagstaff, Arizona, for a study of the social, foraging, and roosting behavior in a false vampire bat.

No. 1119: To Dr. Eugenie Clark, University of Maryland, College Park,

Maryland, to study the behavior and toxic-repellent effect of a Red Sea fish on sharks.

No. 1120: To Dr. Richard E. W. Adams, University of Texas, San Antonio, Texas, in support of a study of ecological change and cultural history of the Río Bec region, Yucatán Peninsula.

No. 1121: To Dr. Frank H. Talbot, The Australian Museum, Sydney, New South Wales, Australia, for an ichthyological expedition to Lord Howe Island, New South Wales.

No. 1123: To Theodore A. Wertime, American Embassy, Athens, Greece, for a study of man's uses of fire to shape earths and metals.

No. 1124: To Dr. Jeremy A. Sabloff, Harvard University, Cambridge, Massachusetts, for a study of Pre-Columbian culture change on Cozumel, Mexico.

No. 1125: To David T. Richardson, Maine Department of Sea and Shore Fisheries, Augusta, Maine, to study feeding habits and population dynamics of Maine's harbor and gray seals.

No. 1126: To Dr. Donald H. Menzel, Harvard University, Cambridge, Massachusetts, for an expedition to observe the African total solar eclipse of June 30, 1973.

No. 1127: To Dr. Robert G. Jaeger, University of Wisconsin, Madison, Wisconsin, to study the relation of activity periods to phototactic behavior in frogs.

No. 1128: To Dr. James M. Adovasio, University of Pittsburgh, Pittsburgh, Pennsylvania, for an archeological-site survey of Mesolithic occupations on Cyprus.

No. 1129: To Lewis A. Krevolin, Dutchess Community College, Poughkeepsie, New York, for reconstruction of Meso-American pottery techniques.

No. 1130: To Dr. William Alexander Calder, Jr., University of Arizona, Tucson, Arizona, for a study of heat exchanges of nesting hummingbirds in the Rocky Mountains.

No. 1131: To Dr. John M. Legler, University of Utah, Salt Lake City, Utah, to study the taxonomy, distribution, and ecology of Australian fresh-water turtles.

No. 1132: To Dr. John D. Dwyer, St. Louis University, St. Louis, Missouri, for a botanical exploration of Maya Mountains, British Honduras.

No. 1133: To Dr. Erik H. Erikson, Jr., Juniata College, Huntingdon, Pennsylvania, to study the petrology and geochemistry of the Mount Stuart batholith, Washington.

No. 1134: To Dr. James D. Lazell, Jr., Massachusetts Audubon Society,

Lincoln, Massachusetts, for a study of the ecology and relationships of isolated tropical raccoons.

No. 1135: To Dr. George B. Schaller, New York Zoological Society, New York City, to study the biology of large, high-altitude mammals in Pakistan and Nepal.

No. 1136: To Dr. David C. Grove, University of Illinois, Urbana, Illinois, to continue his study of the archeology of Chalcatzingo, Morelos, Mexico.

Index